THE CHARLTON
STANDARD CATALOGUE OF

BESWICK
POTTERY

SECOND EDITION

BY
DIANA AND JOHN CALLOW

PUBLISHER
W.K. CROSS

The Charlton Press

TORONTO, ONTARIO • PALM HARBOR, FLORIDA

Canadian Cataloguing In Publication Data

Callow, Diana
    The Charlton standard catalogue of Beswick pottery

2nd ed.
Includes index.
ISBN 0-88968-219-4

1. Beswick (Firm) - Catalogs. 2. Pottery, British - Catalogs. I. Callow, John, 1923 or 4-   . II. Title.

NK4210.B44C34 1999   738'.029'42   C99-932197-8

EDITORIAL

Editor	Jean Dale
Assistant Editor	Cindy Raycroft
Graphic Technician	Davina Rowan
Photography	John Callow

ACKNOWLEDGMENTS

The Charlton Press wishes to thank those who have helped and assisted with the first edition of *The Charlton Standard Catalogue of Beswick Pottery*.

CONTRIBUTORS TO SECOND EDITION

The Publisher would like to thank the following individuals or companies who graciously supplied photographs or allowed us access to their collections for photographic purposes. We offer sincere thanks to:

Linda Brown, Gloucester, England; **Gathorne Burns**, Winnipeg, Manitoba; **Margaret Carroll**, South Yorkshire, England; **Joyce Garrad**, Gloucester, England; **Pat Griffin**, Leicester, England; **Linda Isgrove,** Birmingham, England; **Ian Hutchison**, Wellington, New Zealand; **Nigel Kellett**, Leicester, England; **Andy McCabe**, Nottingham, England; **Kathleen McCullough**, Winnipeg, Manitoba; **Ray Self**, Norfolk, England; **Elizabeth Wicks**, Bayside Antiques Centre, Melbourne, Australia.

A SPECIAL NOTE TO COLLECTORS

We welcome and appreciate any comments or suggestions in regard to *The Charlton Standard Catalogue of Beswick Pottery*. As you proceed through the book you will find many illustration squares which contain only a line drawing from the Beswick shape book. It is our goal to replace these line drawings over time with actual photographs. We would greatly appreciate your help in this endeavour. If you would like to participate in pricing or supply previously unavailable data or information, please contact Jean Dale at (416) 488-1418.

Printed in Canada
in the Province of Ontario

The Charlton Press

Editorial Offices:
2040 Yonge Street, Suite 208
Toronto, Ontario M4S 1Z9
Telephone: (416) 488-1418 Fax: (800) 488-4656
Telephone: (800) 442-6042 Fax: (800) 442-1542
Web site: www.charltonpress.com
E-mail: chpress@charltonpress.com

Vase, model 30

HOW TO USE THIS CATALOGUE

THE LISTINGS

This book has been designed to serve two specific purposes. First, to furnish the Beswick enthusiast with accurate listings containing vital information and photographs to aid in the building of a rewarding collection. Secondly, this publication provides Beswick collectors and dealers with current market prices for the complete line of Beswick pottery.

Within the individual listings, the pieces are listed in order of their shape number. After this number comes the item's name or description. Next comes **Designer**, the dates of **Issue and withdrawal** (if the exact date of withdrawal is not known we indicate the last time the piece was seen advertised through the designation "by"), **Size** (either height or diameter depending on the shape), and **Colour**(s). The **Series** to which the piece belongs (if applicable) is listed next. Lastly, the suggested **Retail price** is given in American, Canadian and British funds.

A NOTE ON THE PHOTOGRAPHS

In some cases, drawings of models have been used to represent unobtainable pieces. The reader is cautioned that all photographs so utilized are to be used for model characteristics only. More specific details concerning a piece (i.e. size) should be determined from the information listed below the photograph.

A WORD ON PRICING

As stated, one of the purposes of this catalogue is to give readers the most accurate, up-to-date retail prices for Beswick pottery in the United States, Canada and the United Kingdom.

To accomplish this, The Charlton Press continues to access an international pricing panel of experts who submit prices based on both dealer and collector retail-price activity, as well as current auction results in the U.S., Canada, and the U.K. These market prices are carefully averaged to reflect accurate valuations for models in each of these markets.

The prices published herein are for models in mint condition. Collectors are cautioned that a repaired or restored piece may be worth as little as 25 per cent of the value of the same model in mint condition.

A further word on pricing: As mentioned previously, this is a catalogue giving prices for models in the currency of a particular market (U.S. dollars for the American market and sterling for the U.K. market). The bulk of the prices given herein are not determined by currency exchange calculations, but by actual market activity in the market concerned.

THE INTERNET AND PRICING

The internet is changing the way business is being done in the collectable marketplace. Linking millions of collectors around the world through chat rooms, antique and collector malls, internet auctions and producer web sites, e-commerce has become big business.

Some of the effects caused by the internet and e-commerce on the collectable business are as follows:

1. Collectors deal directly with other collectors, changing the dynamics of the traditional customer/dealer relationship.

2. Information concerning new issues, finds and varieties is readily available, twenty-four hours a day. Collectors' wants are made known instantly to a wide spectrum of dealers and collectors.

3. Prices:

    (a) Price differentials dissappear between global market areas as collectors and the delivery services team up to stretch the purchasing power of the collectable dollar/pound.

    (b) Prices of common to scarce items will adjust downward to compensate for the temporary expansion of merchandise supply. Conversely, prices of rare and extremely rare items will increase, a result of additional exposure to demand.

    (c) After a time even the prices of the common items will rise due to the growing worldwide demand for collectables.

4. Internet auction sites listing millions of items for sale on a daily basis continue to grow as more and more collectors discover the viability of using this method to buy and sell merchandise.

5. Traditional marketing strategies (retail stores, direct mail retailers, collectable shows and fairs, and collectable magazines and papers) face increased pressure in a more competitive environment.

The internet is user-friendly: no travelling required, twenty-four hour accessibility, no face-to-face contact or other pressure to buy or sell. Without a doubt, the arrival of e-commerce will change the way a collector collects.

Butterfly wall plaque, model 594

CONTENTS

Shape 193 (left), Shape 145 (centre), Shape 97 (right)

INTRODUCTION

We have been collecting Beswick Ware for many many years, drawn into the hobby when we first realized the quality of the Beswick products. We soon developed into Beswick addicts. At that time we pursued our hobby in isolation, visiting Collectors Fairs trying to add to our increasing family of "Beswicks." As we progressed along the way we thirsted for information. We had acquired Collectors Book No. 4 and a few odd bits and pieces - really only scraps of information - and thought it was time to make a real effort to gather the knowledge we were seeking. We therefore wrote to Royal Doulton asking for information about specific models.

Subsequently it was suggested that we should visit the Beswick factory at Gold Street, Longton, Stoke-on-Trent and on the first of several visits we discovered that little direct information on early production was available. Fortunately, there we met and were greatly assisted by the late Pamela Colclough, who had accumulated a small archive of early price lists etc. In addition we were able to study and make notes from the "Shape Book," a record started at the factory in the early nineteen thirties, containing sketches of most of the pieces, together with entries which gave the designer's names and the modelling dates.

We learnt that only from the 1930s had any form of backstamp been used, and that most of these had been in use for many years and were then still current. Therefore,

backstamps cannot generally be used as a means of dating.

We quickly realized that we needed to locate other collectors, who like ourselves, were interested in finding out more about the Beswick models. This we thought hopefully would in turn lead to discovering additional information.

Based on our previous experience as members of a collecting society, we decided to take the plunge and start a collector's club of our own for Beswick enthusiasts. The Beswick Collectors Circle, as it was named, was started during 1985 and continued until our retirement as Co-ordinators at the end of 1995.

The aim of this present book, written by Collectors for Collectors, is to provide a guide to Beswick decorative and other ware covering the period from the foundation of the company in 1894 to 1973. By 1973 the take-over by Royal Doulton had taken place and all production of this type of ware had ceased.

We hope that this book will serve as a useful guide and as a means by which you will be able to identify the models quickly. The arrangement of the chapters has been chosen with this object in mind and to make this process as easy as possible. Many of the models have been illustrated by using photographs and where this has not been possible we have done our best to show you what these shapes would have looked like by a variety of other means.

History of the Company

The following short history of the company is based on contemporary articles from *The Pottery Gazette*.

The earliest reference to the company we have found is the advertisement illustrated below, which is from the January 1st, 1894 issue of *The Pottery Gazette*.

This is the year now accepted for the start of the company, although Beswick catalogues of the 1960s give 1896 as the year of its foundation. The content of the advertisement however leads one to suppose that the firm of J. W. BESWICK was already well established as a manufacturer of pottery, so great is the variety of articles on offer.

Success must have followed on very quickly for James Wright Beswick. His company rapidly grew as a manufacturer of earthenware and majolica with a reputation for quality at a competitive price. By August, 1896 we read that "owing to increase of business" a second premises had been taken, the Britannia Works in High Street, Longton, where china was produced. Only two years later at the beginning of 1898 the Gold Street works, still the home of Beswick today, had been acquired and by 1899 was in full operation.

J. W. BESWICK,

BALTIMORE WORKS, ALBION STREET, LONGTON,

MANUFACTURER OF

Majolica and Earthenware Specialities.   **Leading Lines in Majolica Jugs.**
Gilt Jugs in all Decorations. Figures of all descriptions. Flower Pots and Pedestals in all Colours. Hanging Pots with or without Chains. Cheese Stands, Bread Trays, Spittoons, Green Glaze Plates and Comports, Hand-painted Vases in Newest Styles of Decoration, &c. &c.

SPECIAL LINES IN CHINA, JET, AND ROCKINGHAM,
SUITABLE FOR HOME AND EXPORT.

PRICES SENT ON APPLICATION.

Advertisement from the Pottery Gazette January 1894

The year 1899 also marked the end of production at the Baltimore Works. Production of china was restarted in 1908 at the King Street Works, formerly of Bridgett & Bates, and continued for a while under the old name. From 1915 china was produced at the Warwick Works, Chadwick Street until 1930, when production of all china ceased. (Note this guide does not deal with any of the china, such as "Warwick" china, marketed with a backstamp of Beswick & Sons and a crown).

By 1905 the Britannia Works had also been given up and production concentrated at Gold Street where additions and alterations had been made to the premises.

When James Wright Beswick died in 1920, at the age of seventy-five, the firm was taken over by his son John, whose name lives on today. John died in 1934 and was succeeded by his son, John Ewart Beswick, who became Chairman and Managing Director.

"Mr. Ewart," as he was always known, had worked in the business since leaving school, as also had Mr. Ewart's uncle, Mr. Gilbert Beswick who was half-brother to John. "Mr. Gilbert" also joined in the management of the company at that time and was later appointed Sales Director about 1960. When in the late 1960s, Ewart Beswick was ready to retire, no member of the immediate family was available to carry on the business, and the company was incorporated into the Royal Doulton Group.

Initially a private company, Beswick became a private limited company in 1938. It was converted to a public limited company in 1957 and became part of the Royal Doulton Group in 1969.

The Early Years - 1894 to 1934

A description of the exhibit at "The Furnishing Trades Exhibition and Market" at the Agricultural Hall, Islington, London, in March, 1898, at which about twenty exhibits only, were devoted to pottery, reads as follows:

"Mr. J.W. Beswick, of Albion Street and High Street, Longton, made a good display with his majolica ware. Flower pots, suspension pots, jugs, spittoons, baskets, pedestals and pots, umbrella stands and bread trays showed the variety of his manufactures. His earthenware exhibits comprised samples of toilet ware — many shapes and decorations — dinner and tea ware and a good assortment of jugs. His other exhibits comprised C.C ware, china tea ware and jet and Rockingham ware. In these were shown some nicely-shaped teapots. Fancy goods included vases, pots, figures, cheese stands and covers and bread trays. Altogether it was a very good and nicely-assorted exhibit."

The figures mentioned above were probably the Staffordshire type mantle-piece ornaments in the shape of generals, gardeners, milkmaids, dogs, etc., which had been popular fifty years before, and surprisingly for which there was still a demand. A special line were the "Staffordshire dogs," made in nine sizes. These were facing left and right in pairs, in white and gold or red and black, and were very similar in shape to those in production today.

The following illustrations from *The Pottery Gazette* for February 1901 and March 1905 show some of the products listed above.

An assortment of Beswick Ware including Flown Blue

Left to right: Spiral shaped teacup and saucer, "Queen" teapot, "Britannia" flower pot, "Roseberry" flower pot, "Durban" flower pot, "Paris" cup and saucer. Bottom (left to right): Staffordshire dog, "Jap" vase, "Alexandra" vase, umbrella stand, "York" vase, "Victoria" vase and Swan flower pot

Left to right - "Trent" Jug, "Princess" Flower Pot and "Acme" Jug

"Acme" shaped Toilet Set - Jug and Ewer

By 1908 we read that " Mr. J. W. Beswick is a manufacturer of useful domestic ware in great variety. He makes goods of the popular class, both as to appearance and price. He aims at giving good value, and, though he does not manufacture the highest grades, he has some very good lines. He is well known for his jugs, and produces many excellent patterns on good useful shapes."

J. W. Beswick was known principally as a manufacturer of earthenware, and in the illustration, shown below, from *The Pottery Gazette* for April,1913 everything, with the exception of the ewer and basin, was entirely new for that year.

Production of such items would have spanned a number of years and therefore it is not possible to know exactly in which year any particular piece would have been made.

Unfortunately, these items of early manufacture do not carry a backstamp or any marking by which they can be easily recognized. One needs to have some knowledge of the shapes produced (see page xvi to xx) and the decorations employed, before early pieces can be identified.

On later pieces shape names and/or numbers may be impressed or a decoration number may be present, as an aid to identification. The various patterns used were interchangeable with the various shapes, and vice versa.

The clock set is described as having a blue ground with painted game figures, stippled in gold, and four sizes were available. The vase on the left is in the "Aden" shape and the one on the right "Alexandra". The flowerpots are "Douglas" and "Fulham" shapes. An example of the "Douglas" shape in a decoration typical of the mid-1920s can be seen on page 440. It was available in five sizes ranging from 6 ½" to 10 ½"

Below may be seen a variety of shapes:

*Two shapes of toilet ware dating from 1925 are shown above, the "York" and "Victory,"
the latter may also be seen in a different decoration in the colour plate No 4/4*

*A selection of items dating from June 1928. Left to Right - "Rita" Vase (7" tall), "Regent" Bowl
(8 ½" diameter), "Len" Vase (8 ½" tall) and "Rena" Vase (7" tall)*

*A selection of Vases dating from September 1929. Left to Right - "Lille" (10 ½" tall), "Rhos" (9" tall),
"Stafford" (6" tall), "Regal" (6" tall) and "Roslin (10 ½" tall)*

Also we have the coloured plates which show more of the shapes available. The vase 9" tall with the shape name "Blythe" (see plate 2/4) must have been popular, as many examples have been seen in various decorations. The pair of vases shape name "Albany," 11 ½" tall, decorated with a pattern of carmine roses picked out in gilt on a jet-black background carry a much earlier decoration number, 3072. This decoration was evidently a success when introduced, for it continued to be available until 1930, which probably explains why so many pieces decorated with this design have survived to turn up relatively often at fairs.

The "Bluebird" pattern (decoration number 6155) is shown on another pair of vases in the "Sale" shape (see plate 3/2). This decoration is a lithographed design in attractive colours, and is also fairly common today. As well as being employed on vases, as in this illustration, it was used on teapots, candlesticks and pieces for a dressing table or trinket set. This style of decoration must have been well-liked, because we have noticed its use on a number of pieces, which have not been made at the Beswick factory. The Beswick decoration number should remove all doubt as to origin.

At the time the Shape Book was started, in the early 1930s, shape names were being replaced by shape numbers, although there was a period of overlap.

For example the jug, shown here, with the name "Ruth" and the backstamp "Beswick Handcraft," later carried the impressed number "72," alone or together with the name "Ruth."
This jug, in a satin matt finish, has a cream background with orange trim on the base, rim and handle. The decoration is in blue, brown, orange and green.

Fashions change, in pottery as in all things, and whereas in the early days, a pronounced demand was encountered for pottery of the more highly coloured type, as the 1930s approached, a softer, less flamboyant style of decoration was being demanded.

The vase shown below reflects this change. It is impressed with the shape name "Rhos" and is beautifully decorated with hand-painted blue, white, yellow and black flowers. On a mottled grey background it is finished in a matt glaze. Surprisingly the flowers, the rim and the base are still picked out in gilt.

This style of decoration marked the transition between the earlier more ornate products and the large number of jugs, vases etc. decorated with matt glazes, in well over two hundred shapes, which followed.

Rhos Vase

Prices continued to be aimed at a level to sell readily in the popular markets, while at the same time the quality of the products was maintained or even improved, with new designs and decorations being shown at the British Industries Fairs. These new shapes continued to be modelled at a rapidly increasing rate, and employed lithographed designs which were inexpensive, or were decorated in hand-painted styles in underglaze or enamel colours, which reflected a tendency to move towards a superior product.

The advertisement from *The Pottery Gazette* dated May 1st, 1930, shown on the following page, marks the introduction of the "Beswick Ware" logo. This logo was also used for many years as a backstamp.

This advertisement from The Pottery Gazette (May 1, 1930) marks the introduction of the "Beswick Ware" logo. This logo was also used for many years as a backstamp.

The arrangement of the pieces in this illustration probably accounts for the use of the name "Cosy" which is impressed on the base, because the individual items nestle together in depressions in the tray. The decoration is in a strong orange typical of the period with white, black and gold.

At the same time, as the above advertisement suggests, due to the less prosperous nature of the times, there was a move away from purely ornamental wares to those of greater utility. We find that as the demand for ornamental wares declined, John Beswick turned his attention increasingly to tableware, with the single exception of dinner sets, and as had always been his custom, to novelties in a large variety of styles.

The Pottery Gazette for October 1931 reported an increasing business in such lines as "cosy" sets (teapot, hot-water jug and cream on a tray), egg sets, cruet sets, triple trays and the like.

By 1932, all sorts of new and attractive lines were much in evidence — lines which were both useful and ornamental. For example the "Wild Rose" design finished off in silver, which can be seen in the photograph for the Preserve (Shape 53, Miscellaneous Chapter). Also there was a hollyhock decoration in a similar finish and a marigold design with an orange edge.

In place of the grounded and panelled, stippled and gilt vases and clock sets, the new shapes had pleasing lines and simple decorations.

The Salad Ware series was prominent among the new creations and a range known as "Gardena" Ware, modelled in the form of flowers embossed and tinted in pastel shades was also introduced at this time. Items in this series are shown here.

New jug-vases in six different styles of decoration were launched to compete with Continental designs.

Displayed on the John Beswick stand at the British Industries Fair in 1933, a newly modelled series of tableware known as "Flowerkist" attracted the attention of Queen Mary, who purchased a quantity of this pattern. One can see that it was a most appealing design of sweetpeas on a background resembling wickerwork. (The royal patronage was later recognized by the use of a backstamp stating "As purchased by Her Majesty The Queen").

Both the Queen and the Duchess of York (the present Queen Mother) also purchased items of Salad Ware, some with a green ground and some with primrose.

Also featured on the stand were pieces of a range of table sundries modelled to depict thatched cottages. The forerunner for the Cottage Ware series is shown here.

"Gardena" Ware

'Thatched Cottage' - a forerunner to the Cottage Ware Series

Beswick shapes shown in an advertisement in 1934

1933 also saw the introduction of a number of jugs and vases decorated with a matt glaze. So successful were they, that a firm of pottery distributors, G. Hardy & Co., of Nottingham, negotiated with John Beswick to have a number of these ornamental lines and other novelties produced to their own shapes and designs. These were originally sold under the name of "Trentham Art Ware," but when the arrangement ended, about seven years later, many pieces remained in production to be sold under the Beswick name.

Sadly John Beswick did not live to see the great growth in these and similar lines and in the new novelties that were introduced as, after a long illness, he died in October 1934. In the years that followed there was great activity and each year that passed saw the introduction of an increasing number of new shapes in ornamental ware and novelties. These new shapes were mostly the work of modellers working on a freelance basis. Production was supervised by James Hayward, the Decorating Manager, who was responsible for the continued development of the matt glazes, which had proved so successful. Examples of these can be found in a great variety of mostly soft colours, in browns, blues, greens and yellows, to name but a few.

The War Years 1939-1945

Restrictions on the home front and the need to export as much as possible, resulted in many changes of emphasis in production. Fortunately the company continued to operate successfully during these very difficult times.

The outbreak of war in 1939 coincided with what, at first sight, would seem to be a surprising and dramatic expansion in, and a change in the nature of, the products from the Beswick factory. The stimulus for all this activity was the need for Britain at that time to export in order to survive, and in the period to the end of 1945, around three hundred new shapes were added. With the European companies being prevented from exporting, Beswick seized their chance to expand their markets overseas, and particularly into the then Dominions.

War time controls imposed on the home market by the Board of Trade, restricted domestic sales to everyday articles. Beswick was no exception and even their breakfast and tea-ware with a minimum decoration of three gold lines, was later reduced to one gold line! Production of vases, jugs and bowls in a great variety of shapes and decorations in the plain, embossed and incised styles for which Beswick had been noted for a number of years continued and eighty per cent of their output was accounted for by export.

On a personal note

In 1985 when we founded The Beswick Collectors Circle we had no idea of the impact which would result from our actions. We soon found out that the world was full of Beswick Collectors and the interest in Beswick Ware was greater than we could have ever foreseen.

Little notices, on the factory's products, soon turned up at Collectors Fairs - a new innovation for Beswick pieces in those days - and the word was spreading rapidly that Beswick was ready to take its place in the collecting world. This happened almost overnight.

The Circle was the first club to be formed for collectors of Beswick, and in the ten years during which we were the Co-ordinators, we saw the introduction of special Auctions for Beswick Ware, Collectors Fairs with dealers specialising in Beswick, books written especially for Beswick collectors, special Beswick models being commissioned, and the House of Beswick established in the world of collecting for all time.

Our aim was to get the products of Beswick appreciated for their quality, both in the modelling and in the decorations applied to the great variety of shapes - something for everyone to enjoy.

When we retired from The Circle in 1995 a new Beswick Club was formed and the interest in Beswick goes from "strength to strength". We hope that for years to come many people will enjoy the hobby as much as we have done and still do, especially the search for that elusive piece.

We wish you all, as we used to say, "Happy Beswicking."

Diana Callow

John Callow

Diana and John Callow

A Guide to Identification

For pieces produced prior to 1930, after which time the script "Beswick Ware" backstamp is likely to be present, only a hand-painted decoration number or an impressed shape name may be found. By 1900, the decoration numbering had already reached around the 1000 mark, by 1914 around 2500, and by 1932 was approaching 7000!

To assist in identification we have included:

Shape Names: An alphabetical listing of a selection of shape names, together with the corresponding shape numbers where known.

Shape names or numbers may be impressed on the underside of a piece. In some instances the shape number may be stamped.

Shape Illustrations: Illustrations of a variety of early shapes. Many of these shapes continued in production after the introduction of the shape book and were allocated shape numbers.

Backstamps: Illustrations of the variety of backstamps, in rough chronological order, used by Beswick.

SHAPE NAMES AND NUMBERS

Shape Name	Shape Number	Item	Shape Name	Shape Number	Item	Shape Name	Shape Number	Item
Acme		Toilet set	Eric		Flower holder	Regent		Plant pot
Aden		Vase	Eric		Clock case	Rena		Vase
Albany		Handled vase	Eton		Flower holder	Rheims		Plant pot
Alexandra		Vase	Eton		Vase	Rhos	57	Vase
Alpha	64	Vase	Exeter		Vase	Rita		Covered jar
Arran	68	Vase	Flora	58	Vase	Rome	53	Preserve
Arras		Vase	Fulham		Plant pot	Rose	56	Vase
Athens		Vase	Hague		Vase	Roslin	54	Vase
Avon			Holborn		Handled vase	Rouen		Handled vase
Baltic		Plant Pot	Iris	104		Royal	63	
Bell	110	Vase	Italian		Handled vase	Ruby	115	Teapot or Vase
Blythe	106	Vase	Kelt	67		Ruth	72	Jug
Bow		Vase	Kew	113		Ryde	55	Vase
Bude	52	Vase	Laurie		Covered vase	Rye		Vase
Castle Brush			Leeds		Vase	Sale		Handled vase
Ciro	70	Vase	Len	59	Vase	Sandon		Flower holder
Cleo	65	Vase	Leyden	50	Vase	Sparta	107	Vase
Clyde			Lille	105	Vase	Stafford		Flower holder
Crete	66	Vase	Lily	109	Vase	Sudan		Flower holder
Cuba		Covered Vase	Looe	49		Toy		Clock case
Deal		Vase	Louvain		Covered jar	Toy		Flower holder
Delhi		Vase	Lynn		Handled vase	Trent		Shallow bowl
Delta	71	Vase	Lynton	111	Vase	Troy		Vase
Doris		Flower Holder	Malta		Vase	Tyne	103	
Dresden	122	Vase	Mona	112	Ash tray	Vera		Flower holder
Douglas		Plant pot	Monmouth		Flower holder	Victoria		Covered vase
Durbar		Covered vase	Nankin		Covered vase	Victory		Toilet set
Dutch			Octagon			Warwick		Clock case
Edam		Vase	Opal	51	Vase	Windsor		Plant pot
Egypt		Covered vase	Oxford		Flower holder	Windsor	60	Vase
Eler	69	Vase	Pearl		Vase	Wye		Vase
Elite	73	Vase	Pekin		Covered vase	York		Toilet set
Ena		Flower holder	Princess		Plant pot	York	108	Vase
Ena		Plant pot	Regal	61	Vase	Zenith	261	Jug

SHAPES

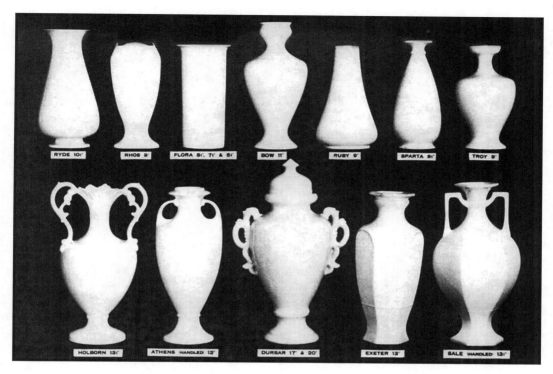

RYDE 10½" · RHOS 9" · FLORA 8½", 7½" & 6½" · BOW 11" · RUBY 9" · SPARTA 9½" · TROY 9"

HOLBORN 13½" · ATHENS (HANDLED) 13" · DURBAR 17" & 20" · EXETER 13" · SALE (HANDLED) 13½"

ROSE 8½", 7½" & 6½" · LYNTON 7½" · BLYTHE 9" · LILY 5½" · LEEDS 9" · RENA 7½" · WINDSOR 9"

ROUEN 16" & 15" · VICTORIA 20", 18" & 16½" · NANKIN 20", 18" & 16½" · PEKIN 19", 18" & 17"

MALTA 11" & 7"

PEARL 7"

LEN 8", 7" & 5"

REGAL 6"

CUBA 20" & 17"

RYE 13"

EGYPT ON PED. 21"

ITALIAN 13"

LAURIE 17"

DAFFODIL BOWL 8", 7" & 6"

DORIS 5½"

VERA ON PED 11"

TOY 5½"

SANDON 9"

STAFFORD 6"

SUDAN 5"

OXFORD OFF PED 8"

ERIC 5"

ENA (HANDLED) 6"

ENA DIAM 9"

WINDSOR 7½", 5½", 4½", 4" & 3½" DIAM

BALTIC 9½", 8½", 7½" & 6½" DIAM

DOUGLAS 10½", 9½", 8½", 7½" & 6½" DIAM

PRINCESS 9½" DIAM

RHEIMS 11½", 10" & 8½" DIAM

REGENT 9½", 8½" & 7½" DIAM

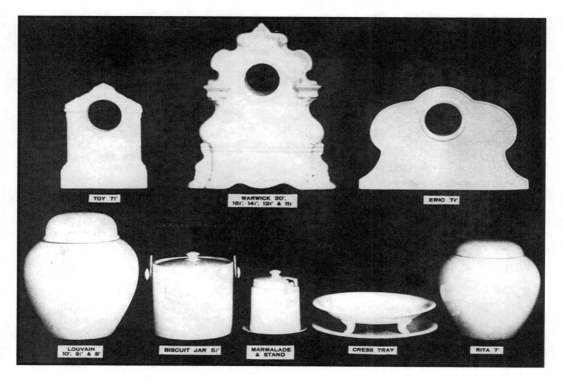

TOY 7½"

WARWICK 20", 16½", 14½", 12½" & 11½"

ERIC 7½"

LOUVAIN 10", 9½" & 8"

BISCUIT JAR 5½"

MARMALADE & STAND

CRESS TRAY

RITA 7"

BACKSTAMPS

Backstamp 1 — Beswick Ware ENGLAND

Backstamp 1 is of the earliest printed backstamp. It may also be found with "ENGLAND" replaced by "MADE IN ENGLAND" and with the addition of "MADE IN ENGLAND" impressed in the base.

Backstamp 2 — Beswick Handcraft
ENGLAND

Backstamp 2 shows a version used on more highly decorated pieces, in this case on a jug, "Ruth." The colours used to decorate the piece are strong, in the style of deco flowers and leaves.

Backstamp 3 — Impressed name and
MADE IN ENGLAND

Backstamp 3 illustrates a style which gave the name of the decoration "Wild Rose" together with, in some cases, the decoration number. The shape name, in this case "ROME" is impressed, with "MADE IN ENGLAND."

Backstamp 4 — "H. M. THE QUEEN"

Backstamp 4 shows a backstamp announcing royal patronage, The Queen mentioned here is Queen Mary, the wife of King George V.

Backstamp 5 — "H.M. QUEEN MARY"

Backstamp 5 is the backstamp which can be found on items of the "Sundial" pattern. The form of words was necessary because after the death of King George V, Queen Mary became the Queen Mother. The registration number corresponds with the year 1938.

Backstamp 6 — TRENTHAM ART WARE

Backstamp 6 is the backstamp used for the Trentham Art Wares. A gummed label with similar wording was also used.

Backstamp 7 — Circular
BESWICK ENGLAND

**BESWICK
ENGLAND**

Backstamp 8 — Oval
BESWICK ENGLAND

BESWICK ENGLAND

Backstamp 9 — BESWICK ENGLAND

Backstamp 10 — BESWICK CREST
ENGLAND

SEALS

In addition to the first small gummed seal, green with gold lettering, an alternative oval style with gold lettering on a green background was used. The small green seal was replaced by the large oval style.

Seal 1 — Small gummed seal
(first style) green with gold lettering

Seal 2 — Small gummed seal
(second style) green wil gold lettering

Seal 3 — Large gummed seal

ROYAL DOULTON COLLECTORS CLUB AND GUILD

Royal Doulton International Collectors Club

Founded in 1980, the Royal Doulton International Collectors Club provides an information service on all aspects of the company's products, past and present. A club magazine, *Gallery*, is published four times a year with information on new products and current events that will keep the collector up-to-date on the happenings in the world of Royal Doulton. Upon joining the club, each new member will receive a free gift and invitations to special events and exclusive offers throughout the year.

To join the Royal Doulton Collectors Club, please contact your local stockist, or contact the club directly at the address or telephone numbers below:

Royal Crown Derby Collectors Guild

The Royal Crown Derby Collectors Guild was established in 1994 to establish closer contact with Royal Crown Derby Collectors. Membership entitles the collector to a yearly subscription to the quarterley *Gallery* magazine, *Royal Crown Derby News*, membership gifts and free admission to the Royal Crown Derby Visitor Centre.

To join the Royal Crown Derby Collectors Guild, please contact the guild at the address or telephone number below:

Minton House
London Road, Stoke-on-Trent
Staffordshire ST4 7QD, England

Telephone:
U.K.: (01782) 292127
U.S.A. and Canada: 1-800-747-3045 (toll free)
Australia: 011-800-142624 (toll free)
Fax: U.K.: (01782) 292099
Attn: Maria Murtagh

Caithness Glass Paperweight Collectors Society
Cathness Glass International
Paperweight Collectors Society

Formed in 1997, by Colin Terris, the society is the clearing house for all information on Caithness Glass Paperweights. Membership of the society entitles the collector to receive *Reflections*, the society's twice yearly magazine, plus three newsletters and a personal tour of the paperweight studios in Perth, Scotland, if you are ever in the area. An annual International Convention is held in Scotland in October.

To join the Caithness Glass Paperweight Collectors Society, please contact the society at one of the addresses or telephone numers below:

In the U.K. and International
Caithness Glass Paperweight Collectors Society
Caithness Glass Inc.
Inveralmond, Perth PH1 3TZ, Scotland
Tel.: (44) (0)1738 637373
Fax: (44) (0)1738 622494

In the U.S.A.

Caithness Glass Paperweight Collectors Society
Caithness Glass Inc.
141 Lanza Avenue, Building No. 12
Garfield, N.J. 07026, U.S.A.
Tel.: 973-340-3330
Fax: 973-340-9415

COLLECTOR CLUB CHAPTERS

Chapters of the RDICC have formed across North America and are worthy of consideration in those areas.

Detroit Chapter
Frank Americk, President
1771 Brody, Allen Park, MI 48101

Edmonton Chapter
Mildred's Collectibles
6813 104 Street, Edmonton, AB

New England Chapter
Charles Wood, President
Charles Briggs, Secretary
21 Walpole Street, Norwood, MA 02062
Tel.: (781) 784-8121

Northern California Chapter
Donald A. Blubaugh, President
P.O. Box 3665, Walnut Creek, CA 94598
Tel.: (925) 945-1687 Fax: (925) 938-6674
e-mail: Blubaugh@usa.net

Northwest, Bob Haynes, Chapter
Alan Matthew, President
15202 93rd Place N.E., Bothell, WA 98011
Tel.: (425) 488-9604

Ohio Chapter
Reg Morris, President
Dick Maschmeier, Treasurer
5556 White Haven Avenue
North Olmstead, Ohio 44070
Tel.: (216) 779 5554

Rochester Chapter
Judith L. Trost, President
103 Garfield Street, Rochester, N.Y. 14611
Tel.: (716) 436-3321

Western Pennsylvania Chapter
John Re, President
9589 Parkedge Drive, Allison Park, PA 15101
Tel.: (412) 366-0201 Fax: (412) 366-2558

ROYAL DOULTON VISITOR CENTRES

Royal Doulton Visitor Centre

Opened in the summer of 1996, the Royal Doulton Visitor Centre houses the largest collection of Royal Doulton figurines in the world. The centre also is home to the Minton Fine Art Studio, which specializes in hand painting and gilding. Demonstration areas offer the collector a first hand insight on how figurines are assembled and decorated. Also at the Visitor Centre is a cinema showing a 20 minute video on the history of Royal Doulton, plus a restaurant, and a retail shop offering both the best quality ware and slight seconds.

Factory tours may be booked, Monday to Friday, at the Visitor Centre.

Nile Street, Burslem
Stoke-on-Trent ST6 2AJ, England
Tel.: (01782) 292434
Fax: (01782) 292424
Attn: Yvonne Wood

Royal Doulton John Beswick Studios

Tours of the John Beswick Factory and Museum are available Monday to Thursday by appointment only. Please book in advance.

Gold Street, Longton
Stoke-on-Trent ST3 2JP, England
Tel.: (01782) 291213
Fax: (01782) 291279
Attn: Joan Barker

Royal Crown Derby Visitor Centre

Opened in the spring of 1998, the Visitor Centre was created to provide an insight into the tradition, history and skills that go into making Royal Crown Derby collectables. The centre houses the largest collection of Royal Crown Derby seen anywhere in the world, a demonstration area for skilled Royal Crown Derby artists and crafts people, restaurants, and shops.

Factory tours may be booked Monday to Friday at the centre, with advance bookings suggested.

194 Ormastson Road
Derby DE23 8JZ, England
Tel.: (01332) 712841
Fax: (01332) 712899
Attn: Stella Birks

Caithness Glass Visitor Centre

The Visitor Centre is home to the largest public display of Caithness Glass paperweights. Over 1200 designs are on display. A special viewing gallery enables visitors to watch the complete paperweight making process.

Inveralmond
Perth PH1 3TZ, Scotland
Tel.: (44) (0)1738 637373
Fax: (44) (0)1738 622494

Factory Shops

Royal Doulton Visitor Centre
Nile Street, Burslem
Stoke-on-Trent ST6 2AJ, England
Tel.: (01782) 292451

Royal Doulton Group Factory Shop
Lawley Street, Longton
Stoke-on-Trent ST3 2PH, England
Tel.: (01782) 291172

Royal Doulton Factory Shop
Minton House, London Road
Stoke-on-Trent ST4 7QD, England
Tel.: (01782) 292121

Royal Doulton Factory Shop
Leek New Road, Baddeley Green
Stoke-on-Trent ST2 7HS, England
Tel.: (01782) 291700

Royal Doulton Factory Shop
Victoria Road, Fenton
Stoke-on-Trent ST4 2PJ, England
Tel.: (01782) 291869

Beswick Factory Shop
Barford Street, Longton
Stoke-on-Trent ST3 2JP, England
Tel.: (01782) 291237

Web Site and E-mail Address

Sites: www.royal-doulton.com
www.caithnessglass.co.uk
E-mail:
Clubs: iss@royal-doulton.com
Visitor Centre: visitor@royal-doulton.com
Consumer Enquiries: enquiries@royal-doulton.com
Museum Curator: heritage@royal-doulton.com
Lawleys by Post: lbp@royal-doulton.com

WHERE TO BUY

Discontinued Doulton collectables can be found in Antique shops, markets, auctions, shows and fairs. Specialist dealers in Royal Doulton collectables attend many of the events listed below.

For auction happenings it is necessary to subscribe to Auction Houses that hold 20th Century or Doulton Auctions.

UNITED KINGDOM
Auction Houses

BBR Auctions
Elsecar Heritage Centre
Nr. Barnsley
South Yorkshire S74 8HJ, England
Te.: (01226) 745156
Fax: (01226) 351561
Attn: Alan Blakeman

Bonhams
65-69 Lots Road, Chelsea
London SW10 0RN, England
Tel.: (0171) 393-3900
Fax: (0171) 393-3906
www.bonhams.com
Attn: Neil Grenyer

Christie's South Kensington
85 Old Bromtpon Road
London SW7 3LD, England
Tel.: (0171) 581-7611
Fax.: (0171) 321-3321
www.christies.com
Attn: Michael Jeffrey

Potteries Specialist Auctions
271 Waterloo Road
Stoke-on-Trent ST6 3HR
Staffordshire, England
Tel.: (01782) 286622
Fax: (01782) 213777
Attn: Steve Anderson

Louis Taylor
Britannia House
10 Town Road, Hanley
Stoke-on-Trent ST1 2QG, England
Tel.: (01782) 21411
Fax: (01782) 287874
Attn: CLive Hillier

Phillips
101 New Bond Street
London W1Y 0AS, England
Tel.: (0171) 629-6602
Fax: (0171) 629-8876
www.phillips-auctions.com
Attn: Mark Oliver

Sotheby's
34-35 New Bond Street
London W1A 2AA, England
Tel.: (0171) 293-5000
Fax: (0171) 293-5989
www.sothebys.com
Attn: Christina Donaldson

Sotheby's Sussex
Summers Place
Billinghurst, Sussex RH14 9AF
England
Tel.: (01403) 833500
Fax: (01403) 833699

Thomson Roddick & Laurie
60 Whitesands
Dumfries DG1 2RS, Scotland
Tel.: (01387) 255366
Fax: (01387) 266236
Attn: Sybelle Medcalf

Peter Wilson Auctioneers
Victoria Gallery, Market Street
Nantwich, Cheshire CW5 5DG
England
Tel.: (01270) 623878
Fax: (01270) 610508
Attn: Stella Ashbrook or Robert Stone

Antique Fairs

Doulton and Beswick Collectors Fair
National Motorcycle Museum, Meriden, Birmingham
Usually March and August.
For information on times and dates:
Doulton and Beswick Dealers Association
Te.: (0181) 303 3316

Doulton and Beswick Collectors Fair
The Queensway Hall Civic Centre, Dunstable
Bedforshire. Usually in October.
For information on times and location:
UK Fairs Ltd., 10 Wilford Bridge Spur,
Melton, Woodbridge, Suffolk, 1P12 1RJ
Tel.: (01394) 386663

20th Centry Fairs
266 Glossop Road, Sheffield S10 2HS, England
Usually the last week in May, or the first week in June.
For information on times and dates:
Tel.: (0114) 275-0333
Fax: (0114) 275-4443

International Antique & Collectors Fair
Newark, Nottinghamshire
Usually six fairs annually. For information on times and dates:
International Antique & Collectors Fair Ltd.
P.O. Box 100, Newark, Nottinghamshire NG2 1DJ
Tel.: (01636) 702326

West London Wade Beswick & Doulton Fair
Brunel University, Kingston Lane
Uxbridge, Middlesex
For information on times and dates:
B & D Fairs, P.O. Box 273, Uxbridge
Middlesex, UB9 4LP
Tel.: (01895) 834694 or 834357

Yesterdays Doulton Fair
Usually November.
For information on times and dates:
Doulton and Beswick Dealers Association
Tel.: (0181) 303-3316

London Markets

Alfie's Antique Market
13-25 Church Street, London
Tuesday - Saturday

New Caledonia Market
Bermondsey Square, London
Friday Morning

Camden Passage Market
London
Wednesday and Saturday

Portobello Road Market
Portobello Road, London
Saturday

UNITED STATES
Auction Houses

Christie's East
219 East 67th Street
New York, NY 10021
Tel.: (212) 606-0400
www.christies.com
Attn: Timothy Luke

Sotheby's Arcade Auctions
1334 York Avenue
New York, NY 10021
Tel.: (212) 606-7000
www.sothebys.com
Attn: Andrew Cheney

Collectable Shows

Atlantique City
New Atlantic City Convention Centre
Atlantic City, NJ
Usually March and October.
For information on times and dates:
Brimfield and Associates
P.O. Box 1800, Ocean City, NJ 08226
Tel.: (609) 926-1800
www.atlantiquecity.com

O'Hare National Antiques Show & Sale
Rosemont Convention Centre, Chicago, Illinois
Usually April, August and November.
For information on times and dates:
Manor House Shows Inc.
P.O. Box 7320, Fort Lauderdale, FL 33338
Tel.: (954) 563-6747

Royal Doulton Convention & Sale
John S. Knight Convention Centre
77 E. Mill Street, Akron, OH 44308
Usually August.
For information on times and dates:
Colonial House Productions
182 Front Street, Berea, Ohio 44017
Tel.: (800) 344-9299

Florida Doulton Convention & Sale
Sheraton Inn
1825 Griffin Road, Dania, Florida
Usually mid-January
For information on times and dates:
Pascoe & Company
932 Ponce De Leon Blvd., Coral Gables, FL
Tel.: (305) 445-3229
Charles Dombeck, 9720 Ridge Walk Court
Davie, Florida 33328 Tel.: (954) 452-9174

CANADA
Auction Houses

Maynards
415 West 2nd Avenue
Vancouver, BC. V5Y 1E3
Tel.: (604) 876-1311

Ritchie's
288 King Street East, Toronto, Ontario M5A 1K4
Tel.: (416) 364-1864 Fax: (416) 364-0704
Attn: Caroline Kaiser

Collectable Shows

Canadian Art & Collectible Show & Sale
Kitchener Memorial Auditorium, Kitchener, Ontario
Usually early May.
For information on times and location:
George or Jackie Benninger
P.O. Box 130, Durham, Ontario, N0G 1R0
Tel.: (519) 369-6950

Canadian Doulton & Collectable Fair
Toronto, Ontario
Usually early September.
For information on times and location:
George or Jackie Benninger
P.O. Box 130, Durham, Ontario N0G 1R0
Tel.: (519) 369-6950

FURTHER READING

Storybook Figures

The Charlton Standard Catalogue of Bunnykins, by Jean Dale and Louise Irvine
The Charlton Standard Catalogue of Royal Doulton Storybook Figurines, by Jean Dale
Collecting Cartoon Classics and other Character Figures, by Louise Irvine
Royal Doulton Bunnykins Figures, by Louise Irvine
Bunnykins Collectors Book, by Louise Irvine
Beatrix Potter Figures and Giftware, edited by Louise Irvine
The Beswick Price Guide, by Harvey May

Animals, Figures and Character Jugs

Royal Doulton Figures, by Desmond Eyles, Louise Irvine and Valerie Baynton
The Charlton Standard Catalogue of Beswick Animals, by Diane & John Callow and Marilyn & Peter Sweet
The Charlton Standard Catalogue of Royal Doulton Animals, by Jean Dale
The Charlton Standard Catalogue of Royal Doulton Beswick Figurines, by Jean Dale
The Charlton Standard Catalogue of Royal Doulton Beswick Jugs, by Jean Dale
Collecting Beswick - A Guide to Horses, Ponies and Foals, by Marilyn Sweet
Collecting Character and Toby Jugs, by Jocelyn Lukins
Collecting Doulton Animals, by Jocelyn Lukins
Doulton Flambé Animals, by Jocelyn Lukins
The Character Jug Collectors Handbook, by Kevin Pearson
The Doulton Figure Collectors Handbook, by Kevin Pearson

General

The Charlton Standard Catalogue of Beswick Pottery, by Diane and John Callow
Discovering Royal Doulton, by Michael Doulton
The Doulton Story, by Paul Atterbury and Louise Irvine
Royal Doulton Series Wares, by Louise Irvine (Vols. 1-5)
Limited Edition Loving Cups and Jugs, by Louise Irvine and Richard Dennis
Doulton for the Collector, by Jocelyn Lukins
Doulton Kingsware Flasks, by Jocelyn Lukins
Doulton Burslem Advertising Wares, by Jocelyn Lukins
Doulton Lambeth Advertising Wares, by Jocelyn Lukins
The Doulton Lambeth Wares, by Desmond Eyles
The Doulton Burslem Wares, by Desmond Eyles
Hannah Barlow, by Peter Rose
George Tinworth, by Peter Rose
Sir Henry Doulton Biography, by Edmund Gosse
Phillips Collectors Guide, by Catherine Braithwaite
Royal Doulton, by Jennifer Queree
John Beswick: A World of Imagination. Catalogue reprint (1950-1996)
Royal Doulton, by Julie McKeown

Magazines and Newsletters

Rabbiting On (Bunnykins Newsletter) Contact Leah Selig: 2 Harper Street, Merrylands 2160
   New South Wales, Australia. Tel./Fax 61 2 9637 2410 (International), 02 637 2410 (Australia)
Collect it! (Contact subscription department at: P.O. Box 3658, Bracknell, Berkshire RG12 7XZ.
   Telephone: (1344) 868280 or e-mail: collectit@dialpipex.com
Collecting Doulton Magazine, contact Doug Pinchin, P.O. Box 310, Richmond, Surrey TW9 1FS, England
Doulton News, published by Thorndon Antiques & Fine China Ltd., edited by David Harcourt
   P.O. Box 12-076 (109 Molesworth Street), Wellington, New Zealand
Beswick Quarterly (Beswick Newsletter) Contacr Laura Rock-Smith: 10 Holmes Court, Sayville
   N.Y. 11782-2408, U.S.A. Tel./Fax (516) 589-9027

SECTION ONE
SERIES WARE

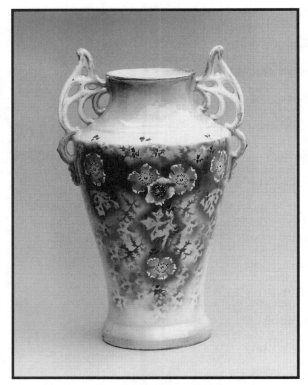

Victoria No. 1 Deco 3013

CM SERIES

In addition to the "contemporary" models of animals and birds (see *The Charlton Standard Catalogue of Beswick Animals*) which formed part of this series, Colin Melbourne also modelled a collection of nineteen ornamental pieces, mainly bowls and vases.

These items, as with the animals and birds, represented a break with the Beswick tradition and ventured into an area where there were unsatisfied demands. It was an attempt to produce commercially, wares which had before that time been the province of the studio potter.

Their appeal relied on their shape, enhanced by the texture of the glaze and the decoration, for which James Hayward, the Decorating Manager at that time, was responsible. The colours were subdued and subtle with glazes combining the use of gloss and matt finishes, in a variety of colours. Examples are also known decorated in copper lustre. The shapes were intended to match the contemporary scene of the time, and an advertisement in January, 1957 proclaimed "Modern in Conception - High Aesthetic Merit and Workmanship."

Today these shapes are either very much admired or thoroughly disliked, there does not seem to be room for half measures! Following their introduction their popularity proved to be relatively short-lived, as most had been withdrawn by 1963.

Shape 1392 Vase

Designer: Colin Melbourne in 1956
Issued: 1957 - by 1963
Height: 9 ½", 24.0 cm
Colour: Assorted colours, including copper lustre

Market	Range
U.S.A.	$65.00 - 100.00
Canada	$100.00 - 150.00
U.K.	£40.00 - 60.00

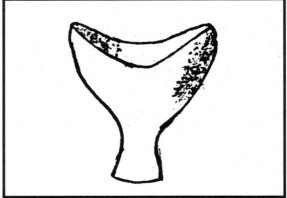

Shape 1393 Vase

Designer: Colin Melbourne in 1956
Issued: 1957 - by 1963
Height: 5 ¾", 14.6 cm
Colour: Assorted colours, including copper lustre

Market	Range
U.S.A.	$45.00 - 65.00
Canada	$65.00 - 100.00
U.K.	£25.00 - 45.00

Shape 1394 Vase

Designer: Colin Melbourne in 1956
Issued: 1957 - by 1963
Height: 7", 17.8 cm
Colour: Assorted colours, including copper lustre

Market	Range
U.S.A.	$45.00 - 65.00
Canada	$65.00 - 100.00
U.K.	£25.00 - 45.00

Shape 1395 Vase

Designer: Colin Melbourne in 1956
Issued: 1957 - by 1962
Height :   11 ¾", 29.8 cm
Colour: Assorted colours, including copper lustre

Market	Range
U.S.A.	$65.00 - 100.00
Canada	$100.00 - 150.00
U.K.	£40.00 - 60.00

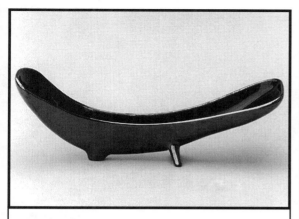

Shape 1396 Bowl

Designer: Colin Melbourne in 1956
Issued: 1957 - by 1963
Length: 10 ½", 26.7 cm
Colour: Assorted colours, including copper lustre

Market	Range
U.S.A.	$65.00 - 100.00
Canada	$100.00 - 150.00
U.K.	£40.00 - 60.00

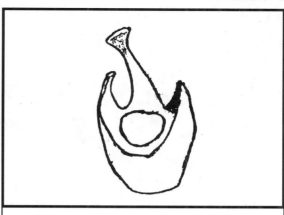

Shape 1397 Vase

Designer: Colin Melbourne in 1956
Issued: 1957 - by 1963
Height :   7 ¾", 19.7 cm
Colour: Assorted colours, including copper lustre

Market	Range
U.S.A.	$45.00 - 65.00
Canada	$65.00 - 100.00
U.K.	£25.00 - 45.00

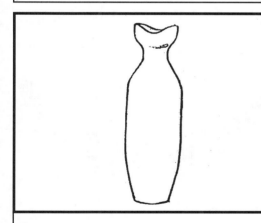

Shape 1398 Vase

Designer: Colin Melbourne in 1956
Issued: 1957 - by 1963
Height: 11 ½", 29.2 cm
Colour: Assorted colours, including copper lustre

Market	Range
U.S.A.	$65.00 - 100.00
Canada	$100.00 - 150.00
U.K.	£40.00 - 60.00

Shape 1399 Vase

Designer: Colin Melbourne in 1956
Issued: 1957 - by 1963
Height :   6", 15.0 cm
Colour: Assorted colours, including copper lustre

Market	Range
U.S.A.	$45.00 - 65.00
Canada	$65.00 - 100.00
U.K.	£25.00 - 45.00

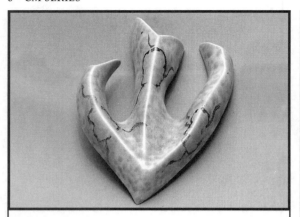

Photograph not
available
at press time

Shape 1400 Wall vase

Designer:	Colin Melbourne in 1956
Issued:	1957 - by 1963
Height:	7 ½", 19.1 cm
Colour:	Assorted colours, including copper lustre

Market	Range
U.S.A.	$45.00 - 65.00
Canada	$65.00 - 100.00
U.K.	£25.00 - 45.00

Shape 1401 Vase

Designer:	Colin Melbourne in 1956
Issued:	1957 - by 1963
Size:	Unknown
Colour:	Assorted colours, including copper lustre

Market	Range
U.S.A.	$45.00 - 65.00
Canada	$65.00 - 100.00
U.K.	£25.00 - 45.00

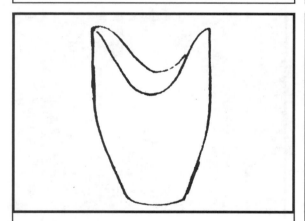

Shape 1402 Vase

Designer:	Colin Melbourne in 1956
Issued:	1957 - by 1963
Height:	7 ½", 19.1 cm
Colour:	Assorted colours, including copper lustre

Market	Range
U.S.A.	$45.00 - 65.00
Canada	$65.00 - 100.00
U.K.	£25.00 - 45.00

Shape 1403 Bowl

Designer:	Colin Melbourne in 1956
Issued:	1957 - by 1969
Length:	14 ½", 36.8 cm
Colour:	Assorted colours, including copper lustre

Market	Range
U.S.A.	$65.00 - 100.00
Canada	$100.00 - 150.00
U.K.	£40.00 - 60.00

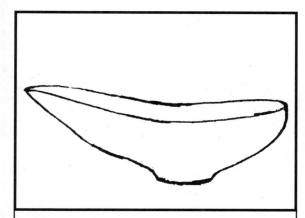

Shape 1404 Bowl

Designer:	Colin Melbourne in 1956
Issued:	1957 - by 1966
Length:	9 ¾", 24.7 cm
Colour:	Assorted colours, including copper lustre

Market	Range
U.S.A.	$65.00 - 100.00
Canada	$100.00 - 150.00
U.K.	£40.00 - 60.00

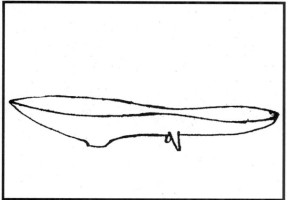

Shape 1405 Bowl

Designer:	Colin Melbourne in 1956
Issued:	1957 - by 1963
Length:	14", 35.5 cm
Colour:	Assorted colours, including copper lustre

Market	Range
U.S.A.	$65.00 - 100.00
Canada	$100.00 - 150.00
U.K.	£40.00 - 60.00

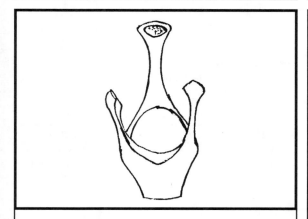

Shape 1408 Pot holder

Designer:	Colin Melbourne in 1956
Issued:	1957 - by 1963
Height:	14", 35.5 cm
Colour:	Assorted colours, including copper lustre

Market	Range
U.S.A.	$65.00 - 100.00
Canada	$100.00 - 150.00
U.K.	£40.00 - 60.00

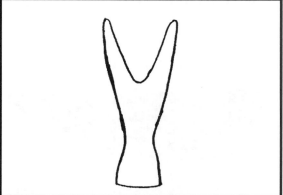

Shape 1466 Vase

Designer:	Colin Melbourne in 1956
Issued:	1957 - by 1963
Height :	8 ¾", 22.2 cm
Colour:	Assorted colours, including copper lustre

Market	Range
U.S.A.	$65.00 - 100.00
Canada	$100.00 - 150.00
U.K.	£40.00 - 60.00

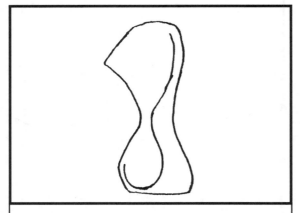

Shape 1477 Lamp base

Designer: Colin Melbourne in 1957
Issued: 1957 - by 1963
Size: Unknown
Colour: Assorted colours, including copper lustre

Market	Range
U.S.A.	$45.00 - 65.00
Canada	$65.00 - 100.00
U.K.	£25.00 - 45.00

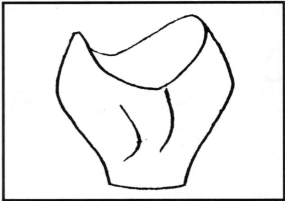

Shape 1478 Pot vase

Designer: Colin Melbourne in 1957
Issued: 1957 - by 1963
Height: 6 ½", 16.5 cm
Colour: Assorted colours, including copper lustre

Market	Range
U.S.A.	$45.00 - 65.00
Canada	$65.00 - 100.00
U.K.	£25.00 - 45.00

Shape 1479 Bowl

Designer: Colin Melbourne in 1957
Issued: 1957 - by 1966
Length: 8 ½", 21.6 cm
Colour: Assorted colours, including copper lustre

Market	Range
U.S.A.	$45.00 - 65.00
Canada	$65.00 - 100.00
U.K.	£25.00 - 45.00

Note: Price ranges are retail market indicators of prices for models under the following conditions:
- Lower end of range = price of monochrome models
- Higher end of range = price of multicoloured models

COTTAGE WARE

Items of tableware modelled to depict thatched cottages were first introduced at the British Industries Fair in April, 1933, and were an immediate success. Their popularity is obvious by the fact that most items continued to be available until they were all withdrawn at the beginning of 1971. Examples of another item, modelled as a cottage with a removable roof, have also been found. This is an earlier piece, as it does not carry a shape number, it is illustrated on page xiii of the introduction.

The "Cottage Ware" series had an embossed and hand-painted decoration with trees and flowers. The thatch was usually light brown, with the tops of the chimneys painted in dark brown. Shape numbers 243, 247, 248 and 1128 however, have been found with grey chimney tops.

Some shapes were produced during the 1930s only, with the thatch in "helio-blue." These items have a more detailed and colourful decoration, and in our experience are very rare.

The numbered series consisted of 23 items, all in a gloss finish and included a cheese dish in the shape of Log Cabin and a cruet of "Tudor" houses.

Shape 239   Teapot, large

Designer:	Mr. White in 1932
Issued:	1933 - 1970
Height:	6″, 15.0 cm
Colour:	Cream, light and dark brown

Description	U.S. $	Can. $	U.K. £
Teapot, large	110.00	165.00	65.00

Shape 240   Teapot, small

Designer:	Mr. White in 1932
Issued:	1933 - 1970
Height :	5 ¼″, 13.3 cm
Colour:	Cream, light and dark brown

Description	U.S. $	Can. $	U.K. £
Teapot, small	95.00	150.00	55.00

Shape 241   Hot water jug

Designer:	Mr. White in 1932
Issued:	1933 - 1970
Height:	6 ¾″, 17.2 cm
Colour:	Cream, light and dark brown

Description	U.S. $	Can. $	U.K. £
Hot water jug	110.00	165.00	65.00

Shape 242   Milk jug

Designer:	Mr. White in 1932
Issued:	1933 - 1970
Height:	4 ½″, 11.9 cm
Colour:	Cream, light and dark brown

Description	U.S. $	Can. $	U.K. £
Milk jug	65.00	100.00	40.00

Shape 243   Covered sugar, round

Designer:	Mr. White in 1932
Issued:	1933 - 1970
Height:	4 ¾", 12.1 cm
Colour:	Cream, light and dark brown

Description	U.S. $	Can. $	U.K. £
Covered sugar round	110.00	165.00	65.00

Note: Also known with grey chimney top.

Shape 244   Covered preserve, rectangular

Designer:	Mr. White in 1932
Issued:	1. 1933 - 1970
	2. 1930s only
Height :	3 ¾", 9.5 cm
Colour:	1. Cream, light and dark brown
	2. Helio-blue

Colour	U.S. $	Can. $	U.K. £
1. Cream and browns	65.00	100.00	40.00
2. Helio-blue		Very Rare	

Shape 245   Open Sugar

Designer:	Mr. White in 1932
Issued:	1. 1933 - 1970
	2. 1930s only
Height:	2 ¾", 7.0 cm
Colour:	1. Cream, light and dark brown
	2. Helio-blue

Colour	U.S. $	Can. $	U.K. £
1. Cream and browns	50.00	75.00	30.00
2. Helio-blue		Very Rare	

Shape 246   Cream jug

Designer:	Mr. White in 1932
Issued:	1933 - 1970
Height :	2 ½", 6.4 cm
Colour:	Cream, light and dark brown

Description	U.S. $	Can. $	U.K. £
Cream jug	40.00	60.00	25.00

Shape 247   Covered butter, round

Designer:	Mr. White in 1932
Issued:	1933 - 1970
Height:	4 ¾", 12.1 cm
Colour:	Cream, light and dark brown, and green

Description	U.S. $	Can. $	U.K. £
Covered butter, round	100.00	150.00	60.00

Note: Also known with grey chimney top.

Shape 248   Covered muffin, round

Designer:	Mr. White in 1932
Issued:	1933 - 1969
Height :	5 ½", 14.0 cm
Colour:	Cream, light and dark brown, and green

Description	U.S. $	Can. $	U.K. £
Covered muffin, round	150.00	225.00	85.00

Note: Also known with grey chimney top.

Shape 249   Biscuit barrel, square

Designer:	Mr. White in 1932
Issued:	1933 - 1970
Height:	7", 17.8 cm
Colour:	Cream, light and dark brown, and green

Description	U.S. $	Can. $	U.K. £
Chrome handle	120.00	175.00	70.00
Rafia handle	125.00	190.00	75.00
Without handle	100.00	150.00	60.00

Note: This biscuit barrel came with either a chrome, a
raffia handle, or without a handle.

Shape 250   Cheese dish, large

Designer:	Mr. White in 1932
Issued:	1. 1933 - 1970
	2. 1930s only
Height :	6 ¼", 15.9 cm
Colour:	1. Cream, light and dark brown, and green
	2. Helio-blue

Colour	U.S. $	Can. $	U.K. £
1. Cream and browns	85.00	125.00	50.00
2. Helio-blue		Very Rare	

Shape 251   Cheese dish, medium

Designer: Mr. White in 1932
Issued: 1933 - 1970
Height: 5 ¼", 13.3 cm
Colour: Cream, light and dark brown, and green

Description	U.S. $	Can. $	U.K. £
Cheese dish, medium	75.00	115.00	45.00

Shape 252   Log cabin cheese dish

Designer: Mr. White in 1932
Issued: 1. 1933 - 1970
            2. 1930s only
Height :   5", 12.7 cm
Colour: 1. Cream, light and dark brown, and green
            2. Helio-blue

Colour	U.S. $	Can. $	U.K. £
1. Cream, brown, green	65.00	100.00	40.00
2. Helio-blue		Very Rare	

Shape 253   Shakespeare cruet set
**   (three pieces on a base)**

Designer: Mr. White in 1932
Issued: 1933 - 1970
Height: 3 ¼", 8.3 cm
Colour: Cream, light and dark brown, and green

Description	U.S. $	Can. $	U.K. £
Shakespeare cruet set	65.00	100.00	40.00

Shape 254   Tobacco jar with lid, round

Designer: Albert Hallam in 1932
Issued: 1933 - by 1954
Height :   5", 12.7 cm
Colour: Cream, light and dark brown, and green

Description	U.S. $	Can. $	U.K. £
Tobacco jar with lid		Very Rare	

Photograph not
available
at press time

Shape 255   Tobacco jar

Designer: Albert Hallam in 1932
Issued: 1933 - by 1954
Size: Unknown
Colour: Cream, light and dark brown, and green

Description	U.S. $	Can. $	U.K. £
Tobacco jar		Very Rare	

Shape 273   Cheese dish, small

Designer: Mr. Symcox in 1932
Issued: 1933 - 1970
Height :   4 ½", 11.9 cm
Colour: Cream, light and dark brown, and green

Description	U.S. $	Can. $	U.K. £
Cheese dish, small	75.00	100.00	45.00

Shape 1115   Cream jug

Designer: Arthur Gredington in 1948
Issued: 1948 - 1970
Height: 3 ½", 8.9 cm
Colour: Cream, light and dark brown, and green

Description	U.S. $	Can. $	U.K. £
Cream jug	40.00	50.00	20.00

Shape 1128   Covered sugar

Designer: Unknown
Issued: 1948 - 1970
Height :   3 ¾", 9.5 cm
Colour: Cream, light and dark brown, and green

Description	U.S. $	Can. $	U.K. £
Covered sugar	60.00	90.00	35.00

Note: Based on shape 245, and the lid from shape 243.
     Also known with grey chimney top.

Shape 1149   Cup and saucer

Designer:	Albert Hallam in 1949
Issued:	1949 - 1962
Height:	Cup — 2 ¾", 7.0 cm
Diameter:	Saucer — 5 ¾", 14.6 cm
Colour:	Cream, light and dark brown, and green

Description	U.S. $	Can. $	U.K. £
Cup and saucer	110.00	165.00	65.00

Shape 1196   Plate, small house

Designer:	Unknown
Issued:	c.1951 - 1962
Diameter:	6 ½", 16.5 cm
Colour:	Cream, light and dark brown, and green

Description	U.S. $	Can. $	U.K. £
Plate	85.00	125.00	50.00

Shape 1211   Plate, large house

Designer:	Albert Hallam in 1951
Issued:	1951 - 1962
Diameter:	8", 20.3 cm
Colour:	Cream, light and dark brown, and green

Description	U.S. $	Can. $	U.K. £
Plate	85.00	125.00	50.00

Stand for Teapot

Designer:	Unknown
Issued:	Unknown
Diameter:	6 ¼", 15.9 cm
Colour:	Green

Description	U.S. $	Can. $	U.K. £
Stand for teapot	35.00	50.00	20.00

Cottage Ware Series Ware

Shape 247 Covered Butter   Shape 244 Covered Preserve   Shape 250 Cheese dish, large

GEORGE SMITH'S
FLOWER CONTAINERS

George Smith was the design consultant for a series of pottery containers produced especially for use in flower arranging. The collection included classical shapes for traditional arrangements, as well as unusual shapes intended to complement the more abstract style of presentation popular in the late 1960s. The colours of the containers were carefully chosen to enhance both floral and foliage displays and a brochure was issued in 1968 illustrating some of the containers with examples of their use.

There were twenty designs in total, the last four being added only a short while before they were all withdrawn.

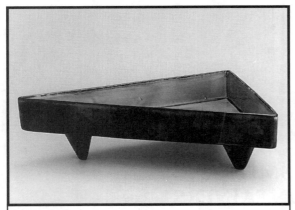

**Shape 1985 Flower container, triangular in shape
                with three feet**

Modeller:	Albert Hallam in 1964
Issued:	1965 - 1972
Size:	14" x 8" x 4", 35.5 x 20.3 x 10.1 cm
Colour:	1. Metallic blue 2. Metallic black/blue
	3. Metallic black/mustard
	4. White - matt

Market	Range
U.S.A.	$30.00 - 85.00
Canada	$45.00 - 110.00
U.K.	£15.00 - 40.00

Shape 1986 Chalice vase

Modeller:	Albert Hallam in 1964
Issued:	1965 - by 1972
Height :	12 ½", 31.7 cm
Colour:	White - matt

Description	U.S. $	Can. $	U.K. £
Chalice vase	60.00	90.00	35.00

Shape 1987 Bowl on pedestal

Modeller:	Albert Hallam in 1964
Issued:	1965 - by 1972
Size:	10" x 10 ½", 25.4 x 26.7 cm
Colour:	White - matt

Description	U.S. $	Can. $	U.K. £
Pedestal bowl	60.00	90.00	35.00

Shape 1988 Melon bowl

Modeller:	Albert Hallam in 1964
Issued:	1965 - by 1972
Size:	10" x 5 ½", 25.4 x 14 cm
Colour:	1. Matt green/glossy mustard
	2. Matt grey/glossy blue
	3. White - matt

Market	Range
U.S.A.	$30.00 - 85.00
Canada	$45.00 - 110.00
U.K.	£15.00 - 40.00

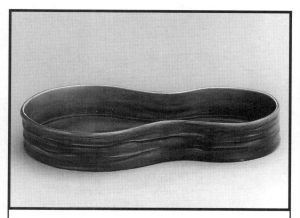

Shape 1989 Lake bowl

Modeller: Albert Hallam in 1964
Issued: 1965 - 1972
Size: 12 ¼" x 7 ½" x 2", 31.1 x 19.1 x 5 cm
Colour: 1. Matt green/glossy mustard
                2. Matt grey/glossy blue
                3. Metallic black 4. White - matt

Market	Range
U.S.A.	$25.00 - 65.00
Canada	$40.00 - 75.00
U.K.	£15.00 - 30.00

Shape 2005 Cherub/Cupid vase

Modeller: Albert Hallam, Mr. Murphy in 1965
Issued: 1965 - by 1972
Height :   12 ½", 31.7 cm
Colour: 1. Metallic black
                2. Opaque white

Market	Range
U.S.A.	$85.00 - 125.00
Canada	$125.00 - 190.00
U.K.	£50.00 - 75.00

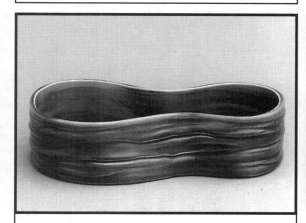

Shape 2068 Lake bowl

Modeller: Albert Hallam in 1966
Issued: 1967 - 1972
Size: 8 ¼" x 2", 21 x 5 cm
Colour: 1. Matt green/glossy mustard
                2. Matt grey/glossy blue
                3. White - matt

Market	Range
U.S.A.	$20.00 - 40.00
Canada	$30.00 - 60.00
U.K.	£10.00 - 25.00

Shape 2069 Bowl

Modeller: Albert Hallam in 1966
Issued: 1967 - by 1972
Size: 8" x 3 ½", 20.3 x 8.9 cm
Colour: 1. Matt green/glossy mustard
                2. Matt grey/glossy blue

Market	Range
U.S.A.	$25.00 - 40.00
Canada	$40.00 - 60.00
U.K.	£15.00 - 25.00

Shape 2081 Round vase

Modeller:	Graham Tongue in 1967
Issued:	1968 - by 1972
Height:	4", 10.1 cm
Colour:	1. Matt green/glossy mustard
	2. Matt grey/glossy blue

Market	Range
U.S.A.	$25.00 - 40.00
Canada	$40.00 - 60.00
U.K.	£15.00 - 25.00

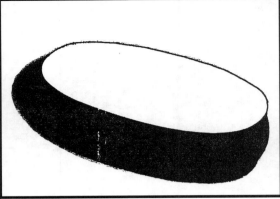

Shape 2153 Oval bowl

Modeller:	Graham Tongue in 1967
Issued:	1968 - 1972
Size :	12" x 3 ½", 30.5 x 8.9 cm
Colour:	1. Golden green/lime green
	2. White - matt

Market	Range
U.S.A.	$20.00 - 35.00
Canada	$30.00 - 50.00
U.K.	£10.00 - 20.00

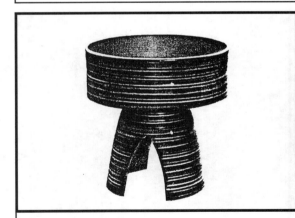

Shape 2158 Bowl on feet

Modeller:	Albert Hallam in 1967
Issued:	1968 - 1972
Height:	6 ½", 16.4 cm
Diameter:	6", 15 cm
Colour:	1. Solid lime green
	2. Solid forest green

Market	Range
U.S.A.	$25.00 - 40.00
Canada	$40.00 - 60.00
U.K.	£15.00 - 25.00

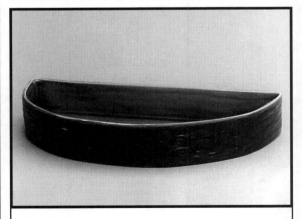

Shape 2159 Semi-circular bowl

Modeller:	Albert Hallam in 1967
Issued:	1968 - by 1972
Size:	12" x 6" x 2", 30.5 x 15 x 5 cm
Colour:	1. Charcoal/celadon
	2. Matt grey/glossy blue

Market	Range
U.S.A.	$20.00 - 40.00
Canada	$40.00 - 60.00
U.K.	£15.00 - 25.00

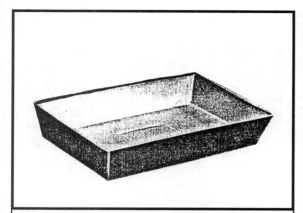

Shape 2160 Rectangular tray

Modeller: Albert Hallam in 1967
Issued: 1968 - by 1972
Size: 13" x 8" x 2 ¼", 33 x 20.3 x 5.7 cm
Colour: 1. Matt golden green/celadon
            2. Matt sage green/mustard

Market	Range
U.S.A.	$20.00 - 40.00
Canada	$30.00 - 60.00
U.K.	£10.00 - 20.00

Shape 2161 Bowl on pedestal

Modeller: Albert Hallam in 1967
Issued: 1968 - 1972
Height :   10 ½", 26.7 cm
Diameter: 4, 10.1 cm
Colour: 1. Solid celadon
            2. Charcoal/celadon

Market	Range
U.S.A.	$25.00 - 35.00
Canada	$40.00 - 50.00
U.K.	£15.00 - 20.00

Shape 2162 Bowl

Modeller: Albert Hallam in 1967
Issued: 1968 - 1972
Height: 7", 17.8 cm
Diameter: 8 ½", 21.6 cm
Colour: Matt golden/celadon

Description	U.S.$	Can. $	U.K.£
Bowl	50.00	75.00	30.00

Shape 2163 Footed tray

Modeller: Albert Hallam in 1967
Issued: 1968 - by 1972
Size: 11 ½" x 7" x 3", 29.2 x 17.8 x 7.6 cm
Colour: 1. Forest green/celadon
            2. Solid celadon

Market	Range
U.S.A.	$25.00 - 40.00
Canada	$40.00 - 60.00
U.K.	£15.00 - 25.00

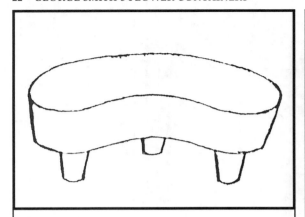

Shape 2335 Bowl

Modeller:	Albert Hallam in 1970
Issued:	1971 - 1972
Size:	11 ¾" x 4", 29.8 x 10.1 cm
Colour:	1. Mushroom/olive green
	2. White - matt

Market	Range
U.S.A.	$25.00 - 40.00
Canada	$40.00 - 60.00
U.K.	£15.00 - 25.00

Shape 2336 Bowl

Modeller:	Albert Hallam in 1970
Issued:	1971 - 1972
Size :	9" x 6", 22.9 x 15 cm
Colour:	1. Brown/blue
	2. White - matt

Market	Range
U.S.A.	$25.00 - 40.00
Canada	$40.00 - 60.00
U.K.	£15.00 - 25.00

Shape 2337 Bowl

Modeller:	Albert Hallam in 1970
Issued:	1971 - 1972
Height:	8", 20.3 cm
Colour:	1. Brown/blue, green
	2. White - matt

Market	Range
U.S.A.	$25.00 - 40.00
Canada	$40.00 - 60.00
U.K.	£15.00 - 25.00

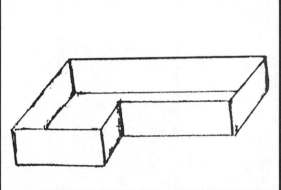

Shape 2338 Bowl

Modeller:	Graham Tongue in 1970
Issued:	1971 - 1972
Size:	11" x 2", 27.9 x 5 cm
Colour:	1. Green/celadon
	2. White - matt

Market	Range
U.S.A.	$20.00 - 40.00
Canada	$30.00 - 60.00
U.K.	£10.00 - 25.00

HEATHER AND GORSE

This series consisted of fourteen shapes, all with a gloss finish. The background colour was either shaded peach or a shaded green. The heather decoration was raised and showed a spray of purple and yellow heather with green foliage and brown stems.

There were also seven undecorated shapes which corresponded with Heather and Gorse shapes as follows:

1900 with 1907, 1901 with 1908, 1902 with 1909, 1903 with 1911, 1904 with 1910, 1905 with 1916 and 1906 with 1912. These shapes (1900-1906) were possibly not put into production.

Prices are for either background colour.

Shape 1907 Elongated dish

Designer:	Albert Hallam in 1963	
Issued:	1964 - 1966/67	
Length :	10", 25.4 cm	
Colour:	Light peach or light green background, purple, yellow and green heather	

Description	U.S.$	Can.$	U.K.£
Elongated dish	35.00	50.00	20.00

Shape 1908 Elongated dish

Designer:	Albert Hallam in 1963	
Issued:	1964 - 1966/67	
Length:	10", 25.4 cm	
Colour:	Light peach or light green background, purple, yellow and green heather	

Description	U.S.$	Can.$	U.K.£
Elongated dish	35.00	50.00	20.00

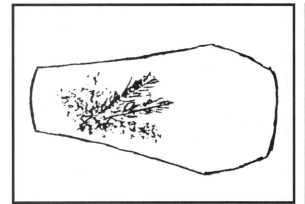

Shape 1909 Dish

Designer:	Albert Hallam in 1963	
Issued:	1964 - 1966/67	
Length:	12", 30.5 cm	
Colour:	Light peach or light green background, purple, yellow and green heather	

Description	U.S.$	Can.$	U.K.£
Dish	35.00	50.00	20.00

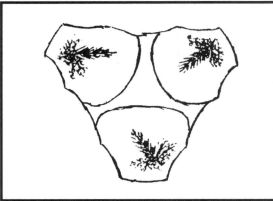

Shape 1910 Triple dish

Designer:	Albert Hallam in 1963	
Issued:	1964 - 1966/67	
Length:	12", 30.5 cm	
Colour:	Light peach or light green background, purple, yellow and green heather	

Description	U.S.$	Can.$	U.K.£
Triple dish	40.00	60.00	25.00

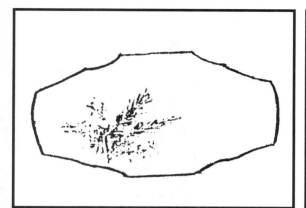

Shape 1911 Dish

Designer:	Albert Hallam in 1963
Issued:	1964 - 1966/67
Lenght:	13", 33.0 cm
Colour:	Light peach or light green background, purple, yellow and green heather

Description	U.S.$	Can.$	U.K.£
Dish	35.00	50.00	20.00

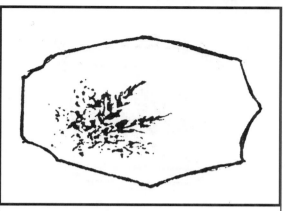

Shape 1912 Dish

Designer:	Albert Hallam in 1963
Issued:	1964 - 1966/67
Length:	8", 20.3 cm
Colour:	Light peach or light green background, purple, yellow and green heather

Description	U.S.$	Can.$	U.K.£
Dish	25.00	40.00	15.00

Shape 1916 Double dish

Designer:	Albert Hallam in 1963
Issued:	1964 - 1966/67
Length:	13", 33.0 cm
Colour:	Light peach or light green background, purple, yellow and green heather

Description	U.S.$	Can.$	U.K.£
Double dish	35.00	50.00	20.00

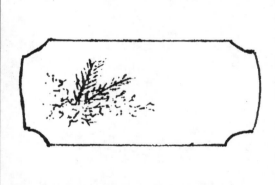

Shape 1924 Sandwich tray

Designer:	Albert Hallam in 1964
Issued:	1964 - 1966/67
Length:	11", 27.9 cm
Colour:	Light peach or light green background, purple, yellow and green heather

Description	U.S.$	Can.$	U.K.£
Sandwich tray	35.00	50.00	20.00

Shape 1925 Preserve with lid

Designer:	Albert Hallam in 1964	
Issued:	1964 - 1966/67	
Height:	3", 7.6 cm	
Colour:	Light peach or light green background, purple, yellow and green heather	

Description	U.S.$	Can.$	U.K.£
Preserve with lid	40.00	60.00	25.00

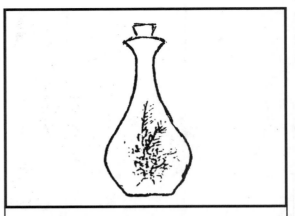

Shape 1926 Vinegar with stopper

Designer:	Albert Hallam in 1964	
Issued:	1964 - 1966/67	
Height:	6", 15.0 cm	
Colour:	Light peach or light green background, purple, yellow and green heather	

Description	U.S.$	Can.$	U.K.£
Vinegar with stopper	40.00	60.00	25.00

Shape 1927-1928 Salt and pepper

Designer:	Albert Hallam in 1964	
Issued:	1964 - 1966/67	
Height:	5 ½", 14.0 cm	
Colour:	Light peach or light green background, purple, yellow and green heather	

Description	U.S.$	Can.$	U.K.£
Salt and pepper	40.00	60.00	25.00

Note: Price listed is for pair.

Shape 1929 Salad bowl, footed

Designer:	Albert Hallam in 1964	
Issued:	1964 - 1966/67	
Size:	Unknown	
Colour:	Light peach or light green background, purple, yellow and green heather	

Description	U.S.$	Can.$	U.K.£
Salad bowl, footed	50.00	75.00	30.00

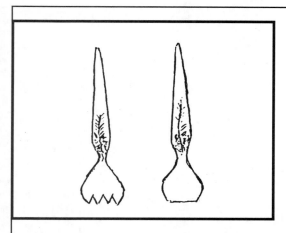

**Shape 1930 Salad servers, decorated with a sprig
of heather only**

Designer: Albert Hallam in 1964
Issued: 1964 - 1966/67
Length: 9", 22.9 cm
Colour: Light peach or light green background,
                purple, yellow and green heather

Description	U.S.$	Can.$	U.K.£
Salad servers	40.00	60.00	25.00

Note: Price ranges are retail market indicators of prices for models under the following conditions:
- Lower end of range = price of monochrome models
- Higher end of range = price of multicoloured models

Heather and Gorse Series Ware
Shape 1908 Elongated dish

Shape 1927 Salt

Shape 1928 Pepper

HORS-D'OEUVRE

The decoration for this attractive and colourful series included combinations of the following fruit and vegetables: bananas, grapes, lemons, pineapples, tomatoes, strawberries, cherries, onions, mushrooms, asparagus and aubergines (eggplant). Also a carafe of wine, a wine glass and a candlestick were used on some of the items. The background was white with a gloss finish, to set off the many colours used for the decorations.

Mostly the seventeen shapes listed here were new introductions styled for use as hors-d'oeuvre ware and decorated as above, others were existing shapes similarly decorated. Also, patterns such as oranges and lemons, and even a blue rose have been seen on Hors D' Oeuvre shapes.

Shape 1444 Plate, contemporary shape
Designer: Albert Hallam in 1956
Issued: 1960 - 1963
Width: 8 ½", 21.6 cm
Colour: White with multi-coloured design

Description	U.S. $	Can. $	U.K. £
Plate, contemporary shape	20.00	30.00	10.00

Shape 1586 Dish with four sections
Designer: Albert Hallam in 1959
Issued: 1960 - 1963
Size: 9 ¾" x 6 ¾", 24.7 x 17.2 cm
Colour: White with multi-coloured designs

Description	U.S. $	Can. $	U.K. £
Dish, four sections	40.00	60.00	25.00

Shape 1617 Dish, square
Designer: Mr. Wood in 1959
Issued: 1960 - 1963
Width: 4", 10.1 cm
Colour: White with multi-coloured design

Description	U.S. $	Can. $	U.K. £
Dish, square	20.00	30.00	10.00

Shape 1623 Meat dish, contemporary shape
Designer: Mr. Wood in 1959
Issued: 1960 - 1963
Size: 12 ½" x 10 ¼", 31.7 x 26.0 cm
Colour: White with multi-coloured design

Description	U.S. $	Can. $	U.K. £
Meat dish, contemporary	35.00	50.00	20.00

Shape 1635 Rectangular dish
Designer: Albert Hallam in 1959
Issued: 1960 - 1963
Size: 7 ¾" x 5 ¼", 19.7 x 13.3 cm
Colour: White with multi-coloured design

Description	U.S. $	Can. $	U.K. £
Rectangular dish	25.00	30.00	10.00

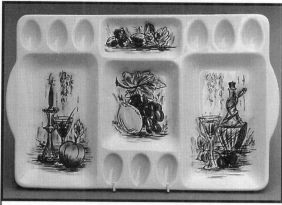

**Shape 1636 Large rectangular dish with four
                sections plus egg holders**
Designer: Albert Hallam in 1959
Issued: 1960 - 1963
Size: 18" x 11 ¾", 45.7 x 29.8 cm
Colour: White and light blue, with multi-coloured
            designs

Description	U.S. $	Can. $	U.K. £
Rectangular dish	65.00	100.00	40.00

**Shape 1637 Large round dish with six sections
                around a centre one**
Designer: Albert Hallam in 1959
Issued: 1960 - 1963
Diameter: 14 ½", 36.8 cm
Colour: White with multi-coloured designs

Description	U.S. $	Can. $	U.K. £
Round dish, six sections	50.00	75.00	40.00

Shape 1638 Large dish with five sections
Designer: Albert Hallam in 1959
Issued: 1960 - 1963
Size: 13 ¾" x 8 ¾", 34.9 x 22.2 cm
Colour: White with multi-coloured designs

Description	U.S. $	Can. $	U.K. £
Dish, five sections	50.00	75.00	30.00

Photograph not
available
at press time

Shape 1639 Dish with three sections

Designer:	Albert Hallam in 1959
Issued:	1960 - 1963
Size:	10 ¼" x 9", 26.0 x 22.9 cm
Colour:	White with multi-coloured designs

Description	U.S. $	Can. $	U.K. £
Dish, three sections	35.00	50.00	20.00

Shape 1640 Oval dish

Designer:	Albert Hallam in 1959
Issued:	1960 - 1963
Size:	8" x 5", 20.3 x 12.7 cm
Colour:	White with multi-coloured design

Description	U.S. $	Can. $	U.K. £
Oval dish	35.00	50.00	20.00

Shape 1665-1666 Pepper and Salt

Designer:	Albert Hallam in 1959
Issued:	1960 - 1963
Height:	4 ½", 11.9 cm
Colour:	White with multi-coloured designs

Description	U.S. $	Can. $	U.K. £
Pepper and Salt	35.00	50.00	20.00

Note: Price listed is for pair.

Shape 1667   Vinegar bottle marked with a "V"

Designer:	Albert Hallam in 1959
Issued:	1960 - 1963
Height:	5", 12.7 cm including stopper
Colour:	White with multi-coloured designs

Description	U.S. $	Can. $	U.K. £
Vinegar bottle	35.00	50.00	20.00

Note: This shape has also been seen without the "V" for
vinegar and would then have been intended for oil.
Priced listed is for each bottle.

Shape 1673 Fruit bowl, round
Designer: Albert Hallam in 1960
Issued: 1960 - 1963
Size: 9 ¼" x 3 ½", 23.5 x 8.9 cm
Colour: White with multi-coloured design

Description	U.S. $	Can. $	U.K. £
Fruit bowl, round	40.00	60.00	25.00

Shape 1674 Dish
Designer: Albert Hallam in 1960
Issued: 1960 - 1963
Size: 10 ¼" x 9", 26.0 x 22.9 cm
Colour: White with multi-coloured design

Description	U.S. $	Can. $	U.K. £
Dish	35.00	50.00	20.00

Shape 1689 Mexican hat, three sections
Designer: Albert Hallam in 1960
Issued: 1960 - 1963
Size: 8 ¼" x 3 ½", 21.0 x 8.9 cm
Colour: White with multi-coloured designs

Description	U.S. $	Can. $	U.K. £
Mexican hat, three sections	40.00	60.00	25.00

Shape 1693 Kidney-shaped dish
Designer: Albert Hallam in 1960
Issued: 1960 - 1963
Size: 9 ½" x 4 ½", 24.0 x 11.9 cm
Colour: White with multi-coloured design

Description	U.S. $	Can. $	U.K. £
Kidney-shaped dish	25.00	40.00	15.00

Hors-d'oeuvre Series Ware
Shape 1586 Dish with four sections

HUNTSMAN SERIES

The "Huntsman" series, sometimes referred to by collectors as the "Country" series, followed on closely after the Cottage Ware, and was designed in 1934.

The huntsman brandishing his crop and surrounded by his hounds created a colourful scene. The horse and hounds were in a pale brown. The leaves on the trees were green, and the grass was a paler green, with dark brown used for the tree trunks and the handles. The knobs were very attractive and made a lovely finishing touch, as they were in the shape of acorns.

There are only thirteen shapes in this series, all in a gloss finish. We believe that it would have been the intention to expand the set, but that the outbreak of war in 1939 brought about its early retirement. Except for the sugar dredger and the cruet set, where space was limited, the hunting scene was fully shown on all the pieces.

Shape 285   Jug

Designer:	Mr. Fletcher in 1934		
Issued:	1935 - by 1954		
Size:	5 ½", 14.0 cm		
Colour:	Light cream and assorted colours		

Description	U.S. $	Can. $	U.K. £
Jug	110.00	150.00	60.00

Shape 325   Teapot

Designer:	Mr. Fletcher in 1934		
Issued:	1935 - by 1954		
Height :	6 ¼", 15.9 cm		
Colour:	Light cream and assorted colours		

Description	U.S. $	Can. $	U.K. £
Teapot	140.00	210.00	85.00

Shape 326   Hot water jug

Designer:	Mr. Fletcher in 1934		
Issued:	1935 - by 1954		
Size:	Unknown		
Colour:	Light cream and assorted colours		

Description	U.S. $	Can. $	U.K. £
Hot water jug	140.00	210.00	85.00

Shape 327/336 Covered cheese dish in two sizes

Designer:	Mr. Fletcher in 1934		
Issued:	1935 - by 1954		
Size:	1. Large — unknown		
	2. Small — unknown		
Colour:	Light cream and assorted colours		

Description	U.S. $	Can. $	U.K. £
1. Shape 327, large	110.00	165.00	65.00
2. Shape 336, small	100.00	150.00	60.00

Shape 328 **Biscuit barrel, wicker covered handle**

Designer: Mr. Fletcher in 1934
Issued: 1935 - by 1954
Size: Unknown
Colour: Light cream and assorted colours

Description	U.S. $	Can. $	U.K. £
Biscuit barrel	160.00	235.00	95.00

Shape 329 **Sugar bowl**

Designer: Mr. Fletcher in 1934
Issued: 1935 - by 1954
Size: Unknown
Colour: Light cream and assorted colours

Description	U.S. $	Can. $	U.K. £
Sugar bowl	85.00	125.00	50.00

Shape 330 **Cream jug**

Designer: Mr. Fletcher in 1934
Issued: 1935 - by 1954
Size: Unknown
Colour: Light cream and assorted colours

Description	U.S. $	Can. $	U.K. £
Cream jug	85.00	125.00	50.00

Shape 331 **Preserve pot with lid**

Designer: Mr. Fletcher in 1934
Issued: 1935 - by 1954
Size: Unknown
Colour: Light cream and assorted colours

Description	U.S. $	Can. $	U.K. £
Preserve with lid	110.00	165.00	65.00

Shape 332   Covered butter

Designer:	Mr. Fletcher in 1934
Issued:	1935 - by 1954
Size:	Unknown
Colour:	Light cream and assorted colours

Description	U.S. $	Can. $	U.K. £
Covered butter	120.00	175.00	70.00

Shape 333   Sugar dredger

Designer:	Mr. Fletcher in 1934
Issued:	1935 - by 1954
Height:	5 ¼", 13.3 cm
Colour:	Light cream and assorted colours

Description	U.S. $	Can. $	U.K. £
Sugar dredger	85.00	125.00	50.00

Shape 334   Covered muffin dish

Designer:	Mr. Fletcher in 1934
Issued:	1935 - by 1954
Size:	Unknown
Colour:	Light cream and assorted colours

Description	U.S. $	Can. $	U.K. £
Covered muffin dish	140.00	215.00	85.00

Shape 335   Cruet set, salt, pepper and mustard on base

Designer:	Mr. Fletcher in 1934
Issued:	1935 - by 1954
Size:	Unknown
Colour:	Light cream and assorted colours

Description	U.S. $	Can. $	U.K. £
Cruet set	140.00	215.00	85.00

KASHAN

This range of ornamental ware was almost the last to be modelled and produced under the Beswick backstamp, following the change of ownership from Beswick to Royal Doulton in 1969. The origin of the name Kashan has not yet come to light, but the name probably relates to the style of the pottery, which is somewhat oriental in character. The designs, which are strongly incised, produce an immediate visual impact.

The range consisted of twelve items, of which nine were vases. All the items were available in four decorations: Turquoise/stone, solid green or pewter - gloss; white - matt.

Shape 2250 Vase
Designer: James Hayward, Albert Hallam in 1968
Issued: 1969 - 1972
Height: 9", 22.9 cm
Colour: 1. Pewter   3. Turquoise/stone
         2. Solid green   4. White

Colour	U.S. $	Can. $	U.K. £
1. Pewter	75.00	115.00	45.00
2. Solid green	75.00	115.00	45.00
3. Turquoise/stone	100.00	150.00	60.00
4. White		Rare	

Shape 2251 Vase
Designer: J. Hayward, A. Hallam, G. Tongue in 1968
Issued: 1969 - 1972
Height : 7", 17.8 cm
Colour: 1. Pewter   3. Turquoise/stone
         2. Solid green   4. White

Colour	U.S. $	Can. $	U.K. £
1. Pewter	60.00	90.00	35.00
2. Solid green	60.00	90.00	35.00
3. Turquoise/stone	75.00	115.00	45.00
4. White		Rare	

Shape 2252 Vase
Designer: James Hayward, Albert Hallam in 1968
Issued: 1969 - 1972
Height: 5 ½", 14.0 cm
Colour: 1. Pewter   3. Turquoise/stone
         2. Solid green   4. White

Colour	U.S. $	Can. $	U.K. £
1. Pewter	50.00	75.00	30.00
2. Solid green	50.00	75.00	30.00
3. Turquoise/stone	65.00	100.00	40.00
4. White		Rare	

Shape 2255 Vase
Designer: James Hayward, Graham Tongue in 1968
Issued: 1969 - 1972
Height: 10", 25.4 cm
Colour: 1. Pewter   3. Turquoise/stone
         2. Solid green   4. White

Colour	U.S. $	Can. $	U.K. £
1. Pewter	75.00	115.00	45.00
2. Solid green	75.00	115.00	45.00
3. Turquoise/stone	100.00	150.00	60.00
4. White		Rare	

Shape 2256 Vase
Designer: James Hayward, Graham Tongue in 1969
Issued: 1969 - 1972
Height: 8", 20.3 cm
Colour: 1. Pewter   3. Turquoise/stone
             2. Solid green   4. White

Colour	U.S. $	Can. $	U.K. £
1. Pewter	75.00	115.00	45.00
2. Solid green	75.00	115.00	45.00
3. Turquoise/stone	100.00	150.00	60.00
4. White		Rare	

Shape 2257 Vase
Designer: James Hayward, Albert Hallam in 1969
Issued: 1969 - 1972
Height :   11", 27.9 cm
Colour: 1. Pewter   3. Turquoise/stone
             2. Solid green   4. White

Colour	U.S. $	Can. $	U.K. £
1. Pewter	75.00	115.00	45.00
2. Solid green	75.00	115.00	45.00
3. Turquoise/stone	100.00	150.00	60.00
4. White		Rare	

Shape 2258 Bowl oval
Designer: James Hayward, Graham Tongue in 1969
Issued: 1969 - 1972
Size: 5" x 12" x 6", 12.7 x 30.5 x 15.0 cm
Colour: 1. Pewter   3. Turquoise/stone
             2. Solid green   4. White

Colour	U.S. $	Can. $	U.K. £
1. Pewter	75.00	115.00	45.00
2. Solid green	75.00	115.00	45.00
3. Turquoise/stone	100.00	150.00	60.00
4. White		Rare	

Shape 2259 Vase
Designer: J. Hayward, A. Hallam, G. Tongue in 1969
Issued: 1969 - 1972
Height :   6 ½", 16.5 cm
Colour: 1. Pewter   3. Turquoise/stone
             2. Solid green   4. White

Colour	U.S. $	Can. $	U.K. £
1. Pewter	60.00	90.00	35.00
2. Solid green	60.00	90.00	35.00
3. Turquoise/stone	75.00	115.00	45.00
4. White		Rare	

Shape 2266 Plant pot

Designer: Graham Tongue in 1969
Issued: 1969 - 1972
Height: 4 ½", 11.9 cm
Colour: 1. Pewter   3. Turquoise/stone
        2. Solid green   4. White

Colour	U.S. $	Can. $	U.K. £
1. Pewter	40.00	60.00	25.00
2. Solid green	40.00	60.00	25.00
3. Turquoise/stone	60.00	90.00	35.00
4. White		Rare	

Photograph not
available
at press time

Shape 2296 Vase

Designer: Graham Tongue in 1969
Issued: 1970 - 1972
Height : 6 ½" x 16.5 cm
Colour: 1. Pewter   3. Turquoise/stone
        2. Solid green   4. White

Colour	U.S. $	Can. $	U.K. £
1. Pewter	60.00	90.00	35.00
2. Solid green	60.00	90.00	35.00
3. Turquoise/stone	75.00	115.00	45.00
4. White		Rare	

Photograph not
available
at press time

Shape 2296C Ginger jar with cover

Designer: Graham Tongue in 1969
Issued: 1970 - 1972
Height: 7 ¼", 18.4 cm
Colour: 1. Pewter   3. Turquoise/stone
        2. Solid green   4. White

Colour	U.S. $	Can. $	U.K. £
1. Pewter	100.00	150.00	60.00
2. Solid green	100.00	150.00	60.00
3. Turquoise/stone	110.00	175.00	70.00
4. White		Rare	

Shape 2303 Vase

Designer: Graham Tongue in 1970
Issued: 1971 - 1972
Height : 11 ¾", 29.8 cm
Colour: 1. Pewter   3. Turquoise/stone
        2. Solid green   4. White

Colour	U.S. $	Can. $	U.K. £
1. Pewter	75.00	115.00	45.00
2. Solid green	75.00	115.00	45.00
3. Turquoise/stone	100.00	150.00	60.00
4. White		Rare	

PALM TREE

This distinctive series containing eighteen shapes was produced in the following colourways:

1. Biscuit, light blue or white - matt
2. Turquoise with gilt, grey with gilt, cobalt with gilt or ruby with gilt - gloss
3. British racing green, yellow, light green - gloss; pale green - matt

In the pricing tables, the numbers 1, 2 and 3 refer to the colourways as listed above.

The matt glazes were satin finished and the shaded colouring was soft and very pleasing. On the darker background, for example ruby, much gilding was used and more colours - such as black, blue and green - appeared on the palm leaves, which created a very dramatic effect. This is a popular series with collectors and it is quite a challenge to find the rare colourways.

Shape 1063 Wall vase with two drums

Designer:	James Hayward in 1946
Issued:	1947 - by 1963
Height:	9 ½", 24 cm
Colour:	See title page

Colourway	U.S. $	Can. $	U.K. £
1. Colour/matt	50.00	75.00	30.00
2. Gilt/gloss	75.00	115.00	45.00
3. Colour/gloss/matt		Rare	

Shape 1064 Vase, large

Designer:	James Hayward in 1946
Issued:	1947 - by 13
Height :	11 ¼", 28.5 cm
Colour:	See title page

Colourway	U.S. $	Can. $	U.K. £
1. Colour/matt	75.00	115.00	45.00
2. Gilt/gloss	125.00	190.00	75.00
3. Colour/gloss/matt		Rare	

Shape 1065 Vase with oval top

Designer:	Albert Hallam in 1946
Issued:	1947 - by 1963
Height:	8", 20.3 cm
Colour:	See title page

Colourway	U.S. $	Can. $	U.K. £
1. Colour/matt	60.00	90.00	35.00
2. Gilt/gloss	110.00	165.00	65.00
3. Colour/gloss/matt		Rare	

Shape 1066 Bowl

Designer:	Albert Hallam in 1946
Issued:	1947 - by 1963
Diameter:	12", 30.5 cm
Colour:	See title page

Colourway	U.S. $	Can. $	U.K. £
1. Colour/matt	60.00	90.00	35.00
2. Gilt/gloss	110.00	165.00	65.00
3. Colour/gloss/matt		Rare	

Shape 1067 Jug, large

Designer:	Albert Hallam in 1946
Issued:	1947 - by 1963
Height:	11", 27.9 cm
Colour:	See title page

Colourway	U.S. $	Can. $	U.K. £
1. Colour/matt	65.00	100.00	40.00
2. Gilt/gloss	110.00	165.00	65.00
3. Colour/gloss/matt		Rare	

Shape 1068 Jug

Designer:	Albert Hallam in 1946
Issued:	1947 - by 1963
Height :	9 ¼", 23.5 cm
Colour:	See title page

Colourway	U.S. $	Can. $	U.K. £
1. Colour/matt	60.00	90.00	35.00
2. Gilt/gloss	110.00	150.00	60.00
3. Colour/gloss/matt		Rare	

Shape 1069 Vase with wide curly oval top

Designer:	Albert Hallam in 1946
Issued:	1947 - by 1963
Height:	8", 20.3 cm
Colour:	See title page

Colourway	U.S. $	Can. $	U.K. £
1 Colour/matt	60.00	90.00	35.00
2. Gilt/gloss	110.00	165.00	65.00
3. Colour/gloss/matt		Rare	

Shape 1070 Basket

Designer:	Albert Hallam in 1946
Issued:	1947 - by 1963
Height :	10 ¼", 26.0 cm
Colour:	See title page

Colourway	U.S. $	Can. $	U.K. £
1. Colour/matt	65.00	100.00	40.00
2. Gilt/gloss	110.00	165.00	65.00
3. Colour/gloss/matt		Rare	

Shape 1071 Vase on square base

Designer:	Albert Hallam in 1946
Issued:	1947 - by 1963
Height:	10 ¼″, 26 cm
Colour:	See title page

Colourway	U.S. $	Can. $	U.K. £
1. Colour/matt	65.00	100.00	40.00
2. Gilt/gloss	120.00	175.00	70.00
3. Colour/gloss/matt		Rare	

Shape 1072 Vase

Designer:	Albert Hallam in 1946
Issued:	1947 - by 1963
Height:	6 ¼″, 15.9 cm
Colour:	See title page

Colourway	U.S. $	Can. $	U.K. £
1. Colour/matt	60.00	90.00	35.00
2. Gilt/gloss	110.00	165.00	65.00
3. Colour/gloss/matt		Rare	

Shape 1073 Jug, medium

Designer:	Albert Hallam in 1946
Issued:	1947 - by 1963
Height:	8 ½″, 21.6 cm
Colour:	See title page

Colourway	U.S. $	Can. $	U.K. £
1. Colour/matt	60.00	90.00	35.00
2. Gilt/gloss	110.00	165.00	65.00
3. Colour/gloss/matt		Rare	

Shape 1074 Jug, small

Designer:	Albert Hallam in 1946
Issued:	1947 - by 1963
Height:	7 ¼″, 18.4 cm
Colour:	See title page

Colourway	U.S. $	Can. $	U.K. £
1. Colour/matt	60.00	90.00	35.00
2. Gilt/gloss	110.00	165.00	65.00
3. Colour/gloss/matt		Rare	

Photograph not
available
at press time

Photograph not
available
at press time

Shape 1267 Bowl

Designer:	James Hayward, Albert Hallam in 1952
Issued:	1953 - by 1963
Size:	7 ½" x 5 ½", 19.1 x 14 cm
Colour:	See title page

Colourway	U.S. $	Can. $	U.K. £
1. Colour/matt	40.00	60.00	25.00
2. Gilt/gloss	100.00	150.00	60.00
3. Colour/gloss/matt		Rare	

Shape 1268 Jug, round with straight sides

Designer:	James Hayward, Albert Hallam in 1952
Issued:	1953 - by 1963
Height:	8", 20.3 cm
Colour:	See title page

Colourway	U.S. $	Can. $	U.K. £
1. Colour/matt	60.00	90.00	35.00
2. Gilt/gloss	110.00	165.00	65.00
3. Colour/gloss/matt		Rare	

Shape 1269 Vase standing with two drums

Designer:	James Hayward, Albert Hallam in 1952
Issued:	1953 - by 1963
Height:	7", 17.8 cm
Colour:	See title page

Colourway	U.S. $	Can. $	U.K. £
1. Colour/matt	60.00	90.00	35.00
2. Gilt/gloss	100.00	150.00	60.00
3. Colour/gloss/matt		Rare	

Shape 1270 Horn of Plenty

Designer:	Albert Hallam in 1952
Issued:	1953 - by 1963
Height:	7 ¼", 18.4 cm
Colour:	See title page

Colourway	U.S. $	Can. $	U.K. £
1. Colour/matt	40.00	75.00	30.00
2. Gilt/gloss	100.00	150.00	60.00
3. Colour/gloss/matt		Rare	

Shape 1271 Jug with guitar and drums

Designer: Albert Hallam in 1952
Issued: 1953 - by 1963
Height: 7 ¾", 19.7 cm
Colour: See title page

Colourway	U.S. $	Can. $	U.K. £
1. Colour/matt	65.00	100.00	40.00
2. Gilt/gloss	125.00	190.00	75.00
3. Colour/gloss/matt		Rare	

Shape 1272 Scorpion jug

Designer: James Hayward, Albert Hallam in 1952
Issued: 1953 - by 1963
Height :   6 ½", 16.5 cm
Colour: See title page

Colourway	U.S. $	Can. $	U.K. £
1. Colour/matt	60.00	90.00	35.00
2. Gilt/gloss	120.00	175.00	70.00
3. Colour/gloss/matt		Rare	

Note: Price ranges are retail market indicators of prices for models under the following conditions:
- Lower end of range = price of monochrome models
- Higher end of range = price of multicoloured models

PETIT POINT

A new range of tableware in a gloss finish was introduced in 1939 which was plain except for an embossed border design. The pattern, which appeared on all the pieces, represented a type of embroidery stitch commonly known as petit point, and gave its name to the series. See for example the teapot, shape 641.

The items were also available with different lithograph designs applied. One known as "Windmill," was a very colourful and ornate Dutch scene (see shape 630), reminiscent of embroidery, while another named "Romance" was very different in style (see shape 681), and was more in the nature of a painting. The plain background varied between cream and white and on some examples the Dutch scene was heavily overlaid with gilt tracery.

As with most of the other series introduced pre-war, information is scarce, however it is likely that the twenty-three shapes of Petit Point were not in production for very long.

Shape 630, Windmill design

Shape 641, Plain white design

Shape 630-631 Teapot in two sizes

Designer: Mr. Owen in 1938
Issued: 1939 - by 1954
Height: 1. Shape 630 — 8 ¼", 21 cm
            2. Shape 631 — unknown
Colour: a. Plain
            b. Plain with multi-coloured decoration

Colour	U.S. $	Can. $	U.K. £
1a. Shape 630 - plain	75.00	100.00	35.00
1b. Shape 630 - multi-coloured	90.00	125.00	45.00
2a. Shape 631 - plain	60.00	90.00	30.00
2b. Shape 631 - multi-coloured	75.00	125.00	40.00

Shape 632/1/2/3 Jug in three sizes

Designer: Mr. Owen in 1938
Issued: 1939 - by 1954
Height: 1. Shape 632/1, large — 6 ¾", 17.2 cm
            2. Shape 632/2, medium — 6", 15 cm
            3. Shape 632/3, small — unknown
Colour: a. Plain
            b. Plain with multi-coloured decoration

Colour	U.S. $	Can. $	U.K. £
1a. Large - plain	50.00	75.00	25.00
1b. Large - multi-coloured	60.00	90.00	30.00
2a. Medium - plain	40.00	60.00	20.00
2b. Medium - multi-coloured	50.00	75.00	25.00
3a. Small - plain	30.00	50.00	15.00
3b. Small - multi-coloured	40.00	60.00	20.00

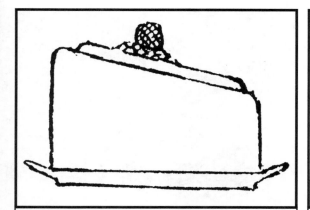

Shape 633-634 Cheese dish in two sizes

Designer:	Mr. Owen in 1938
Issued:	1939 - by 1954
Size:	1. Shape 633, small — unknown
	2. Shape 634, large — unknown
Colour:	a . Plain
	b. Plain with multi-coloured decoration

Colour	U.S. $	Can. $	U.K. £
1a. Shape 633 - plain	50.00	75.00	25.00
1b. Shape 633 - multi-coloured	60.00	90.00	30.00
2a. Shape 634 - plain	60.00	90.00	30.00
2b. Shape 634 - multi-coloured	75.00	110.00	35.00

Photograph not
available
at press time

Shape 635   Bread and butter plate

Designer:	Mr. Owen in 1938
Issued:	1939 - by 1954
Size:	Unknown
Colour:	a. Plain
	b. Plain with multi-coloured decoration

Colour	U.S. $	Can. $	U.K. £
a. Plain	40.00	60.00	20.00
b. Multi-coloured	50.00	75.00	25.00

Photograph not
available
at press time

Shape 636   Cup and saucer

Designer:	Mr. Owen in 1938
Issued:	1939 - by 1954
Size:	Unknown
Colour:	a. Plain
	b. Plain with multi-coloured decoration

Colour	U.S. $	Can. $	U.K. £
a. Plain	40.00	60.00	20.00
b. Multi-coloured	50.00	75.00	25.00

Photograph not
available
at press time

Shape 637   Muffin

Designer:	Mr. Owen in 1938
Issued:	1939 - by 1954
Size:	Unknown
Colour:	a. Plain
	b. Plain with multi-coloured decoration

Colour	U.S. $	Can. $	U.K. £
a. Plain	60.00	90.00	30.00
b. Multi-coloured	75.00	100.00	35.00

Photograph not
available
at press time

Shape 638/1/2 Sugar in two sizes

Designer: Mr. Owen in 1938
Issued: 1939 - by 1954
Size: Unknown
Colour: a. Plain
           b. Plain with multi-coloured decoration

Colour	U.S. $	Can. $	U.K. £
638/1a. Plain	50.00	75.00	25.00
638/1b. Multi-coloured	60.00	90.00	30.00
638/2a. Plain	40.00	60.00	20.00
638/2b. Multi-coloured	50.00	75.00	25.00

Shape 639 Cream jug

Designer: Mr. Owen in 1938
Issued: 1939 - by 1954
Height: 3 ¼″, 8.3 cm
Colour: a. Plain
           b. Plain with multi-coloured decoration

Colour	U.S. $	Can. $	U.K. £
a. Plain	40.00	60.00	20.00
b. Multi-coloured	50.00	75.00	25.00

Photograph not
available
at press time

Shape 640   Breakfast cup and saucer

Designer: Mr. Owen in 1938
Issued: 1939 - by 1954
Size: Unknown
Colour: a. Plain
           b. Plain with multi-coloured decoration

Colour	U.S. $	Can. $	U.K. £
a. Plain	50.00	75.00	25.00
b. Multi-coloured	60.00	90.00	30.00

Shape 641   Teapot

Designer: Mr. Owen in 1938
Issued: 1939 - by 1954
Size: 6 ½″, 16.5 cm
Colour: a. Plain
           b. Plain with multi-coloured decoration

Colour	U.S. $	Can. $	U.K. £
a. Plain	60.00	90.00	30.00
b. Multi-coloured	75.00	125.00	40.00

Photograph not
available
at press time

Shape 642   Coffee pot

Designer: Mr. Owen in 1938
Issued: 1939 - by 1954
Size: Unknown
Colour: a. Plain
             b. Plain with multi-coloured decoration

Colour	U.S. $	Can. $	U.K. £
a. Plain	75.00	100.00	35.00
b. Multi-coloured	100.00	150.00	50.00

Photograph not
available
at press time

Shape 643   Butter dish

Designer: Mr. Owen in 1938
Issued: 1939 - by 1954
Size: Unknown
Colour: a. Plain
             b. Plain with multi-coloured decoration

Colour	U.S. $	Can. $	U.K. £
a. Plain	60.00	90.00	30.00
b. Multi-coloured	75.00	100.00	35.00

Photograph not
available
at press time

Shape 644   Egg stand

Designer: Mr. Owen in 1938
Issued: 1939 - by 1954
Size: Unknown
Colour: a. Plain
             b. Plain with multi-coloured decoration

Colour	U.S. $	Can. $	U.K. £
a. Plain	60.00	90.00	30.00
b. Multi-coloured	75.00	100.00	35.00

Photograph not
available
at press time

Shape 645   Fruit bowl

Designer: Mr. Owen in 1938
Issued: 1939 - by 1954
Size: Unknown
Colour: a. Plain
             b. Plain with multi-coloured decoration

Colour	U.S. $	Can. $	U.K. £
a. Plain	75.00	100.00	35.00
b. Multi-coloured	90.00	125.00	45.00

Photograph not
available
at press time

Photograph not
available
at press time

Shape 646   Fruit saucer

Designer:	Mr. Owen in 1938
Issued:	1939 - by 1954
Size:	Unknown
Colour:	a. Plain
	b. Plain with multi-coloured decoration

Colour	U.S. $	Can. $	U.K. £
a. Plain	30.00	45.00	15.00
b. Multi-coloured	40.00	60.00	20.00

Shape 647   Coffee cup and saucer

Designer:	Mr. Owen in 1938
Issued:	1939 - by 1954
Size:	Unknown
Colour:	a. Plain
	b. Plain with multi-coloured decoration

Colour	U.S. $	Can. $	U.K. £
a. Plain	40.00	60.00	20.00
b. Multi-coloured	50.00	75.00	25.00

Photograph not
available
at press time

Photograph not
available
at press time

Shape 648   Muffin

Designer:	Mr. Owen in 1938
Issued:	1939 - by 1954
Size:	4″, 10.1 cm
Colour:	a. Plain
	b. Plain with multi-coloured decoration

Colour	U.S. $	Can. $	U.K. £
a. Plain	80.00	125.00	40.00
b. Multi-coloured	70.00	110.00	35.00

Shape 649   Sugar, small

Designer:	Mr. Owen in 1938
Issued:	1939 - by 1954
Size:	Unknown
Colour:	a. Plain
	b. Plain with multi-coloured decoration

Colour	U.S. $	Can. $	U.K. £
a. Plain	40.00	60.00	20.00
b. Multi-coloured	50.00	75.00	25.00

Photograph not
available
at press time

Photograph not
available
at press time

Shape 670 **Cream jug, small**

Designer:	Mr. Owen in 1938
Issued:	1939 - by 1954
Size:	Unknown
Colour:	a. Plain
	b. Plain with multi-coloured decoration

Colour	U.S. $	Can. $	U.K. £
a. Plain	40.00	60.00	20.00
b. Multi-coloured	50.00	75.00	25.00

Shape 671 **Toast rack**

Designer:	Mr. Owen in 1938
Issued:	1939 - by 1954
Size:	Unknown
Colour:	a. Plain
	b. Plain with multi-coloured decoration

Colour	U.S. $	Can. $	U.K. £
a. Plain	50.00	75.00	25.00
b. Multi-coloured	75.00	100.00	35.00

Photograph not
available
at press time

Shape 672 **Cress tray and drainer**

Designer:	Mr. Owen in 1938
Issued:	1939 - by 1954
Size:	Unknown
Colour:	a. Plain
	b. Plain with multi-coloured decoration

Colour	U.S. $	Can. $	U.K. £
a. Plain	60.00	90.00	30.00
b. Multi-coloured	80.00	125.00	40.00

Shape 681 **Preserve with lid**

Designer:	Mr. Owen in 1939
Issued:	1939 - by 1954
Height:	5 ¾", 14.6 cm
Colour:	a. Plain
	b. Plain with multi-coloured decoration

Colour	U.S. $	Can. $	U.K. £
a. Plain	40.00	60.00	20.00
b. Multi-coloured	60.00	90.00	30.00

Photograph not
available
at press time

Photograph not
available
at press time

Shape 682   Triple Tray

Designer: Mr. Owen in 1939
Issued: 1939 - by 1954
Size: Unknown
Colour: a. Plain
             b. Plain with multi-coloured decoration

Colour	U.S. $	Can. $	U.K. £
a Plain	60.00	90.00	30.00
b. Multi-coloured	75.00	110.00	35.00

Shape 683   Double Tray

Designer: Mr. Owen in 1939
Issued: 1939 - by 1954
Size: Unknown
Colour: a. Plain
             b. Plain with multi-coloured decoration

Colour	U.S. $	Can. $	U.K. £
a. Plain	50.00	75.00	25.00
b. Multi-coloured	60.00	90.00	30.00

Shape 685/1/2/3 Sweet dish in three sizes

Designer: Mr. Owen in 1939
Issued: 1939 - by 1954
Size :   1. Unknown
             2. 7 ½″ x 5 ¾″, 19.1 x 14.6 cm
             3. Unknown
Colour: a. Plain
             b. Plain with multi-coloured decoration

Colour	U.S. $	Can. $	U.K. £
1a. 685/1 - plain	50.00	75.00	25.00
1b. 685/1 - multi-coloured	60.00	90.00	30.00
2a. 685/2 - plain	40.00	60.00	20.00
2b. 685/2 - multi-coloured	50.00	75.00	25.00
3a. 685/3 - plain	30.00	45.00	15.00
3b. 685/3 - multi-coloured	40.00	60.00	20.00

SALAD WARE

A range of lettuce-leafed embossed salad ware in a gloss finish, was introduced during 1932, a time when funds were scarce, so that items of domestic tableware which were both useful and ornamental had an obvious attraction. The last piece (shape 2029) was added to the range in 1965, by which time thirty-seven pieces had been modelled. It is likely that production was interrupted during the war years and that some pieces were not reintroduced afterwards. Except for the round salad bowl (shape 210), which is listed in opaque white glaze for 1971, all the remaining range was withdrawn in 1970.

The very first decoration was a darkish solid green ground, but a primrose ground was very soon added. Later, around 1936, the solid green ground was replaced by a lighter shaded green, giving a more delicate effect. The shaded green decoration remained to the end, but other decorations exist, such as white, cream, and a deep yellow-orange. These date from before the war until the fifties. One piece has even been found decorated in three shaded colours, pink, mauve and green!

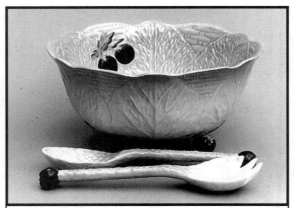

Shape 210	Salad bowl, round
Designer:	Mr. Symcox in 1932
Issued:	1. 1932 - 1971
	2. 1971 - 1971
Diameter:	9", 22.9 cm
Colour:	a. Background solid green, shaded green, white, cream or yellow-orange
	b. Opaque

Description	U.S. $	Can. $	U.K. £
Salad bowl, round	100.00	150.00	60.00

Note: Servers available, 9" long. Price is for bowl only.

Shape 211	Salad bowl, octagonal
Designer:	Mr. Symcox in 1932
Issued:	1932 - by 1965
Diameter:	7 ¾", 19.7 cm
Colour:	Background solid green, shaded green, white, cream or yellow-orange

Description	U.S. $	Can. $	U.K. £
Salad bowl, octagonal	100.00	150.00	60.00

Note: Supplied with or without servers which were 9", 22.9 cm long. Price is for bowl only.

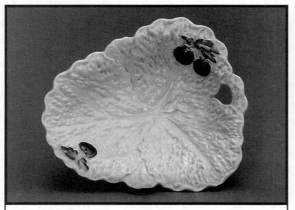

Shape 212	Tomato dish, triangular
Designer:	Mr. Symcox in 1932
Issued:	1932 - 1970
Size:	8" x 9", 20.3 x 22.9 cm
Colour:	Background solid green, shaded green, white, cream or yellow-orange

Description	U.S. $	Can. $	U.K. £
Tomato dish	50.00	75.00	30.00

Note: Early pieces have a "cut-out."

Shape 213	Tomato dish, round
Designer:	Mr. Symcox in 1932
Issued:	1932 - 1970
Diameter:	6 ¾", 17.2 cm
Colour:	Background solid green, shaded green, white, cream or yellow-orange

Description	U.S. $	Can. $	U.K. £
Tomato dish, round	50.00	75.00	30.00

Shape 214-215 Tomato dish, leaf shape, in two sizes

Designer:	Mr. Symcox in 1932
Issued:	1932 - 1970
Size:	1. Shape 214 — 7" x 5 ¾", 17.8 x 14.6 cm
	2. Shape 215 — 5 ½" x 4 ¼", 14 x 10.8 cm
Colour:	Background solid green, shaded green, white, cream or yellow-orange

Description	U.S. $	Can. $	U.K. £
1. Shape 214	35.00	50.00	20.00
2. Shape 215	25.00	40.00	15.00

Shape 216 Tomato dish, rectangular

Designer:	Mr. Symcox in 1932
Issued:	1932 - 1970
Size:	10 ½" x 7 ¼", 26.7 x18.4 cm
Colour:	Background solid green, shaded green, white, cream or yellow-orange

Description	U.S. $	Can. $	U.K. £
Tomato dish, rectangular	60.00	90.00	35.00

Shape 217 Tomato dish

Designer:	Mr. Symcox in 1932
Issued:	1932 - 1970
Size :	9" x 7 ½", 22.9 x 19.1 cm
Colour:	Background solid green, shaded green, white, cream or yellow-orange

Description	U.S. $	Can. $	U.K. £
Tomato dish	60.00	90.00	35.00

Shape 218 Tomato dish, diamond shape

Designer:	Mr. Symcox in 1932
Issued:	1932 - 1965
Size:	7 ¾" x 4 ¼", 19.7 x 10.8 cm
Colour:	Background solid green, shaded green, white, cream or yellow-orange

Description	U.S. $	Can. $	U.K. £
Tomato dish, diamond	40.00	60.00	25.00

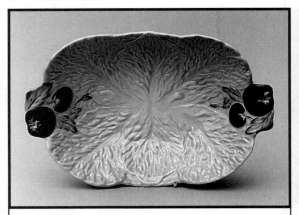

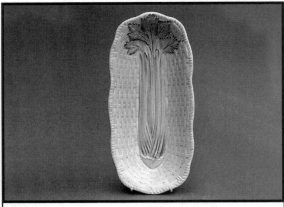

Shape 219	**Tomato dish, oblong**
Designer:	Mr. Symcox in 1932
Issued:	1932 - 1970
Size:	12″ x 8″, 30.5 x 20.3 cm
Colour:	Background solid green, shaded green, white, cream or yellow-orange

Description	U.S. $	Can. $	U.K. £
Tomato dish, oblong	60.00	90.00	35.00

Shape 220	**Celery dish**
Designer:	Mr. Symcox in 1932
Issued:	1932 - 1970
Size :	12″ x 5 ¾″, 30.5 x 14.6 cm
Colour:	Background solid green, shaded green, white, cream or yellow-orange

Description	U.S. $	Can. $	U.K. £
Celery dish	40.00	60.00	25.00

Shape 221	**Cucumber tray**
Designer:	Mr. Symcox in 1932
Issued:	1932 - 1970
Size :	12 ½″ x 5 ¼″, 31.7 x 13.3 cm
Colour:	Background solid green, shaded green, white, cream or yellow-orange

Description	U.S. $	Can. $	U.K. £
Cucumber tray	40.00	60.00	25.00

Shape 222	**Triple tray**
Designer:	Mr. Symcox in 1932
Issued:	1932 - by 1965
Size:	9 ½″ x 10″, 24 x 25.4 cm
Colour:	Background solid green, shaded green, white, cream or yellow-orange

Description	U.S. $	Can. $	U.K. £
Triple tray	65.00	100.00	40.00

Shape 223	**Triple tray**
Designer:	Mr. Symcox in 1932
Issued:	1932 - 1970
Diameter:	8 ¾", 22.2 cm
Colour:	Background solid green, shaded green, white, cream or yellow-orange

Description	U.S. $	Can. $	U.K. £
Triple tray	60.00	90.00	35.00

Shape 224	**Strawberry double tray**
Designer:	Mr. Symcox in 1932
Issued:	1932 - by 1965
Size:	12 ¾" x 6 ¼", 32.4 x 15.9 cm
Colour:	Background solid green, shaded green, white, cream or yellow-orange

Description	U.S. $	Can. $	U.K. £
Strawberry double tray	50.00	75.00	30.00

Shape 225	**Lettuce cheese dish**
Designer:	Mr. Symcox in 1932
Issued:	1932 - 1970
Size:	7 ¼" x 6" x 4", 18.4 x 15 x 10.1 cm
Colour:	Background solid green, shaded green, white, cream or yellow-orange

Description	U.S. $	Can. $	U.K. £
Cheese dish	65.00	100.00	40.00

Shape 226	**Lettuce cheese dish**
Designer:	Mr. Symcox in 1932
Issued:	1932 - 1970
Size:	6 ½" x 5' x 3 ½", 16.5 x 12.7 x 8.9 cm
Colour:	Background solid green, shaded green, white, cream or yellow-orange

Description	U.S. $	Can. $	U.K. £
Cheese dish	60.00	90.00	35.00

Shape 227	Lettuce butter dish
Designer:	Mr. Symcox in 1932
Issued:	1932 - by 1954
Size:	6 ½" x 3", 16.5 x 7.6 cm
Colour:	Background solid green, shaded green, white, cream or yellow-orange

Description	U.S. $	Can. $	U.K. £
Lettuce butter dish	75.00	115.00	45.00

Shape 228	Lettuce toast rack
Designer:	Mr. Symcox in 1932
Issued:	1932 - 1968
Size:	6" x 4 ¾", 15 x 12.1 cm
Colour:	Background solid green, shaded green, white, cream or yellow-orange

Description	U.S. $	Can. $	U.K. £
Toast rack	40.00	60.00	25.00

Photograph not
available
at press time

Shape 229	Lettuce sauce holder
Designer:	Mr. Symcox in 1932
Issued:	1932 - by 1954
Size:	3 ½" x 3" , 8.9 x 7.6 cm
Colour:	Background solid green, shaded green, white, cream or yellow-orange

Description	U.S. $	Can. $	U.K. £
Sauce holder	40.00	60.00	25.00

Shape 230	Lettuce preserve
Designer:	Mr. Symcox in 1932
Issued:	1932 - 1962
Size:	4 ½" x 3 ½", 11.9 x 8.9 cm
Colour:	Background solid green, shaded green, white, cream or yellow-orange

Description	U.S. $	Can. $	U.K. £
Lettuce preserve	60.00	90.00	35.00

Shape 231	**Cherry preserve**
Designer:	Mr. Symcox in 1932
Issued:	1932 - by 1954
Size	3 ½" x 4", 8.9 x 10.1 cm
Colour:	Background solid green, shaded green, white, cream or yellow-orange

Description	U.S. $	Can. $	U.K. £
Cherry preserve	75.00	115.00	45.00

Shape 232	**Lettuce sauce boat and stand, large**
Designer:	Mr. Symcox in 1932
Issued:	1932 - by 1965
Size:	6 ¾" x 3", 17.2 x 7.6 cm
Colour:	Background solid green, shaded green, white, cream or yellow-orange

Description	U.S. $	Can. $	U.K. £
Sauce boat and stand, large	40.00	60.00	25.00

Shape 233	**Lettuce sauce boat and stand, small**
Designer:	Mr. Symcox in 1932
Issued:	1932 - 1970
Size:	5" x 2 ¼", 12.7 x 5.7 cm
Colour:	Background solid green, shaded green, white, cream or yellow-orange

Description	U.S. $	Can. $	U.K. £
Sauce boat and stand, small	35.00	50.00	20.00

Shape 234	**Lettuce cress tray and stand**
Designer:	Mr. Symcox in 1932
Issued:	1932 - by 1954
Size:	8 ¼" x 2 ½", 21 x 6.4 cm
Colour:	Background solid green, shaded green, white, cream or yellow-orange

Description	U.S. $	Can. $	U.K. £
Cress tray and stand	60.00	90.00	35.00

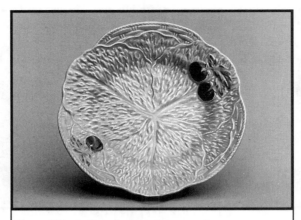

Shape 235   Lettuce dessert plate, round

Designer: Mr. Symcox in 1932
Issued: 1932 - by 1954
Diameter: 8 ½", 21.6 cm
Colour: Background solid green, shaded green, white,
             cream or yellow-orange

Description	U.S. $	Can. $	U.K. £
Dessert plate, round	35.00	50.00	20.00

Shape 236/1/2/3 Lettuce plates, square three sizes

Designer: Mr. Symcox in 1932
Issued: 1932 - by 1965
Length: 1. Shape 236/1 — 9 ½", 24 cm
             2. Shape 236/2 — 8 ½", 21.6 cm
             3. Shape 236/3 — 8", 20.3 cm
Colour: Background solid green, shaded green, white,
             cream or yellow-orange

Description	U.S. $	Can. $	U.K. £
1. Shape 236/1	40.00	60.00	25.00
2. Shape 236/2	35.00	50.00	20.00
3. Shape 236/3	25.00	40.00	15.00

Note: Price ranges are retail market indicators of prices for models under the following conditions:
- Lower end of range = price of monochrome models
- Higher end of range = price of multicoloured models

Photograph not
available
at press time

Shape 237   **Tomato comport, rectangular**

Designer: Mr. Symcox in 1932
Issued: 1932 - by 1965
Size: 10 ½" x 7", 26.7 x 17.8 cm
Colour: Background solid green, shaded green, white, cream or yellow-orange

Description	U.S. $	Can. $	U.K. £
Tomato comport	60.00	90.00	35.00

Shape 238   **Tomato cruet set, salt, pepper, mustard and base**

Designer: Mr. Symcox in 1932
Issued: 1932 - 1970
Size: 6" x 3 ¼", 15 x 8.3 cm
Colour: Background solid green, shaded green, white, cream or yellow-orange

Description	U.S. $	Can. $	U.K. £
Tomato cruet set	65.00	100.00	40.00

Shape 269-270-271 Tomato dish, oval in three sizes

Designer: Mr. Symcox in 1932
Issued: 1932 - 1970
Size: 1. Shape 269 — 7" x 5 ½", 17.8 x 14 cm
       2. Shape 270 — 8 ¼" x 6 ¼", 21 x 15.9
       3. Shape 271 — 10 ¼" x 8", 26 x 20.3 cm
Colour: Background solid green, shaded green, white, cream or yellow-orange

Description	U.S. $	Can. $	U.K. £
1. Shape 269	35.00	50.00	20.00
2. Shape 270	40.00	60.00	25.00
3. Shape 271	50.00	75.00	30.00

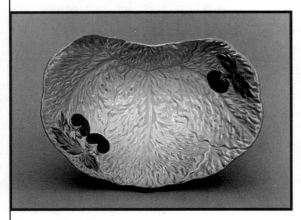

Shape 337-338-339 Tomato dish, kidney-shape, 3 sizes

Designer:	Mr. Symcox c.1934
Issued:	1934 - 1970
Size:	1. Shape 337 — 12″ x 8″, 30.5 x 20.3 cm
	2. Shape 338 — 10 ½″ x 7″, 26.7 x 17.8 cm
	3. Shape 339 — 9″ x 6″, 22.9 x 15 cm
Colour:	Background solid green, shaded green, white, cream or yellow-orange

Description	U.S. $	Can. $	U.K. £
1. Shape 337	50.00	75.00	30.00
2. Shape 338	40.00	60.00	25.00
3. Shape 339	35.00	50.00	20.00

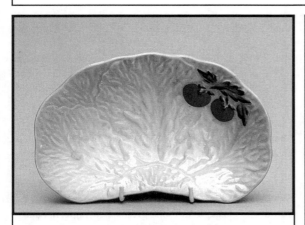

Shape 463   Tomato dish, kidney-shape, large

Designer:	Mr. Symcox in 1937
Issued:	1937 - 1970
Size:	7″ x 4 ½″, 17.8 x 11.9 cm
Colour:	Background solid green, shaded green, white, cream or yellow-orange

Description	U.S. $	Can. $	U.K. £
Tomato dish, kidney-shape	35.00	50.00	20.00

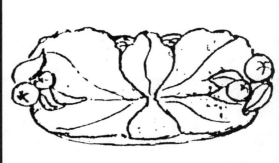

Shape 2029   Salad plate

Designer:	Albert Hallam in 1965
Issued:	1965 - 1970
Length:	7 ½″, 19.1 cm
Colour:	Background solid green, shaded green, white, cream or yellow-orange

Description	U.S. $	Can. $	U.K. £
Salad Plate		Rare	

SPRINGTIME

This series brought a "breath of spring" when it first appeared in 1961, and was aptly named. The range included items decorated with narcissi, with daffodils, with crocus and with anemones, all in their natural colours. The individual pieces were supplied with either a yellow or a green background in a gloss finish. The Double Dish (shape 1704) however was a hybrid, being half yellow and half green.

There was a total of twenty-two items in the series, of which eight were listed as dishes. Several of these were quite large, with novel shapes and scalloped edges. One small difference in detail to note is that in the case of shape 1710, the petals were yellow on the green version, and pale cream on the yellow version. This was necessary to provide a contrast with the background colour.

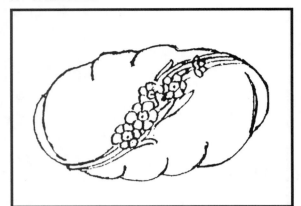

Shape 1704 Double dish, Narcissi

Designer:	Albert Hallam in 1960
Issued:	1961 - by 1966
Size :	12" x 8", 30.5 x 20.3 cm
Colour:	Yellow or green background with flowers in natural colours

Description	U.S. $	Can. $	U.K. £
Double dish, Narcissi	85.00	125.00	50.00

Shape 1705 Oval dish, Narcissi

Designer:	Albert Hallam in 1960
Issued:	1961 - by 1966
Size:	11" x 9", 27.9 x 22.9 cm
Colour:	Yellow or green background with flowers in natural colours

Description	U.S. $	Can. $	U.K. £
Oval dish, Narcissi	60.00	90.00	35.00

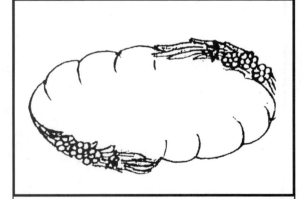

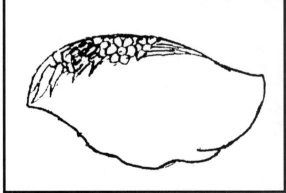

Shape 1706 Bowl, Narcissi

Designer:	Albert Hallam in 1960
Issued:	1961 - by 1966
Size:	13" x 8 ½", 33 x 21.6 cm
Colour:	Yellow or green background with flowers in natural colours

Description	U.S. $	Can. $	U.K. £
Bowl, Narcissi	65.00	100.00	40.00

Shape 1707 Dish, Narcissi

Designer:	Albert Hallam in 1960
Issued:	1961 - by 1966
Size:	10" x 7", 25.4 cm x 17.8 cm
Colour:	Yellow or green background with flowers in natural colours

Description	U.S. $	Can. $	U.K. £
Dish, Narcissi	50.00	75.00	30.00

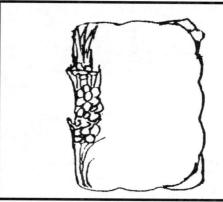

Shape 1708 Comport, Narcissi

Designer:	Albert Hallam in 1960
Issued:	1961 - by 1966
Size:	11" x 4", 27.9 x 10.1 cm
Colour:	Yellow or green background with flowers in natural colours

Description	U.S. $	Can. $	U.K. £
Comport, Narcissi	100.00	150.00	60.00

Shape 1709 Dish, Narcissi

Designer:	Albert Hallam in 1960
Issued:	1961 - by 1966
Size:	8 ½" x 5 ¾", 21.6 x 14.6 cm
Colour:	Yellow or green background with flowers in natural colours

Description	U.S. $	Can. $	U.K. £
Dish, Narcissi	35.00	50.00	20.00

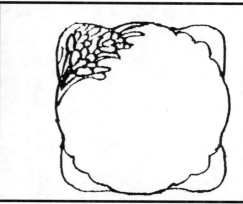

Shape 1710 Triple dish, Daffodil

Designer:	Albert Hallam in 1960
Issued:	1961 - by 1966
Size:	11 ½" x 10 ½", 29.2 x 26.7 cm
Colour:	Yellow or green background with flowers in natural colours

Description	U.S. $	Can. $	U.K. £
Triple dish, Daffodil	40.00	60.00	25.00

Shape 1711 Dish, Crocus

Designer:	Albert Hallam in 1960
Issued:	1961 - by 1966
Width:	6 ½", 16.5 cm
Colour:	Yellow or green background with flowers in natural colours

Description	U.S. $	Can. $	U.K. £
Dish, Crocus	35.00	50.00	20.00

Shape 1712 Sandwich tray, Crocus

Designer:	Albert Hallam in 1960
Issued:	1961 - by 1966
Size :	11″ x 5 ¾″, 27.9 x 14.6 cm
Colour:	Yellow or green background with flowers in natural colours

Description	U.S. $	Can. $	U.K. £
Sandwich tray, Crocus	40.00	60.00	25.00

Shape 1713 Covered butter dish, Anemone

Designer:	Albert Hallam in 1960
Issued:	1961 - by 1966
Size:	5 ½″ x 2 ¼″, 14.0 x 5.7 cm
Colour:	Yellow or green background with flowers in natural colours

Description	U.S. $	Can. $	U.K. £
Covered butter dish, Anemone	65.00	100.00	40.00

Shape 1714 Cheese dish, Anemone

Designer:	Albert Hallam in 1960
Issued:	1961 - by 1966
Size:	6 ½″ x 3 ½″, 16.5 x 8.9 cm
Colour:	Yellow or green background with flowers in natural colours

Description	U.S. $	Can. $	U.K. £
Cheese dish, Anemone	65.00	100.00	40.00

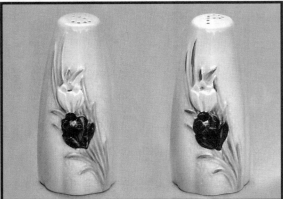

Shape 1715-1716 Salt and pepper, Crocus

Designer:	Albert Hallam in 1960
Issued:	1961 - by 1966
Height :	4 ½″, 11.9 cm
Colour:	Yellow or green background with flowers in natural colours

Description	U.S. $	Can. $	U.K. £
1. Shape 1715 — Salt	35.00	40.00	15.00
2. Shape 1716 — Pepper	35.00	40.00	15.00

Shape 1717 Preserve with lid, Crocus

Designer:	Albert Hallam in 1960
Issued:	1961 - by 1966
Size:	4 ¼" x 3 ½", 10.8 x 8.9 cm
Colour:	Yellow or green background with flowers in natural colours

Description	U.S. $	Can. $	U.K. £
Preserve with lid	50.00	75.00	30.00

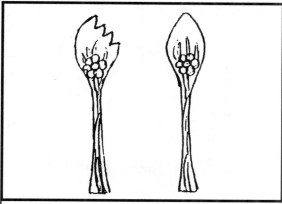

Shape 1718 Servers, Narcissi

Designer:	Albert Hallam in 1960
Issued:	1961 - by 1966
Length:	9", 22.9 cm
Colour:	Yellow or green background with flowers in natural colours

Description	U.S. $	Can. $	U.K. £
Servers, Narcissi	85.00	125.00	50.00

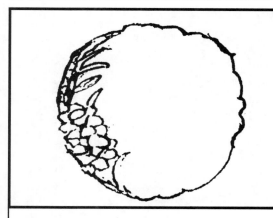

Shape 1725 Sweet dish, Daffodil

Designer:	Albert Hallam in 1960
Issued:	1961 - by 1966
Size:	5 ½" x 5 ½", 14 x 14 cm
Colour:	Yellow or green background with flowers in natural colours

Description	U.S. $	Can. $	U.K. £
Sweet dish, Daffodil	50.00	75.00	30.00

Shape 1726 Hostess set, Daffodil

Designer:	Albert Hallam in 1960
Issued:	1961 - by 1966
Size:	Unknown
Colour:	Yellow or green background with flowers in natural colours

Description	U.S. $	Can. $	U.K. £
Hostess set, Daffodil		Rare	

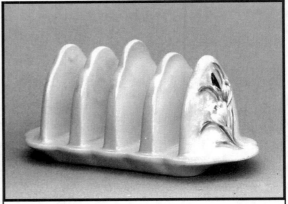

**Shape 1727 Cruet set — Salt, Pepper, Mustard
and Base, Crocus**

Designer:	Albert Hallam in 1960
Issued:	1961 - by 1966
Size:	5 ½" x 3" x 2 ¾", 14 x 7.6 x 7 cm
Colour:	Yellow or green background with flowers in natural colours

Description	U.S. $	Can. $	U.K. £
Cruet set, Crocus	75.00	115.00	45.00

Shape 1728 Toast rack, Crocus

Designer:	Albert Hallam in 1960
Issued:	1961 - by 1966
Size:	6" x 3", 15 x 7.6 cm
Colour:	Yellow or green background with flowers in natural colours

Description	U.S. $	Can. $	U.K. £
Toast rack, Crocus	50.00	75.00	30.00

Shape 1729 Jug (one pint), Anemone

Designer:	Albert Hallam in 1960
Issued:	1961 - by 1966
Size:	Unknown
Colour:	Yellow or green background with flowers in natural colours

Description	U.S. $	Can. $	U.K. £
Jug (one pint), Anemone	75.00	115.00	45.00

Shape 1747 Vinegar with stopper, Crocus

Designer:	Albert Hallam in 1961
Issued:	1961 - by 1966
Height:	6", 15 cm
Colour:	Yellow or green background with flowers in natural colours

Description	U.S. $	Can. $	U.K. £
Vinegar with stopper, Crocus	40.00	60.00	25.00

Shape 1795 Salad bowl, Daffodil

Designer:	Albert Hallam in 1961
Issued:	1962 - by 1966
Size:	Unknown
Colour:	Yellow or green background with flowers in natural colours

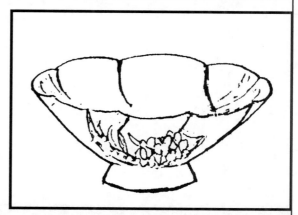

Description	U.S. $	Can. $	U.K. £
Salad bowl, Daffodil	125.00	200.00	75.00

Note: Price ranges are retail market indicators of prices for models under the following conditions:
- Lower end of range = price of monochrome models
- Higher end of range = price of multicoloured models

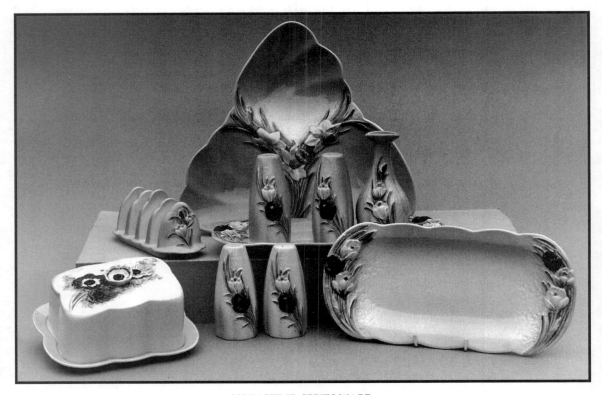

SPRINGTIME SERIES WARE

Shape 1710 Triple dish, Daffodil

Shape 1728, 1715, 1716, 1747 Toast rack, salt, pepper and vinegar, Crocus

Shape 1714 Cheese dish, Anemone   Shape 1712 Sandwich tray, Crocus

STRAWBERRY FAIR

Strawberry Fair, as the name suggests, was decorated with a motif of red strawberries, white flowers with a blue edge, and leaves shaded in different greens, on a white background. The pattern was raised and overall there was a design of strings formed as part of the background and carried over to the outside of pieces where appropriate, e.g. the Salad Bowl (shape 1573).

The series consisted of twenty-two pieces, all in a gloss finish. It was a very attractive design and the shapes of many of the dishes were made more interesting by being irregular in shape. Nevertheless, however delightful the design, it would appear to have been wrong for the period, and the series had gone by 1963.

Shape 1565 Teapot

Designer:	Albert Hallam in 1958
Issued:	1959 - by 1963
Size:	Unknown
Colour:	White background, red strawberries, white daisies, green leaves

Description	U.S. $	Can. $	U.K. £
Teapot	125.00	200.00	75.00

Shape 1566 Sandwich tray

Designer:	Albert Hallam in 1958
Issued:	1959 - by 1963
Size:	11" x 5 ½", 27.9 x 14 cm
Colour:	White background, red strawberries, white daisies, green leaves

Description	U.S. $	Can. $	U.K. £
Sandwich tray	60.00	90.00	35.00

Shape 1567 Sandwich plate

Designer:	Albert Hallam in 1958
Issued:	1959 - by 1963
Width:	5", 12.7 cm
Colour:	White background, red strawberries, white daisies, green leaves

Description	U.S. $	Can. $	U.K. £
Sandwich plate	35.00	50.00	20.00

Shape 1568 Cruet set - salt, pepper, mustard on a base

Designer:	Albert Hallam in 1958
Issued:	1959 - by 1963
Size:	4 ½" x 4 ¼" x 2 ¾", 11.9 x 10.8 x 7.0 cm
Colour:	White background, red strawberries, white daisies, green leaves

Description	U.S. $	Can. $	U.K. £
Cruet set	50.00	75.00	30.00

Note: The above photo is missing the mustard pot.

Shape 1569 Cream jug

Designer: Albert Hallam in 1958
Issued: 1959 - by 1963
Size: 2 ¾", 7.0 cm
Colour: White background, red strawberries, white
             daisies, green leaves

Description	U.S. $	Can. $	U.K. £
Cream jug	40.00	60.00	25.00

Photograph not
available
at press time

Shape 1570 Sugar

Designer: Albert Hallam in 1958
Issued: 1959 - by 1963
Size: Unknown
Colour: White background, red strawberries, white
             daisies, green leaves

Description	U.S. $	Can. $	U.K. £
Sugar	40.00	60.00	25.00

Photograph not
available
at press time

Shape 1571 Stand for teapot

Designer: Albert Hallam in 1958
Issued: 1959 - by 1963
Size: Unknown
Colour: White background, red strawberries, white
             daisies, green leaves

Description	U.S. $	Can. $	U.K. £
Stand for teapot	35.00	50.00	20.00

Photograph not
available
at press time

Shape 1572 Cheese dish

Designer: Albert Hallam in 1958
Issued: 1959 - by 1963
Size: Unknown
Colour: White background, red strawberries, white
             daisies, green leaves

Description	U.S. $	Can. $	U.K. £
Cheese dish	85.00	125.00	50.00

Photograph not
available
at press time

Shape 1573 Salad bowl, footed

Designer: Albert Hallam in 1958
Issued: 1959 - by 1963
Diameter: 9 ¼", 23.5 cm
Colour: White background, red strawberries, white
            daisies, green leaves

Description	U.S. $	Can. $	U.K. £
Salad bowl, footed	85.00	125.00	50.00

Shape 1574 Salad servers

Designer: Albert Hallam in 1958
Issued: 1959 - by 1963
Size: Unknown
Colour: White background, red strawberries, white
            daisies, green leaves

Description	U.S. $	Can. $	U.K. £
Salad servers	85.00	125.00	50.00

Shape 1575 Preserve with lid

Designer: Albert Hallam in 1958
Issued: 1959 - by 1963
Size: 4" x 3 ¾", 10.1 x 9.5 cm
Colour: White background, red strawberries, white
            daisies, green leaves

Description	U.S. $	Can. $	U.K. £
Preserve with lid	60.00	90.00	35.00

Shape 1576 Butter dish, rectangular

Designer: Albert Hallam in 1958
Issued: 1959 - by 1963
Size: 5" x 3 ¼" , 12.7 x 8.3 cm
Colour: White background, red strawberries, white
            daisies, green leaves

Description	U.S. $	Can. $	U.K. £
Butter dish, rectangular	60.00	90.00	35.00

Shape 1577 Dish

Designer:	Albert Hallam in 1959
Issued:	1959 - by 1963
Size:	10" x 8 ¾", 25.4 x 22.2 cm
Colour:	White background, red strawberries, white daisies, green leaves

Description	U.S. $	Can. $	U.K. £
Dish	35.00	50.00	20.00

Shape 1578 Sweet dish

Designer:	Albert Hallam in 1959
Issued:	1959 - by 1963
Size:	5", 12.7 cm
Colour:	White background, red strawberries, white daisies, green leaves

Description	U.S. $	Can. $	U.K. £
Dish	25.00	40.00	15.00

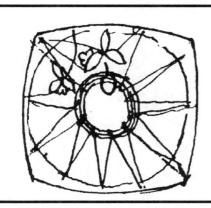

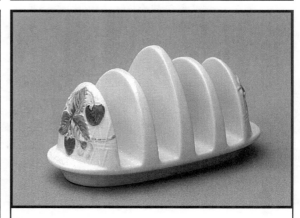

Shape 1579 Sweet dish, square

Designer:	Albert Hallam in 1959
Issued:	1959 - by 1963
Size:	4 ½", 11.9 cm
Colour:	White background, red strawberries, white daisies, green leaves

Description	U.S. $	Can. $	U.K. £
Sweet dish, square	35.00	40.00	15.00

Shape 1580 Toast rack

Designer:	Albert Hallam in 1959
Issued:	1959 - by 1963
Size:	Unknown
Colour:	White background, red strawberries, white daisies, green leaves

Description	U.S. $	Can. $	U.K. £
Toast rack	60.00	90.00	35.00

Photograph not
available
at press time

Shape 1581/1/2/3 Jug in three sizes

Designer:	Mr. Garbet in 1959
Issued:	1959 - by 1963
Size:	Unknown
Colour:	White background, red strawberries, white daisies, green leaves

Description	U.S. $	Can. $	U.K. £
1. Shape 1581/1	85.00	125.00	50.00
2. Shape 1581/2	65.00	100.00	40.00
3. Shape 1581/3	60.00	90.00	35.00

Shape 1582 T.V. Set

Designer:	Albert Hallam in 1959
Issued:	1959 - by 1963
Size:	Unknown
Colour:	White background, red strawberries, white daisies, green leaves

Description	U.S. $	Can. $	U.K. £
TV Set	85.00	125.00	50.00

Photograph not
available
at press time

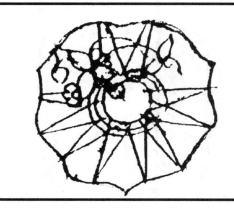

Shape 1583 Dish

Designer:	Albert Hallam in 1959
Issued:	1959 - by 1963
Size:	11 ½", 29.2 cm
Colour:	White background, red strawberries, white daisies, green leaves

Description	U.S. $	Can. $	U.K. £
Dish	60.00	90.00	35.00

Shape 1584 Dish

Designer:	Albert Hallam in 1959
Issued:	1959 - by 1963
Size:	5 ½", 14.0 cm
Colour:	White background, red strawberries, white daisies, green leaves

Description	U.S. $	Can. $	U.K. £
Dish	35.00	50.00	20.00

Photograph not
available
at press time

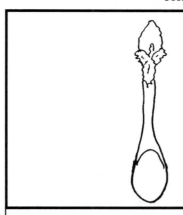

Shape 1585 Contemporary cup with new handle

Designer:	Albert Hallam in 1959
Issued:	1959 - by 1963
Size:	Unknown
Colour:	Plain

Description	U.S. $	Can. $	U.K. £
Contemporary cup with new handle	25.00	40.00	15.00

Note: This shape is part of the TV Set (shape 1582).

Shape 1629 Spoon

Designer:	Albert Hallam in 1959
Issued:	1959 - by 1963
Length:	4 ½", 11.9 cm
Colour:	White background, red strawberries, white daisies, green leaves

Description	U.S. $	Can. $	U.K. £
Spoon		Rare	

Note: Price ranges are retail market indicators of prices for models under the following conditions:
- Lower end of range = price of monochrome models
- Higher end of range = price of multicoloured models

Strawberry Ware Series Ware

Shape 1568 Pepper   Shape 1582 TV Set   Shape 1568 Salt

SUNDIAL

The Sundial tableware formed one of the more stylized ranges from the Beswick factory. Modelled in the then popular "Aztec" style, production was unlikely to have survived long after the outbreak of the Second World War.

The range consisted of eighteen items, all in gloss finish, including three different sizes of teapots, two sizes of butter dishes and two sizes of cheese dishes, but lacked teacups, saucers and plates.

In this colourful and distinctive group the colours are honey-beige (wall), green (grass), with orange and brown used on every piece. The flowers represent a herbaceous border, and are orange, dark red and blue in colour. A rose tree featured on all the designs, and a common feature where it could be incorporated was a sundial, hence the name. The dial and Roman numerals around the perimeter were painted dark brown while the gnomon (the piece that casts the shadow, when the sun is shining) was painted black and served as a knob.

The backstamp on some items read - "As purchased by H.M. Queen Mary" with the registration number 826924, corresponding to the year 1938.

Shape 530   Sugar dredger

Designer: Mr. Watkin in 1938
Issued: 1938 - by 1954
Height: 5", 12.7 cm
Colour: Cream, yellow, red, green, brown and black

Description	U.S. $	Can. $	U.K. £
Sugar dredger	100.00	150.00	60.00

Shape 531-541-579 Teapot in three sizes

Designer: Mr. Watkin, 541 in 1937, 531-579 in 1938
Issued: 1938 - by 1954
Height: 1. Shape 531 — 6 ½", 16.5 cm
           2. Shape 541 — unknown
           3. Shape 579 — unknown
Colour: Cream, yellow, red, green, brown and black

Description	U.S. $	Can. $	U.K. £
1. Shape 531	100.00	150.00	60.00
2. Shape 541	90.00	135.00	55.00
3. Shape 579	80.00	125.00	50.00

Shape 532   Hot water jug

Designer: Mr. Watkin in 1937
Issued: 1938 - by 1954
Height: 6", 15 cm
Colour: Cream, yellow, red, green, brown and black

Description	U.S. $	Can. $	U.K. £
Hot water jug	100.00	150.00	60.00

Shape 533 Cream jug

Designer:	Mr. Watkin in 1937
Issued:	1938 - by 1954
Height:	3 ½", 8.9 cm
Colour:	Cream, yellow, red, green, brown and blue

Description	U.S. $	Can. $	U.K. £
Cream jug	50.00	75.00	30.00

Shape 534 Covered sugar

Designer:	Mr. Watkin in 1937
Issued:	1938 - by 1954
Height:	4", 10.1 cm
Colour:	Cream, yellow, red, green, brown and black

Description	U.S. $	Can. $	U.K. £
Covered sugar	65.00	100.00	40.00

Shape 535 Preserve with lid

Designer:	Mr. Watkin in 1937
Issued:	1938 - by 1954
Height:	4", 10.1 cm
Colour:	Cream, yellow, red, green, brown and black

Description	U.S. $	Can. $	U.K. £
Preserve with lid	65.00	100.00	40.00

Shape 536 Biscuit jar with lid

Designer:	Mr. Watkin in 1937
Issued:	1938 - by 1954
Height:	6 ½", 16.5 cm
Colour:	Cream, yellow, red, green, brown and black

Description	U.S. $	Can. $	U.K. £
Biscuit jar with lid	125.00	190.00	75.00

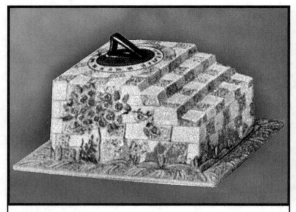

Shape 537-542 Cheese dish, two sizes

Designer:	Mr. Watkin in 1937
Issued:	1938 - by 1954
Size:	1. Shape 537 — 5", 12.7 cm
	2. Shape 542 — 4", 10.1 cm
Colour:	Cream, yellow, red, green, brown and black

Description	U.S. $	Can. $	U.K. £
1. Shape 537, large	100.00	150.00	60.00
2. Shape 542, small	85.00	125.00	50.00

Shape 538 Covered butter

Designer:	Mr. Watkin in 1937
Issued:	1938 - by 1954
Size:	4", 10.1 cm
Colour:	Cream, yellow, red, green, brown and black

Description	U.S. $	Can. $	U.K. £
Covered butter	85.00	125.00	50.00

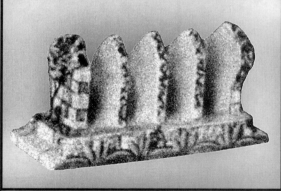

Shape 539 Cruet set, salt, pepper, mustard on base

Designer:	Mr. Watkin in 1937
Issued:	1938 - by 1954
Size:	6 ¼" x 2 ¼" x 3", 15.9 x 5.7 x 7.6 cm
Colour:	Cream, yellow, red, green, brown and black

Description	U.S. $	Can. $	U.K. £
Cruet set	75.00	100.00	40.00

Shape 540 Toast rack, four slice

Designer:	Mr. Watkin in 1937
Issued:	1938 - by 1954
Size:	Unknown
Colour:	Cream, yellow, red, green, brown and black

Description	U.S. $	Can. $	U.K. £
Toast rack, four slice	50.00	75.00	30.00

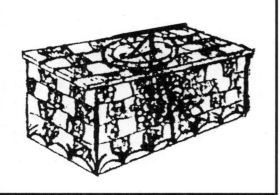

Shape 580   Covered butter, rectangular

Designer: Mr. Watkin in 1938
Issued: 1938 - by 1954
Size: Unknown
 Colour: Cream, yellow, red, green, brown and black

Description	U.S. $	Can. $	U.K. £
Covered butter, rectangular	85.00	125.00	50.00

Photograph not
available
at press time

Shape 581   Covered muffin

Designer: Mr. Watkin in 1938
Issued: 1938 - by 1954
Size: Unknown
Colour: Cream, yellow, red, green, brown and black

Description	U.S. $	Can. $	U.K. £
Covered muffin		Very Rare	

Shape 582   Bowl

Designer: Mr. Watkin in 1938
Issued: 1938 - by 1954
Size: 10 ½″ x 5″, 26.7 x 12.7 cm
Colour: Cream, yellow, red, green, brown and black

Description	U.S. $	Can. $	U.K. £
Bowl	75.00	115.00	45.00

Shape 586   Stand for teapot

Designer: Mr. Watkin in 1938
Issued: 1938 - by 1954
Width: 5 ¼″ , 13.3 cm
Colour: Green and cream

Description	U.S. $	Can. $	U.K. £
Stand for teapot	35.00	50.00	20.00

Note: This stand was designed to be used with teapot
          shapes 531 and 579.

Tit-Willow Series Ware
Shape 1838 Dish
Shape 1841 Salad servers

Shape 1832 Dish

Shape 1843 Dish

TIT-WILLOW

This series of eighteen items, all in a gloss finish, was in production for a very short time, which seems rather surprising to us, as we think it is very appealing. It is the only example of a realistic bird being used as part of the design on tableware. The bird, together with the willow in a raised motif, all on a subtle shaded background, combined to produce a most pleasing effect.

The background is a blend of shaded yellow and turquoise with a touch of pink. The bird was mainly brown, with a black head and blue wings, and brown again featured in the colour of the foliage. It is interesting to note how the position of the bird varies in relation to the willow branch. However alone among the items, the salt, pepper and servers were birdless!

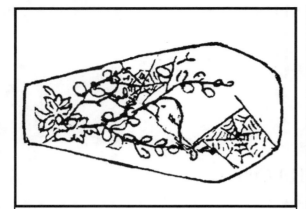

Shape 1830 Dish

Designer: Albert Hallam in 1962
Issued: 1963 - by 1966
Length: 12", 30.5 cm
Colour: Yellow, turquoise, pink, brown and black

Description	U.S. $	Can. $	U.K. £
Dish	65.00	100.00	40.00

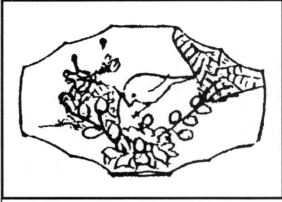

Shape 1831 Dish

Designer: Albert Hallam in 1962
Issued: 1963 - by 1966
Length: 10", 25.4 cm
Colour: Yellow, turquoise, pink, brown and black

Description	U.S. $	Can. $	U.K. £
Dish	65.00	100.00	40.00

Shape 1832 Dish

Designer: Albert Hallam in 1962
Issued: 1963 - by 1966
Size: 7" x 6 ½", 17.8 x 16.5 cm
Colour: Yellow, turquoise, pink, brown and black

Description	U.S. $	Can. $	U.K. £
Dish	50.00	75.00	30.00

Shape 1833 Double dish

Designer: Albert Hallam in 1962
Issued: 1963 - by 1966
Size: 13" x 8", 33 x 20.3 cm
Colour: Yellow, turquoise, pink, brown and black

Description	U.S. $	Can. $	U.K. £
Double dish	75.00	115.00	45.00

Shape 1834 Sandwich tray

Designer: Albert Hallam in 1962
Issued: 1963 - by 1966
Length: 11", 27.9 cm
Colour: Yellow, turquoise, pink, brown and black

Description	U.S. $	Can. $	U.K. £
Sandwich tray	75.00	115.00	45.00

Shape 1835-1836 Salt and pepper

Designer: Albert Hallam in 1962
Issued: 1963 - by 1966
Height: 4 ½", 11.9 cm
Colour: Yellow, turquoise, pink and brown

Description	U.S. $	Can. $	U.K. £
Salt	25.00	40.00	15.00
Pepper	25.00	40.00	15.00

Shape 1837 Preserve with lid

Designer: Albert Hallam 1962
Issued: 1963 - by 1966
Size: 3", 7.6 cm
Colour: Yellow, turquoise, pink, brown and black

Description	U.S. $	Can. $	U.K. £
Preserve with lid	60.00	90.00	35.00

Shape 1838 Dish

Designer: Albert Hallam in 1962
Issued: 1963 - by 1966
Size: 13" x 8", 33 x 20.3 cm
Colour: Yellow, turquoise, pink, brown and black

Description	U.S. $	Can. $	U.K. £
Dish	75.00	115.00	45.00

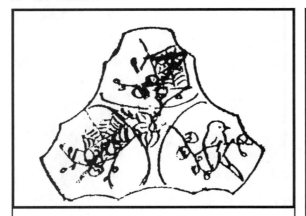

Shape 1839 Triple dish

Designer: Albert Hallam in 1962
Issued: 1963 - by 1966
Size: Unknown
Colour: Yellow, turquoise, pink, brown and black

Description	U.S. $	Can. $	U.K. £
Triple dish	75.00	115.00	45.00

Shape 1840 Salad bowl

Designer: Albert Hallam in 1962
Issued: 1963 - by 1966
Diameter: 10 ½", 26.7 cm
Colour: Yellow, turquoise, pink, brown and black

Description	U.S. $	Can. $	U.K. £
Salad bowl	100.00	150.00	60.00

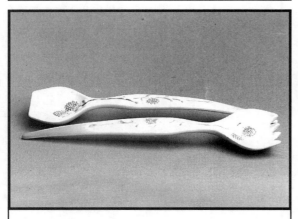

Shape 1841 Salad servers

Designer: Albert Hallam in 1962
Issued: 1963 - by 1966
Lenght: 9", 22.9 cm
Colour: Yellow, turquoise, pink and brown

Description	U.S. $	Can. $	U.K. £
Salad servers	85.00	125.00	50.00

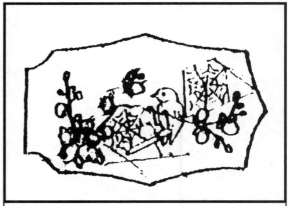

Shape 1842 Dish

Designer: Albert Hallam in 1962
Issued: 1963 - by 1966
Length: 8", 20.3 cm
Colour: Yellow, turquoise, pink, brown and black

Description	U.S. $	Can. $	U.K. £
Dish	60.00	90.00	35.00

Shape 1843 Dish

Designer:	Albert Hallam in 1962
Issued:	1963 - by 1966
Size:	6" x 5 ½", 15 x 14 cm
Colour:	Yellow, turquoise, pink, brown and black

Description	U.S. $	Can. $	U.K. £
Dish	50.00	75.00	30.00

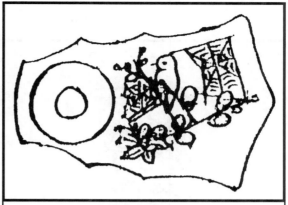

Shape 1844 Hostess or TV set
(TV tray plus Eton cup)

Designer:	Albert Hallam in 1962
Issued:	1963 - by 1966
Size:	Unknown
Colour:	Yellow, turquoise, pink, brown and black

Description	U.S. $	Can. $	U.K. £
Hostess or TV set	85.00	125.00	50.00

Shape 1846 Vinegar with stopper

Designer:	Albert Hallam in 1962
Issued:	1963 - by 1966
Height:	5 ½", 14 cm
Colour:	Yellow, turquoise, pink, brown and black

Description	U.S. $	Can. $	U.K. £
Vinegar with stopper	50.00	75.00	30.00

Shape 1864 Vase

Designer:	Albert Hallam in 1963
Issued:	1963 - by 1966
Height:	7 ½", 19.1 cm
Colour:	Yellow, turquoise, pink, brown and black

Description	U.S. $	Can. $	U.K. £
Vase	75.00	115.00	45.00

Shape 1865 Covered jar

Designer: Albert Hallam in 1963
Issued: 1963 - by 1966
Height: 6 ½", 16.5 cm
Colour: Yellow, turquoise, pink, brown and black

Description	U.S. $	Can. $	U.K. £
Covered jar	100.00	150.00	60.00

Note: Price ranges are retail market indicators of prices for models under the following conditions:
- Lower end of range = price of monochrome models
- Higher end of range = price of multicoloured models

TURQUOISE CATHAY

Turquoise Cathay was a new series of giftware announced for 1972. The items were in a delicate pale aquamarine colour glaze with a gloss finish, which became deeper as it radiated towards the edge of a lid or the base of a vase. The design of raised floral and geometric motifs had its origin in the early Chinese dynastic ceramics. The amalgamation of ancient and modern design combined with modern technology produced the unusual effect of this attractive range.

There were 12 items in the series, all of which are now difficult to find, because they were available for such a short time.

Shape 2382 Candlestick

Designer: Graham Tongue in 1971
Issued: 1972 - 1972
Diameter: 2 ½, 6.4 cm
Height: 3 ½, 8.9 cm
Colour: Aquamarine

Description	U.S. $	Can. $	U.K. £
Candlestick	40.00	60.00	25.00

Shape 2383 Candlestick

Designer: Graham Tongue in 1971
Issued: 1972 - 1972
Diameter: 3 ½, 8.9 cm
Height: 2, 5 cm
Colour: Aquamarine

Description	U.S. $	Can. $	U.K. £
Candlestick	25.00	40.00	15.00

Shape 2384 Bowl

Designer: Graham Tongue in 1971
Issued: 1972 - 1972
Diameter: 5, 12.7 cm
Height: 1 ¼, 3.1 cm
Colour: Aquamarine

Description	U.S. $	Can. $	U.K. £
Bowl	35.00	50.00	20.00

Shape 2385 Vase

Designer: Graham Tongue, Harry Sales in 1971
Issued: 1972 - 1972
Height: 7 ½, 19.1 cm
Colour: Aquamarine

Description	U.S. $	Can. $	U.K. £
Vase	50.00	75.00	30.00

Shape 2386 Covered box with lid

Designer:	Graham Tongue in 1971	
Issued:	1972 - 1972	
Diameter:	4, 10.1 cm	
Height:	3 ½, 8.9 cm	
Colour:	Aquamarine	

Description	U.S. $	Can. $	U.K. £
Covered box with lid	35.00	50.00	20.00

Shape 2387 Bowl

Designer:	Graham Tongue, Harry Sales in 1971	
Issued:	1972 - 1972	
Diameter:	6, 15 cm	
Height:	2 ¾, 7 cm	
Colour:	Aquamarine	

Description	U.S. $	Can. $	U.K. £
Bowl	50.00	75.00	30.00

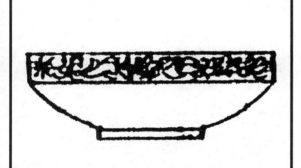

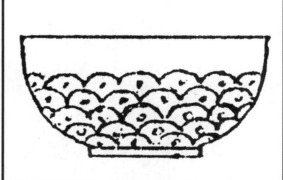

Shape 2388 Bowl

Designer:	Graham Tongue in 1971	
Issued:	1972 - 1972	
Diameter:	4 ¼, 10.8 cm	
Height:	1 ¾, 4.4 cm	
Colour:	Aquamarine	

Description	U.S. $	Can. $	U.K. £
Bowl	35.00	50.00	20.00

Shape 2389 Bowl

Designer:	Graham Tongue in 1971	
Issued:	1972 - 1972	
Diameter:	4 ½, 11.9 cm	
Height:	2, 5 cm	
Colour:	Aquamarine	

Description	U.S. $	Can. $	U.K. £
Bowl	35.00	50.00	20.00

Shape 2390 Preserve with lid

Designer: Graham Tongue in 1971
Issued: 1972 - 1972
Height: 4 ½, 11.9 cm
Colour: Aquamarine

Description	U.S. $	Can. $	U.K. £
Preserve with lid	50.00	75.00	30.00

Shape 2392 Vase

Designer: Graham Tongue in 1971
Issued: 1972 - 1972
Height: 7 ½, 19.1 cm
Colour: Aquamarine

Description	U.S. $	Can. $	U.K. £
Vase	50.00	75.00	30.00

Shape 2408 Ginger jar, large

Designer: Graham Tongue in 1972
Issued: 1972 - 1972
Height: 7, 17.8 cm
Colour: Aquamarine

Description	U.S. $	Can. $	U.K. £
Ginger jar, large	85.00	125.00	50.00

Shape 2409 Ginger jar, small

Designer: Graham Tongue, Harry Sales in 1972
Issued: 1972 - 1972
Height: 4, 10.1 cm
Colour: Aquamarine

Description	U.S. $	Can. $	U.K. £
Ginger jar, small	60.00	90.00	35.00

VENETIAN WARE

The Venetian Series was designed soon after the beginning of the war in order to replace in overseas markets the particular types of ornamental wares previously available from Germany, Czecho-Slovakia and Italy. Two distinct styles of gloss decoration were used, one design incorporating scrolls and a stylistic bird, the other floral and leaf patterns. Three of the floral designs were illustrated in the Pottery Gazette for September, 1940 on a page with the caption :

"Britain **CAN** Export - Buy British Ware."

The decorations were carried out in a scratched or Sgraffito style in green, blue, yellow and red on a white or beige ground, and were typically Italian in character. Except perhaps for the large tray/plaques, all the floral designs were also produced in white matt.

Information is scarce on these early pieces, of which there were thirty-five in the series. The bird design was withdrawn earlier than the floral pattern and each is identified against the shapes in which it was produced, "Bird" with a (B), and "Floral" with an (F). Since the series was produced initially for export, examples rarely appear.

Shape 770 (B) Vase, two handles each consisting of three loops

Designer:	Unknown in 1939
Issued:	1940 - by 1954
Size:	Unknown
Colour:	Green, blue, yellow and red on beige background

Description	U.S. $	Can. $	U.K. £
Vase	160.00	235.00	95.00

Shape 771 (B) Jug, handle consisting of two loops

Designer:	Mr. Symcox in 1939
Issued:	1940 - by 1954
Size:	Unknown
Colour:	Green, blue, yellow and red on beige background

Description	U.S. $	Can. $	U.K. £
Jug	140.00	215.00	85.00

Photograph not
availabe
at press time

Shape 772 (B) Jug

Designer:	Unknown in 1939
Issued:	1940 - by 1954
Size:	Unknown
Colour:	Green, blue, yellow and red on beige background

Description	U.S. $	Can. $	U.K. £
Jug		Rare	

Shape 773 (B) Vase

Designer:	Mr. Symcox in 1939
Issued:	1940 - by 1954
Size:	Unknown
Colour:	Green, blue, yellow and red on beige background

Description	U.S. $	Can. $	U.K. £
Vase	125.00	190.00	75.00

Shape 774 (B) Jug

Designer: Mr. Symcox in 1939
Issued: 1940 - by 1954
Size: Unknown
Colour: Green, blue, yellow and red on beige
             background

Description	U.S. $	Can. $	U.K. £
Jug	150.00	225.00	90.00

Shape 775 (B) Vase

Designer: Mr. Symcox in 1940
Issued: 1940 - by 1954
Size: Unknown
Colour: Green, blue, yellow and red on beige
             background

Description	U.S. $	Can. $	U.K. £
Vase	140.00	215.00	85.00

Shape 776 (B) Vase with 2 handles

Designer: Mr. Watkin in 1940
Issued: 1940 - by 1954
Size: Unknown
Colour: Green, blue, yellow and red on beige
             background

Description	U.S. $	Can. $	U.K. £
Vase	140.00	215.00	85.00

Shape 777 (B) Jug

Designer: Mr. Watkin in 1940
Issued: 1940 - by 1954
Size: Unknown
Colour: Green, blue, yellow and red on beige
             background

Description	U.S. $	Can. $	U.K. £
Jug	140.00	215.00	85.00

Shape 778 (B) Bowl with fancy edge

Designer: Mr. Symcox in 1940
Issued: 1940 - by 1954
Diameter: 12 ½ ", 31.7 cm
Colour: Green, blue, yellow and red on beige
             background

Description	U.S. $	Can. $	U.K. £
Bowl	125.00	190.00	75.00

Photograph not
available
at press time

Shape 779 (B) Vase with 2 handles

Designer: Unknown in 1940
Issued: 1940 - by 1954
Size: Unknown
Colour: Green, blue, yellow and red on beige
             background

Description	U.S. $	Can. $	U.K. £
Vase		Rare	

Shape 780 (B) Jug

Designer: Mr. Symcox in 1940
Issued: 1940 - by 1954
Size: Unknown
Colour: Green, blue, yellow and red on beige
             background

Description	U.S. $	Can. $	U.K. £
Jug	140.00	215.00	85.00

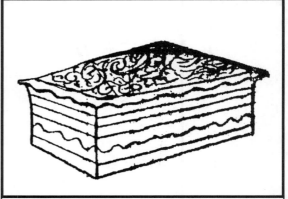

Shape 781 (B) Cigarette box , bird design on lid

Designer: Unknown in 1940
Issued: 1940 - by 1954
Size :   Unknown
Colour: Green, blue, yellow and red on beige
             background

Description	U.S. $	Can. $	U.K. £
Cigarette box	125.00	190.00	75.00

Photograph not
available
at press time

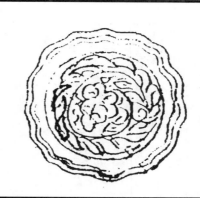

Shape 782 (B) Tray/Plaque

Designer:	Unknown in 1940
Issued:	1940 - by 1954
Diameter:	12 ¼", 31.1 cm
Colour:	Green, blue, yellow and red on beige background

Description	U.S. $	Can. $	U.K. £
Tray/Plaque	165.00	235.00	95.00

Shape 783 (B) Ashtray

Designer:	Unknown in 1940
Issued:	1940 - by 1954
Size:	Unknown
Colour:	Green, blue, yellow and red on beige background

Description	U.S. $	Can. $	U.K. £
Ashtray	40.00	60.00	25.00

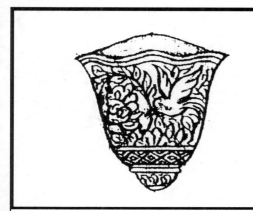

Shape 784 (B) Wall pocket

Designer:	Unknown in 1940
Issued:	1940 - by 1954
Size:	Unknown
Colour:	Green, blue, yellow and red on beige background

Description	U.S. $	Can. $	U.K. £
Wall pocket	100.00	150.00	60.00

Shape 785 (F) Vase with 2 handles

Designer:	Unknown in 1939
Issued:	1940 - by 1963
Height:	9 ¾", 24.7 cm
Colour:	Green, blue, yellow and red on beige background

Description	U.S. $	Can. $	U.K. £
Vase	140.00	215.00	85.00

Shape 786 (F) Jug

Designer:	Unknown in 1939
Issued:	1940 - by 1963
Height:	12 ¼", 31.1 cm
Colour:	Green, blue, yellow and red on beige background

Description	U.S. $	Can. $	U.K. £
Jug	160.00	235.00	95.00

Shape 787 (F) Vase

Designer:	Unknown in 1939
Issued:	1940 - by 1963
Height:	7", 17.8 cm
Colour:	Green, blue, yellow and red on beige background

Description	U.S. $	Can. $	U.K. £
Vase	125.00	190.00	75.00

Shape 788 (F) Vase with 2 handles

Designer:	Mr. Watkin in 1939
Issued:	1940 - by 1963
Height:	10 ½", 26.7 cm
Colour:	Green, blue, yellow and red on beige background

Description	U.S. $	Can. $	U.K. £
Vase	140.00	215.00	85.00

Shape 789 (F) Vase

Designer:	Mr. Watkin in 1939
Issued:	1940 - by 1963
Height:	10 ¾", 27.8 cm
Colour:	Green, blue, yellow and red on beige background

Description	U.S. $	Can. $	U.K. £
Vase	140.00	215.00	85.00

Shape 790 (F)   Jug

Designer: Mr. Watkin in 1939
Issued: 1940 - by 1963
Height: 8 ½", 21.6 cm
Colour: Green, blue, yellow and red on beige
            background

Description	U.S. $	Can. $	U.K. £
Jug	140.00	215.00	85.00

Shape 791 (F)   Vase with 2 handles

Designer: Mr. Symcox in 1939
Issued: 1940 - by 1963
Height: 7 ½", 19.1 cm
Colour: Green, blue, yellow and red on beige
            background

Description	U.S. $	Can. $	U.K. £
Vase	130.00	200.00	80.00

Shape 792 (F)   Vase / Lamp base

Designer: Mr. Symcox in 1939
Issued: 1940 - by 1963
Height: 15 ¼", 38.7 cm
Colour: Green, blue, yellow and red on beige
            background

Description	U.S. $	Can. $	U.K. £
Vase / lamp base	175.00	250.00	100.00

Shape 793 (F)   Vase with 2 handles

Designer: Mr. Watkin in 1939
Issued: 1940 - by 1963
Height: 6", 15 cm
Colour: Green, blue, yellow and red on beige
            background

Description	U.S. $	Can. $	U.K. £
Vase	125.00	190.00	75.00

Shape 794 (F) Bowl

Designer:	Unknown in 1939
Issued:	1940 - by 1963
Diameter:	11″, 27.9 cm
Colour:	Green, blue, yellow and red on beige background

Description	U.S. $	Can. $	U.K. £
Bowl	140.00	215.00	85.00

Shape 795 (F) Jug

Designer:	Mr. Symcox in 1940
Issued:	1940 - by 1963
Height:	9″, 22.9 cm
Colour:	Green, blue, yellow and red on beige background

Description	U.S. $	Can. $	U.K. £
Jug	140.00	215.00	85.00

Shape 796 (F) Jug

Designer:	Mr. Symcox in 1940
Issued:	1940 - by 1963
Height:	7″, 17.8 cm
Colour:	Green, blue, yellow and red on beige background

Description	U.S. $	Can. $	U.K. £
Jug	100.00	150.00	60.00

Shape 797 (F) Ashtray, large

Designer:	Mr. Watkin in 1940
Issued:	1940 - by 1963
Diameter:	5 ¼″, 13.3 cm
Colour:	Green, blue, yellow and red on beige background

Description	U.S. $	Can. $	U.K. £
Ashtray	60.00	90.00	35.00

Photograph not
available
at press time

Shape 798 (F) Wall vase

Designer: Mr. Watkin in 1940
Issued: 1940 - by 1963
Height: 6 ½", 16.5 cm
Colour: Green, blue, yellow and red on beige
background

Description	U.S. $	Can. $	U.K. £
Wall Vase	110.00	165.00	65.00

Shape 799 (F) Ashtray, small

Designer: Unknown in 1940
Issued: 1940 - by 1963
Diameter: 3 ½", 8.9 cm
Colour: Green, blue, yellow and red on beige
background

Description	U.S. $	Can. $	U.K. £
Ashtray, small	65.00	100.00	40.00

Shape 814 (F) Cigarette box

Designer: Mr. Watkin in 1940
Issued: 1940 - by 1963
Size: 5 ½" x 4 ¼", 14.0 x 10.8 cm
Colour: Green, blue, yellow and red on beige
background

Description	U.S. $	Can. $	U.K. £
Cigarette box	110.00	165.00	65.00

Shape 816 (F) Tray / Plaque

Designer: James Hayward, Albert Hallam in 1940
Issued: 1940 - by 1963
Diameter: 12 ¼", 31.7 cm
Colour: Green, blue, yellow and red on beige
background

Description	U.S. $	Can. $	U.K. £
Tray/Plaque	140.00	215.00	85.00

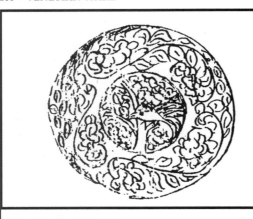

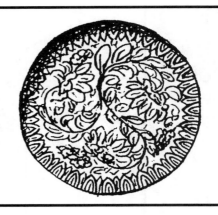

Shape 838 (B) Tray / Plaque

Designer:	Albert Hallam, James Hayward in 1940
Issued:	1940 - by 1954
Diameter:	14", 35.5 cm
Colour:	Green, blue, yellow and red on beige background

Description	U.S. $	Can. $	U.K. £
Tray/Plaque	200.00	300.00	125.00

Shape 839 (F) Tray / Plaque

Designer:	Albert Hallam, James Hayward in 1940
Issued:	1940 - by 1954
Diameter:	14", 35.5 cm
Colour:	Green, blue, yellow and red on beige background

Description	U.S. $	Can. $	U.K. £
Tray/Plaque	200.00	300.00	125.00

Shape 921 (B) Vase / Lamp base

Designer:	Albert Hallam, James Hayward in 1941
Issued:	1941 - by 1954
Height:	7 ½", 19.1 cm
Colour:	Green, blue, yellow and red on beige background

Description	U.S. $	Can. $	U.K. £
Vase / Lamp base	125.00	200.00	75.00

WAYSIDE

The name "Wayside" brings to mind a picture of a typical country lane, and this series surely was inspired by the wonder of nature in the countryside. The background colour chosen for this pretty and attractive series was either a turquoise or primrose with red, purple, pink, yellow and green flowers. Variations have been found in the background, e.g. a pastel turquoise blue or an almost white. A feature of the design were the harebell knobs in blue and yellow. These were used on the butter, preserve and on the teapots. Some of the flowers represented in the decoration were poppies, harebells and violets.

There were twenty-three items in the series, which could be purchased separately or in sets, all in a gloss finish. The sets were put together at the time of purchase. If a Morning Set was ordered, the shop would gather the appropriate pieces to create the set. The four sets were:

1. A fruit set comprising six fruit saucers and a fruit bowl
2. A tea set comprising 21 pieces
3. A tea set comprising 18 pieces
4. A morning set comprising two cups and saucers, a plate, a sugar, a cream jug and a teapot

Shape 870-871 Teapot, two sizes

Designer:	Mr. Watkin in 1940
Issued:	1941 - by 1963
Height:	1. Shape 870 — 6", 15 cm
	2. Shape 871 — 5 ¼", 13.3 cm
Colour:	See title page

Description	U.S. $	Can. $	U.K. £
1. Shape 870	160.00	235.00	95.00
2. Shape 871	140.00	215.00	85.00

Shape 872-873 Cheese dish, two sizes

Designer:	Mr. Watkin in 1940
Issued:	1941 - by 1963
Base Size:	1. Shape 872 — 7" x 8 ¼", 17.8 x 21 cm
	2. Shape 873 — 6" x 6 ¾", 15 x 17.2 cm
Height :	1. Shape 872 — 3 ½, 8.9 cm
	2. Shape 873 — 3", 7.6 cm
Colour:	See title page

Description	U.S. $	Can. $	U.K. £
1. Shape 872	110.00	165.00	65.00
2. Shape 873	95.00	145.00	55.00

Photograph not
available
at press time

Shape 874 /1/2/3 Jug, three sizes

Designer:	Mr. Watkin in 1940
Issued:	1941 - by 1963
Heights:	1. Shape 874/1 — 6 ½", 16.5 cm
	2. Shape 874/2 — 6", 15 cm
	3. Shape 874/3 — 5 ¼", 13.3 cm
Colour:	See title page

Description	U.S. $	Can. $	U.K. £
1. Large	90.00	130.00	55.00
2. Medium	70.00	100.00	45.00
3. Small	65.00	95.00	40.00

Shape 875 Covered butter

Designer:	Mr. Watkin in 1940
Issued:	1941 - by 1963
Size:	6" x 4" x 3 ¾", 15 x 10.1 x 9.5 cm
Colour:	See title page

Description	U.S. $	Can. $	U.K. £
Covered butter	85.00	125.00	50.00

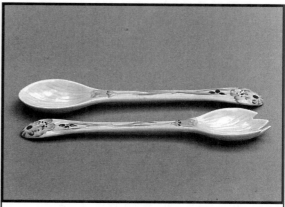

Shape 876	**Salad bowl**		
Designer:	Mr. Watkin in 1940		
Issued:	1941 - by 1963		
Size:	9 ¾" x 4", 24.7 x 10.1 cm		
Colour:	See title page		

Description	U.S. $	Can. $	U.K. £
Salad bowl	100.00	150.00	60.00

Shape 877	**Salad servers**		
Designer:	Mr. Watkin in 1940		
Issued:	1941 - by 1963		
Length:	9", 22.9 cm		
Colour:	See title page		

Description	U.S. $	Can. $	U.K. £
Salad servers	85.00	125.00	50.00

Note: Price listed above is for the pair.

Shape 878	**Open sugar bowl, large**		
Designer:	Mr. Watkin in 1940		
Issued:	1941 - by 1963		
Diameter:	3 ¼", 8.3 cm		
Colour:	See title page		

Description	U.S. $	Can. $	U.K. £
Open sugar bowl, large	40.00	60.00	25.00

Shape 879	**Cream jug**		
Designer:	Mr. Watkin in 1940		
Issued:	1941 - by 1963		
Height :	4", 10.1 cm		
Colour:	See title page		

Description	U.S. $	Can. $	U.K. £
Cream jug	50.00	75.00	30.00

Shape 880   Preserve with lid

Designer:	Mr. Watkin in 1940	
Issued:	1941 - by 1963	
Size:	3 ½" x 4 ½", 8.9 x11.9 cm	
Colour:	See title page	

Description	U.S. $	Can. $	U.K. £
Preserve with lid	60.00	90.00	35.00

Shape 881   Egg set (4 egg cups on a base)

Designer:	Mr. Watkin in 1941	
Issued:	Unknown	
Size:	Unknown	
Colour:	See title page	

Description	U.S. $	Can. $	U.K. £
Egg set	125.00	190.00	75.00

Note: Possibly not put into production.

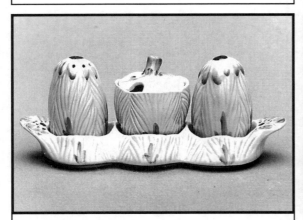

Shape 882   Cruet set, salt, pepper and mustard on base (four pieces)

Designer:	Mr. Watkin in 1941	
Issued:	1941 - by 1963	
Length:	6 ½", 16.5 cm	
Colour:	See title page	

Description	U.S. $	Can. $	U.K. £
Cruet set	65.00	100.00	40.00

Note: These pieces were also supplied as separate items.

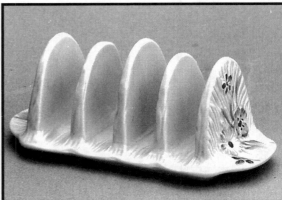

Shape 883   Toast rack, four slice

Designer:	Mr. Watkin in 1941	
Issued:	1941 - by 1963	
Size:	2 ½" x 6", 6.4 x 15 cm	
Colour:	See title page	

Description	U.S. $	Can. $	U.K. £
Toast rack, four slice	60.00	90.00	35.00

Shape 884/1/2   Sweet dish, two sizes

Designer: Mr. Watkin in 1941
Issued: 1941 - by 1963
Length: 1. Shape 884/1 — 9 ¼", 23.5 cm
            2. Shape 884/2 — 7", 17.8 cm
Colour: See title page

Description	U.S. $	Can. $	U.K. £
1. Shape 884/1	60.00	90.00	35.00
2. Shape 884/2	40.00	60.00	25.00

Photograph not
available
at press time

Shape 885   Cup and saucer

Designer: Mr. Watkin in 1941
Issued: 1941 - by 1963
Size: Cup - 3 ¾", 9.5 cm
           Saucer - unknown
Colour: See title page

Description	U.S. $	Can. $	U.K. £
Cup and saucer		Very Rare	

Photograph not
available
at press time

Shape 886-887 Plate, two sizes

Designer: Mr. Watkin in 1941
Issued: 1941 - by 1963
Size: 1. Shape 886 — 5", 12.7 cm
           2. Shape 887 — 6 ¾", 17.2 cm
Colour: See title page

Description	U.S. $	Can. $	U.K. £
1. Shape 886	50.00	75.00	30.00
2. Shape 887	60.00	90.00	35.00

Photograph not
available
at press time

Shape 888   Bread and butter plate

Designer: Mr. Watkin in 1941
Issued: 1941 - by 1963
Diameter: 9", 22.9 cm
Colour: See title page

Description	U.S. $	Can. $	U.K. £
Bread and butter plate	60.00	90.00	35.00

Photograph not
available
at press time

Shape 889   Fruit bowl

Designer: Mr. Watkin in 1941
Issued: 1941 - by 1963
Diameter: 9", 22.9 cm
Colour: See title page

Description	U.S. $	Can. $	U.K. £
Fruit bowl	120.00	175.00	70.00

Shape 890   Fruit saucer

Designer: Mr. Watkin in 1941
Issued: 1941 - by 1963
Diameter: 6 ½", 16.5 cm
Colour: See title page

Description	U.S. $	Can. $	U.K. £
Fruit saucer	40.00	60.00	25.00

Photograph not
available
at press time

Photograph not
available
at press time

Shape 1323   Cream, for the morning set

Designer: Albert Hallam in 1954
Issued: 1954 - by 1963
Size: Unknown
Colour: See title page

Description	U.S. $	Can. $	U.K. £
Cream	50.00	75.00	30.00

Shape 1324   Sugar, for the morning set

Designer: Albert Hallam in 1954
Issued: 1954 - by 1963
Size: Unknown
Colour: See title page

Description	U.S. $	Can. $	U.K. £
Sugar	50.00	75.00	30.00

WILLOW

1938 saw the introduction of the "Willow" series, which was modelled in relief. There were two distinct colourways, the first being in both light and dark blue, on a white background and the second using green, orange, brown and blue also on a white background.

The novelty of the design was that the component subjects of the old willow-pattern plate story were used separately as motifs for the decoration. For example, on the lids of both the teapot (shape 511) and the hot water jug (shape 512), it is possible to see embossed on the lid, the two lovers turned into birds and flying away.

There are eighteen items in this series and all were produced in a gloss finish. Again, as with many series which were modelled around this time, the war intervened and they were discontinued after only a few years. Examples of the more highly coloured decoration have turned up, but the blue version appears to be very rare indeed.

Shape 511   **Teapot on stand**

Designer: Mr. Watkin in 1937
Issued: 1938 - by 1954
Height: 7", 17.8 cm
Colour: 1. Green, orange, brown and blue on a
                 white background
              2. Light and dark blue on white background

Colour	U.S. $	Can. $	U.K. £
1. Green	200.00	300.00	125.00
2. Blue	200.00	300.00	125.00

Shape 512   **Hot water jug**

Designer: Mr. Watkin in 1937
Issued: 1938 - by 1954
Size: 4 ¾" x 3 ¾" x 6 ½", 12.1 x 9.5 x 16.5 cm
Colour: 1. Green, orange, brown and blue on a
                 white background
              2. Light and dark blue on white background

Colour	U.S. $	Can. $	U.K. £
1. Green	175.00	250.00	100.00
2. Blue	175.00	250.00	100.00

Shape 513   **Cream jug**

Designer: Mr. Watkin in 1937
Issued: 1938 - by 1954
Height: 3 ½", 8.9 cm
Colour: 1. Green, orange, brown and blue on a
                 white background
              2. Light and dark blue on white background

Colour	U.S. $	Can. $	U.K. £
1. Green	100.00	150.00	60.00
2. Blue	100.00	150.00	60.00

Shape 514   **Sugar**

Designer: Mr. Watkin in 1937
Issued: 1938 - by 1954
Height :   3 ¾", 9.5 cm
Colour: 1. Green, orange, brown and blue on a
                 white background
              2. Light and dark blue on white background

Colour	U.S. $	Can. $	U.K. £
1. Green	120.00	175.00	70.00
2. Blue	120.00	175.00	70.00

Shape 515 Preserve with lid

Designer:	Mr. Watkin in 1937
Issued:	1938 - by 1954
Size:	4 ½" x 3 ¼" x 4", 11.9 x 8.3 x 10.1 cm
Colour:	1. Green, orange, brown and blue on a white background
	2. Light and dark blue on white background

Colour	U.S. $	Can. $	U.K. £
1. Green	125.00	175.00	75.00
2. Blue	125.00	175.00	75.00

Shape 516 Cheese dish

Designer:	Mr. Watkin in 1937
Issued:	1938 - by 1954
Size:	Unknown
Colour:	1. Green, orange, brown and blue on a white background
	2. Light and dark blue on white background

Colour	U.S. $	Can. $	U.K. £
1. Green	175.00	250.00	100.00
2. Blue	175.00	250.00	100.00

Shape 517 Toast rack

Designer:	Mr. Watkin in 1937
Issued:	1938 - by 1954
Size:	Unknown
Colour:	1. Green, orange, brown and blue on a white background
	2. Light and dark blue on white background

Colour	U.S. $	Can. $	U.K. £
1. Green	175.00	250.00	100.00
2. Blue	175.00	250.00	100.00

Shape 518 Biscuit jar with lid

Designer:	Mr. Watkin in 1937
Issued:	1938 - by 1954
Size:	Unknown
Colour:	1. Green, orange, brown and blue on a white background
	2. Light and dark blue on white background

Colour	U.S. $	Can. $	U.K. £
1. Green	200.00	300.00	125.00
2. Blue	200.00	300.00	125.00

Shape 519	Cruet set, salt, pepper, mustard on base
Designer:	Mr. Watkin in 1937
Issued:	1938 - by 1954
Size:	Unknown
Colour:	1. Green, orange, brown and blue on a white background
	2. Light and dark blue on white background

Colour	U.S. $	Can. $	U.K. £
1. Green	150.00	200.00	85.00
2. Blue	150.00	200.00	85.00

Shape 520	Teapot
Designer:	Mr. Watkin in 1937
Issued:	1938 - by 1954
Size:	Unknown
Colour:	1. Green, orange, brown and blue on a white background
	2. Light and dark blue on white background

Colour	U.S. $	Can. $	U.K. £
1. Green	200.00	300.00	125.00
2. Blue	200.00	300.00	125.00

Shape 521	Covered muffin
Designer:	Mr. Watkin in 1937
Issued:	1938 - by 1954
Size :	Unknown
Colour:	1. Green, orange, brown and blue on a white background
	2. Light and dark blue on white background

Colour	U.S. $	Can. $	U.K. £
1. Green	200.00	300.00	125.00
2. Blue	200.00	300.00	125.00

Shape 522	Cheese dish
Designer:	Mr. Watkin in 1937
Issued:	1938 - by 1954
Size:	Unknown
Colour:	1. Green, orange, brown and blue on a white background
	2. Light and dark blue on white background

Colour	U.S. $	Can. $	U.K. £
1. Green	200.00	300.00	125.00
2. Blue	200.00	300.00	125.00

Shape 523 **Salad / Fruit bowl**

Designer: Mr. Watkin in 1937
Issued: 1938 - by 1954
Size : Unknown
Colour: 1. Green, orange, brown and blue on a
white background
2. Light and dark blue on white background

Description	U.S. $	Can. $	U.K. £
Salad / Fruit bowl	175.00	250.00	100.00

Shape 524 **Butter dish**

Designer: Mr. Watkin in 1937
Issued: 1938 - by 1954
Size: Unknown
Colour: 1. Green, orange, brown and blue on a
white background
2. Light and dark blue on white background

Description	U.S. $	Can. $	U.K. £
Butter dish	200.00	300.00	125.00

Shape 525 **Cup and saucer**

Designer: Mr. Watkin in 1937
Issued: 1938 - by 1954
Size: Unknown
Colour: 1. Green, orange, brown and blue on a
white background
2. Light and dark blue on white background

Description	U.S. $	Can. $	U.K. £
Cup and saucer	125.00	175.00	75.00

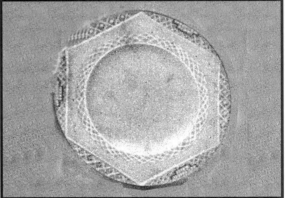

Shape 526 **Plate, small**

Designer: Mr. Watkin in 1937
Issued: 1938 - by 1954
Size: Unknown
Colour: 1. Green, orange, brown and blue on a
white background
2. Light and dark blue on white background

Description	U.S. $	Can. $	U.K. £
Plate, small	75.00	115.00	45.00

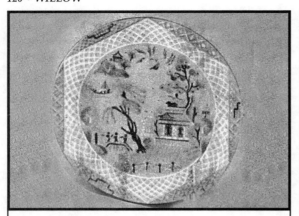

Photograph not
available
at press time

Shape 527   Plate, large

Designer: Mr. Watkin in 1937
Issued: 1938 - by 1954
Size: Unknown
Colour: 1. Green, orange, brown and blue on a
             white background
          2. Light and dark blue on white background

Colour	U.S. $	Can. $	U.K. £
1. Green	140.00	215.00	85.00
2. Blue	140.00	215.00	85.00

Shape 528   Slop bowl

Designer: Mr. Watkin in 1937
Issued: 1938 - by 1954
Size: Unknown
Colour: 1. Green, orange, brown and blue on a
             white background
          2. Light and dark blue on white background

Colour	U.S. $	Can. $	U.K. £
1. Green	110.00	165.00	65.00
2. Blue	110.00	165.00	65.00

Note: Price ranges are retail market indicators of prices for models under the following conditions:
- Lower end of range = price of monochrome models
- Higher end of range = price of multicoloured models

ZORBA

There were thirty-two items in this large series and the shapes were produced in two colourways, brown and olive green, both in a gloss finish. The decoration used geometric shapes of circles and triangles to create a border pattern for the various "modern" shapes. At some time, probably as production was drawing to a close, some pieces were produced in white, these are rare.

The brown finish, called "bronze," was probably the "in colour" at the time, and this is the colourway most often found today. It is amazing to think that so many of these items, which would have been in everyday use, have survived so well. The brown came in different combinations, one shade all over, dark brown and light brown, or in some cases three shades of brown. The dark brown was a satin matt finish. In addition to the individual pieces, Zorba was available in Coffee Sets or Tea Sets. Until a saucer (shape 2344) became available, the Orbit shape was used.

The name for the series conjures up Greek origins and perhaps the inspiration for this design came from that country?

Shape 2211 Coffee pot

Designer:	Graham Tongue in 1968	
Issued:	1970 - 1973	
Base Dia:	4 ½", 11.9 cm	
Height:	9", 22.9 cm	
Colour:	Brown (bronze) or olive green	

Description	U.S. $	Can. $	U.K. £
Coffee pot	25.00	40.00	15.00

Shape 2212 Cup

Designer:	Graham Tongue in 1968	
Issued:	1970 - 1973	
Top Dia:	3", 7.6 cm	
Height :	3", 7.6 cm	
Colour:	Brown (bronze) or olive green	

Description	U.S. $	Can. $	U.K. £
Cup	8.00	12.00	5.00

Shape 2224 Open sugar

Designer:	Graham Tongue in 1968	
Issued:	1970 - 1973	
Diameter:	3 ¾", 9.5 cm	
Height:	2 ½", 6.4 cm	
Colour:	Brown (bronze) or olive green	

Description	U.S. $	Can. $	U.K. £
Open sugar	8.00	12.00	5.00

Shape 2225 Cream jug

Designer:	Graham Tongue in 1968	
Issued:	1970 - 1973	
Height:	3 ¾", 9.5 cm	
Colour:	Brown (bronze) or olive green	

Description	U.S. $	Can. $	U.K. £
Cream jug	8.00	12.00	5.00

Shape 2228 Cheese dish

Designer: Graham Tongue in 1968
Issued: 1970 - 1973
Height: 3 ¾", 9.5 cm
Colour: Brown (bronze) or olive green

Description	U.S. $	Can. $	U.K. £
Cheese dish	25.00	40.00	15.00

Shape 2229 Hot milk jug

Designer: Graham Tongue in 1968
Issued: 1970 - 1973
Base: 4", 10.1 cm
Height : 7 ¼", 18.4 cm
Colour: Brown (bronze) or olive green

Description	U.S. $	Can. $	U.K. £
Hot milk jug	25.00	40.00	15.00

Shape 2234 Covered butter with wide rim

Designer: Graham Tongue in 1968
Issued: 1970 - 1973
Size: 6 ½" x 5" x 4", 16.5 x 12.7 x 10.1 cm
Colour: Brown (bronze) or olive green

Description	U.S. $	Can. $	U.K. £
Covered butter	25.00	40.00	15.00

Shape 2245 Preserve with cover

Designer: Graham Tongue in 1968
Issued: 1970 - 1973
Diameter: 3 ¼", 8.3 cm
Height : 3 ½", 8.9 cm
Colour: Brown (bronze) or olive green

Description	U.S. $	Can. $	U.K. £
Preserve with cover	15.00	25.00	10.00

Photograph not
available
at press time

Shape 2248-2249 Pepper and Salt

Designer: Graham Tongue in 1968
Issued: 1970 - 1973
Height: 5", 12.7 cm
Colour: Brown (bronze) or olive green

Description	U.S. $	Can. $	U.K. £
1. Shape 2248, Pepper	8.00	12.00	5.00
2. Shape 2249, Salt	8.00	12.00	5.00

Shape 2322 Casserole with cover, (3 ½ pint) oval

Designer: Graham Tongue in 1970
Issued: 1971 - 1973
Size: 9" x 6 ½", 5", 22.9 x 16.5 x 12.7 cm
Colour: Brown (bronze) or olive green

Description	U.S. $	Can. $	U.K. £
Casserole with cover	35.00	50.00	20.00

Casserole (6 pint) with cover

Shape 2319-2320-2321 Casserole with cover

Designer: Shape 2319 — Albert Hallam in 1970
          Shape 2320 - 2321 — Graham Tongue in 1970
Issued: 1971 - 1973
Diameter: 1. Shape 2319, 6 pint — 9", 22.9 cm
          2. Shape 2320, 4 pint — 8", 20.3 cm
          3. Shape 2321, 2 ½ pint — 6 ½", 16.5 cm
Height : 1. Shape 2319, 6 pint — 6", 15 cm
          2. Shape 2320, 4 pint — 5", 12.7 cm
          3. Shape 2321, 2 ½ pint — Unknown
Colour: Brown (bronze) or olive green

Description	U.S. $	Can. $	U.K. £
1. Shape 2319, 6 pint	40.00	60.00	25.00
2. Shape 2320, 4 pint	35.00	50.00	20.00
3. Shape 2321, 2 ½ pint	25.00	40.00	15.00

Casserole (4 pint) cover missing

Shape 2323 Gravy boat

Designer: Graham Tongue in 1970
Issued: 1971 - 1973
Height: 3", 7.6 cm
Colour: Brown (bronze) or olive green

Description	U.S. $	Can. $	U.K. £
Gravy boat	20.00	25.00	10.00

Shape 2324 Mug, ½ pint

Designer: Graham Tongue in 1970
Issued: 1971 - 1973
Height :   3 ½", 8.9 cm
Colour: Brown (bronze) or olive green

Description	U.S. $	Can. $	U.K. £
Mug, ½ pint	8.00	12.00	5.00

Shape 2325 Teapot

Designer: Graham Tongue in 1970
Issued: 1971 - 1973
Height: 6 ½", 16.5 cm
Colour: White

Description	U.S. $	Can. $	U.K. £
Teapot	20.00	25.00	10.00

Shape 2326-2327-2328 Plate, three sizes

Designer: Graham Tongue in 1970
Issued: 1971 - 1973
Size: 1. Shape 2326, small - 7", 17.8 cm
             2. Shape 2327, medium - 8 ¾", 22.2 cm
             3. Shape 2328, large - 10 ¾", 27.8 cm
Colour: Brown (bronze) or olive green

Description	U.S. $	Can. $	U.K. £
1. Shape 2326	6.00	10.00	4.00
2. Shape 2327	8.00	12.00	5.00
3. Shape 2328	10.00	15.00	6.00

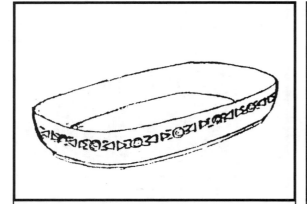

Shape 2329 Gratin dish

Designer: Graham Tongue in 1970
Issued: 1971 - 1973
Size: 10 ½" x 9 ½" x 2", 26.7 x 24 x 5 cm
Colour: Brown (bronze) or olive green

Description	U.S. $	Can. $	U.K. £
Gratin dish	25.00	40.00	15.00

Shape 2330 Ramekin dish

Designer: Graham Tongue in 1970
Issued: 1971 - 1973
Diameter: 5 ¼", 13.3 cm
Height : 3", 7.6 cm
Colour: Brown (bronze) or olive green

Description	U.S. $	Can. $	U.K. £
Ramekin dish	20.00	25.00	10.00

Shape 2331 Soufflé dish, large

Designer: Graham Tongue in 1970
Issued: 1971 - 1973
Diameter: 6 ½", 16.5 cm
Height: 3 ½", 8.9 cm
Colour: Brown (bronze) or olive green

Description	U.S. $	Can. $	U.K. £
Soufflé dish, large	20.00	25.00	10.00

Shape 2332 Soufflé dish, individual

Designer: Graham Tongue in 1970
Issued: 1971 - 1973
Diameter: 3 ½", 8.9 cm
Height : 2", 5.0 cm
Colour: Brown (bronze) or olive green

Description	U.S. $	Can. $	U.K. £
Soufflé dish, individual	8.00	12.00	5.00

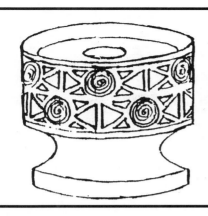

Shape 2341 Candlestick

Designer:	Graham Tongue in 1970
Issued:	1971 - 1973
Height:	2 ½", 6.4 cm
Colour:	Brown (bronze) or olive green

Description	U.S. $	Can. $	U.K. £
Candlestick	10.00	12.00	5.00

Shape 2342 Egg cup

Designer:	Graham Tongue in 1970
Issued:	1971 - 1973
Diameter:	2 ¼", 5.7 cm
Height :	2 ¾", 7.0 cm
Colour:	Brown (bronze) or olive green

Description	U.S. $	Can. $	U.K. £
Egg cup	10.00	12.00	5.00

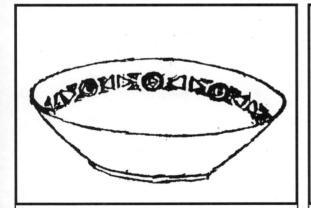

Shape 2343 Coupe

Designer:	Graham Tongue in 1970
Issued:	1971 - 1973
Diameter:	6 ¾", 17.2 cm
Colour:	Brown (bronze) or olive green

Description	U.S. $	Can. $	U.K. £
Coupe	10.00	12.00	5.00

Shape 2344 Saucer

Designer:	Graham Tongue in 1970
Issued:	1971 - 1973
Diameter:	5 ¾", 14.6 cm
Colour:	Brown (bronze) or olive green

Description	U.S. $	Can. $	U.K. £
Saucer	7.00	10.00	4.00

Shape 2353 Lug soup

Designer:	Graham Tongue in 1971
Issued:	1972 - 1973
Diameter:	4 ¼", 10.8 cm
Height:	3" x 7.6 cm
Colour:	Brown (bronze) or olive green

Description	U.S. $	Can. $	U.K. £
Lug soup	10.00	12.00	5.00

Photograph not
available
at press time

Shape 2400 Meat dish

Designer:	Graham Tongue in 1972
Issued:	1972 - 1973
Size:	13 ½" x 10 ½", 34.3 x 26.7 cm
Colour:	Brown (bronze) or olive green

Description	U.S. $	Can. $	U.K. £
Meat dish	25.00	40.00	15.00

Photograph not
available
at press time

Shape 2401 Fruit saucer

Designer:	Graham Tongue in 1972
Issued:	1972 - 1973
Diameter:	5 ½", 14 cm
Colour:	Brown (bronze) or olive green

Description	U.S. $	Can. $	U.K. £
Fruit saucer	10.00	12.00	5.00

Photograph not
available
at press time

Shape 2402 Covered sugar

Designer:	Graham Tongue in 1972
Issued:	1972 - 1973
Size:	Unknown
Colour:	Brown (bronze) or olive green

Description	U.S. $	Can. $	U.K. £
Covered sugar	25.00	40.00	15.00

SECTION TWO

This part of the book has been divided into chapters to make it easier to locate and identify a particular piece. Within these chapters are series and sets, which we have listed separately here for quick reference. The details for an individual piece can be found under the appropriate chapter and shape number.

THE MODELLE RANGE

The style of modelling and the colour unites these shapes. They were:

No. 653 Jug, No. 654 Jug, No. 655 Vase, No. 656 Vase, No. 657 Bowl, No. 675 Vase, No. 676 Jug, No. 677 Vase, No. 678 Vase, No.679 Jug, No. 680 Vase. A total of eleven shapes.

THE FESTIVAL SERIES

This series was so named as it was sold to coincide with the Festival of Britain in 1951. The items were selected from production shapes and were not in any specific colourways. They were:

No. 977 Candlestick, No. 978 Ashtray, No. 979/1/2 Bowl, No. 1051 Deer Vase, No. 1083 Galleon Vase, No. 1095 Nymph Vase, No. 1176 Jug, No. 1184 Column Vase, No. 1185 Flamingo Vase, No. 1186 Shell Vase, No. 1187/1/2/3 Handled Bowl, No. 1189 Square Chequered Vase, No. 1190 Large Urn Vase, No. 1191 Fern Vase, No. 1192 Low fluted bowl, No. 1193 Bellflower Vase, No. 1194 Magnolia Vase, No. 1236 Bowl, No. 1264 Bowl. A total of nineteen shapes.

THE ELIZABETHAN SERIES

All the items in this series, which was launched for the new Elizabethan era in 1953, were in a gloss finish. There were only three colourways under this name: Maroon, Holly Green and Chartreuse. The shapes in this series were:

No. 1191 Vase, No. 1284 Trout Vase, No. 1287 Skater Vase, No. 1288 "Dog Rose" Bowl, No. 1290 "Book" Bowl, No. 1292 Leaf Bowl, No. 1293 Doves Vase, No. 1295 "Maple Bud" Vase, No. 1297 Fan Bowl, No. 1298 Apple Vase, No. 1300 Stardust Vase, No. 1305 Mallard Vase, No. 1306 Pinewood Vase. A total of thirteen shapes.

Note these pieces can also be found in other colourways.

CAPRICE

There were only three colourways under this name — turquoise, orange and yellow. The shapes available were:

No. 128 Vase, No. 1498-2 Bowl, No. 1502/2/3 Vase, No. 1316 Vase, No. 1651 Vase, No. 1654 Vase, No. 1656 Vase, No. 1749 Vase, No. 1750 Vase, No. 1751 Vase, No. 1752 Vase, No. 1896 Plant Pot Holder. A total of twelve shapes issued under this name, between 1968 and 1972 only.

CHRYSANTHEMUM

A set of nine shapes, which were:

No. 1602 Vase, No. 1603 Bowl, No. 1604 Vase, No. 1605 Vase, No. 1606 Vase, No. 1607 Vase, No. 1608 Vase, No. 1609 Wall Vase, No. 1668 Basket.

ROSE

A set of six shapes, which were:

No. 1658 Vase, No. 1659 Basket, No. 1660 Vase, No. 1661 Vase, No. 1662 Vase, No. 1663 Vase.

SHELL

A set of eight shapes, which were:

No. 1996 Bowl, No. 2003 Plant Pot Holder, No. 2012 Vase, No. 2014 Vase, No. 2015 Vase, No. 2016 Plant Pot Holder, No. 2020 Vase, No. 2021 Vase.

KATHI URBACH

A set of seven shapes, which were:

No. 1555 Swan Vase, No. 1556 Swan Vase, No. 1589 Bowl, No. 1590 Vase, No. 1591 Vase, No. 1592 Vase, No. 1593 Bowl.

SHAKESPEARE

A series of ten shapes, which were:

Jugs Nos. 1126, 1146, 1214 and 1366, Mugs Nos. 1127, 1147, 1215 and 1368 plus two wall plaques Nos. 1209 and 1210.

TULIP

A set of six shapes, all vases similar in style, which were:

Nos. 843, 846, 847, 848, 851 and 852.

TRENTHAM ART WARES

A large number of the early Beswick shapes, mostly vases or jugs, with some bowls, wall masks and ashtrays etc., can be found backstamped "Trentham Art Ware." They had the Beswick shape number together with "Made in England," impressed on the base. The origin of these pieces was an agreement made between Beswick and G. Hardy and Company, wholesalers, of Walnut Tree Lane, Nottingham. At the time of the introduction of the matt glaze decoration in 1933, Hardy's were looking to replace foreign ornamental wares with British designs and turned to Beswick as a supplier.

The agreement lasted until 1941 when Beswick were free to market them with their own backstamp.

GENERAL GUIDE TO COLOURS

Many colours were used by Beswick over the years to decorate their pottery — to name a few — blues, greens, browns, yellows, pinks, oranges etc. Shapes were decorated in subtle shades of a single colour, several colours blended together, with definite or indistinct patterns, Art Deco handpainted designs using several colours — the list is endless.

Countless colour combinations were used to decorate the Beswick shapes and the colourways were so varied that we can only give a general guide to changes over the years.

Early 1930s	—	Assorted handpainted decorations, matt glazes (today referred to as satin matt) and matt white.
1963	—	Four new colourways were introduced to the range, these were pink pearl, noire, juniper and black matt.
1966	—	Juniper discontinued. Copper lustre introduced in June.
1967	—	Noire discontinued and pewter introduced.
1968	—	Caprice Series introduced on certain items — colours orange, turquoise or yellow.
1970	—	Pink pearl discontinued.
1972	—	Matt white and pewteramic only.

"Stafford" shape; deco 3072

"Oxford" shape; deco 3072

"Pearl" shape; deco 3072

"Eton" shape; deco 3072

"Monmouth" shape; deco 6155

"Douglas" shape

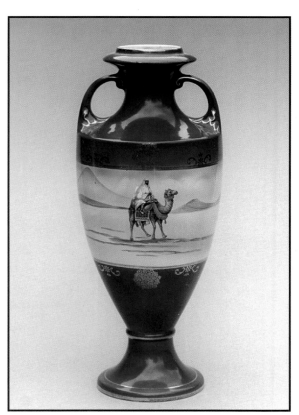

"Athens" shape

"Rye" shape; deco 6451

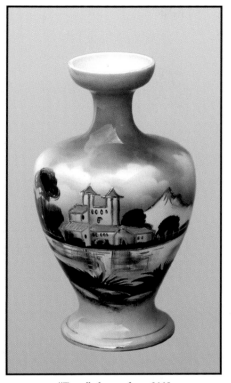

"Troy" shape; deco 6448

"Sale" shape; deco 6115

"Octagon" shape; deco 6451

"Victory" shape; deco 6451

"Cuba" shape; deco 6661   "Durbar" shape; deco 6663   "Egypt" shape; deco 5057

"Holborn" shape; deco 6591   "Victoria" No.1 shape; deco 6045   "Victoria" No. 2 shape; deco 6456

"Pekin" shape; deco 6660　　　　*"Clyde" shape; deco 6466*　　　　*"Nankin" shape; deco 6662*

"Leyden"; deco 6644,　　　*"Louvain"; deco 6644,*　　　*"Edam"; deco 6644,*　　　*"Hague"; deco 6644*

"Eric" shape

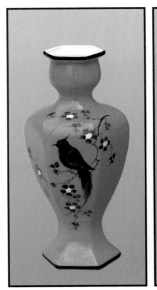

"Deal" shape

"Deal" shape

"Blythe" shape; deco 5057

"Victoria" shape; deco 3013

"Bell" shape

"Kew" shape

"Cosy" shape

"Blythe" shape; deco 6053

"Albany" shape; deco 3072

"Lynn" shape; deco 6338

ASHTRAYS — ASH-BOWLS

A total of sixty-one shapes were designed between about 1934 and 1971. They were produced in a variety of colours and colour combinations with matt glaze (satin matt), gloss, matt and lustre finishes.

Fourteen of these were produced as special commissions, from 1959 onwards, mostly for tobacco companies, and therefore there is little detailed information available. The highlights of this group are the Timpson's Shoemaker, with the delightful figure, and the interesting Les Leston Steering Wheel.

Not surprisingly thirteen shapes incorporated animal and bird models, some of which could be purchased separately (see *The Charlton Standard Catalogue of Beswick Animals*) and six shapes were actually modelled in the shapes of fish or birds.

Shape 83	Ash-bowl
Designer:	Albert Hallam c.1934
Issued:	c.1934 - by 1963
Diameter:	4", 10.1 cm
Colour:	1. Assorted decos, solid colours - satin matt
	2. White - matt

Colour	U.S. $	Can. $	U.K. £
1. Assorted decorations	25.00	40.00	15.00
2. White	20.00	25.00	10.00

Shape 84	Ashtray
Designer:	Mr. Symcox c.1934
Issued:	c.1934 - by 1954
Length:	4 ½", 11.9 cm
Colour:	1. Assorted decos, solid colours - satin matt
	2. White - matt

Colour	U.S. $	Can. $	U.K. £
1. Assorted decorations	35.00	50.00	20.00
2. White	35.00	50.00	20.00

Photograph not
available
at press time

Shape 88	Scottie, ashtray
Designer:	Unknown
Issued:	1934 - 1965
Height :	3 ¼", 8.3 cm
Colour:	1. Assorted decos, solid colours - satin matt
	2. Blue - gloss
	3. White - matt

Colour	U.S. $	Can. $	U.K. £
1. Assorted decorations	50.00	75.00	25.00
2. Blue	60.00	90.00	35.00
3. White	50.00	75.00	30.00

Shape 112	Mona, ashtray
Designer:	Unknown
Issued:	1932 - by 1940
Size:	Unknown
Colour:	1. Assorted decos - satin matt
	2. White - matt

Colour	U.S. $	Can. $	U.K. £
1. Assorted decorations	40.00	60.00	25.00
2. White	40.00	60.00	25.00

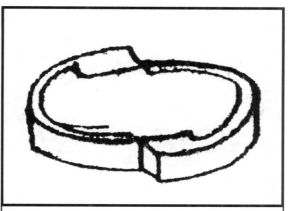

Shape 165   Ashtray

Designer:	Mr. Symcox c.1934
Issued:	c.1934 - by 1954
Size:	14" x 6", 35.5 x 15.0 cm
Colour:	1. Assorted decos, solid colours - satin matt
	2. White- matt

Colour	U.S. $	Can. $	U.K. £
1. Assorted decorations	40.00	60.00	25.00
2. White	40.00	60.00	25.00

Shape 299   Ashtray

Designer:	Mr. Symcox c.1935
Issued:	c.1935 - by 1954
Size:	Unknown
Colour:	1. Assorted decos, solid colours - satin matt
	2. White - matt

Colour	U.S. $	Can. $	U.K. £
1. Assorted decorations	35.00	50.00	20.00
2. White	25.00	40.00	15.00

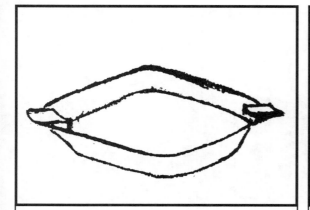

Shape 305   Ashtray

Designer:	Mr. Symcox c.1935
Issued:	c.1935 - by 1963
Length:	6 ¼", 15.9 cm
Colour:	1. Assorted decos, solid colours - satin matt
	2. White - matt

Colour	U.S. $	Can. $	U.K. £
1. Assorted decorations	35.00	50.00	20.00
2. White	25.00	40.00	15.00

Shape 309   Ashtray

Designer:	Mr. Watkin c.1935
Issued:	c.1935 - by 1954
Size:	4" x 3", 10.1 x 7.6 cm
Colour:	1. Assorted decos, solid colours - satin matt
	2. White - matt

Colour	U.S. $	Can. $	U.K. £
1. Assorted decorations	35.00	50.00	20.00
2. White	25.00	40.00	15.00

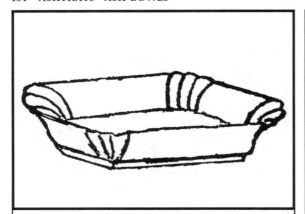

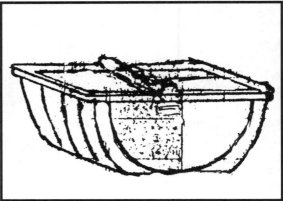

Shape 320/1/2 Ashtray

Designer:	Mr. Symcox c. 1935
Issued:	c.1935 - by 1954
Size:	Unknown
Colour:	1. Assorted decos, solid colours - satin matt
	2. White - matt

Colour	U.S. $	Can. $	U.K. £
1. Assorted decorations	35.00	50.00	20.00
2. White	25.00	40.00	15.00

Shape 321 Ashtray with cover

Designer:	Mr. Symcox in 1935
Issued:	c.1935 - by 1954
Size:	Unknown
Colour:	1. Assorted decos, solid colours - satin matt
	2. White - matt

Colour	U.S. $	Can. $	U.K. £
1. Assorted decorations	40.00	60.00	25.00
2. White	35.00	50.00	20.00

Shape 360 Seal ash bowl

Designer:	Miss Greaves in 1936
Issued:	1936 - by 1954
Size:	5 ¼" x 4 ¾" - 13.3 cm x 12.1 cm
Colour:	1. Assorted decos, solid colours - satin matt
	2. Blue - gloss
	3. White - matt

Colour	U.S. $	Can. $	U.K. £
1. Assorted decorations	100.00	150.00	60.00
2. Blue	110.00	165.00	65.00
3. White	75.00	115.00	45.00

Shape 440 Ashtray

Designer:	Mr. Symcox in 1936
Issued:	1936 - by 1954
Diameter:	4 ¾", 12.1 cm
Height:	2 ¾", 7 cm
Colour:	1. Assorted decos, solid colours - satin matt
	2. White - matt

Colour	U.S. $	Can. $	U.K. £
1. Assorted decorations	40.00	60.00	25.00
2. White	35.00	50.00	20.00

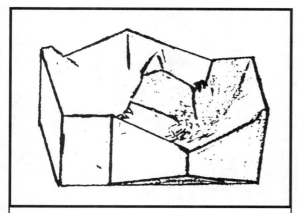

Shape 464   Crompton ashtray

Designer: Albert Hallam in 1937
Issued: 1937 - by 1954
Size: Unknown
Colour: 1. Assorted decos, solid colours - satin matt
    2. White - matt

Colour	U.S. $	Can. $	U.K. £
1. Assorted decorations	40.00	60.00	25.00
2. White	35.00	50.00	20.00

Note: Similar in shape to No. 309.

Shape 497   Pelican match holder and ash-bowl

Designer: Mr. Watkin in 1937
Issued: 1937 - by 1954
Height: 4", 10.1 cm
Colour: 1. Assorted decos, solid colours - satin matt
    2. Blue - gloss
    3. White - matt

Colour	U.S. $	Can. $	U.K. £
1. Assorted decorations	115.00	100.00	65.00
2. Blue	125.00	185.00	75.00
3. White	100.00	150.00	60.00

Shape 617   Duck ashtray

Designer: Mr. Watkin in 1938
Issued: 1938 - by 1954
Height :   3", 7.6 cm
Colour: 1. Assorted decos, solid colours - satin matt
    2. Blue - gloss
    3. White - matt

Colour	U.S. $	Can. $	U.K. £
1. Assorted decorations	125.00	185.00	75.00
2. Blue	150.00	200.00	85.00
3. White	85.00	125.00	50.00

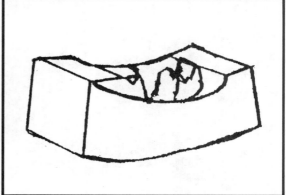

Shape 669   Crompton ashtray

Designer: Mr. Owen in 1939
Issued: 1939 - by 1954
Size: Unknown
Colour: 1. Assorted decos, solid colours - satin matt
    2. White - matt

Colour	U.S. $	Can. $	U.K. £
1. Assorted decorations	40.00	60.00	25.00
2. White	35.00	50.00	20.00

Shape 754	Pheasant ashtray		
Designer:	Mr. Watkin in 1939		
Issued:	1939 - 1970		
Height :	3 ½", 8.9 cm		
Colour:	Teal green and brown - gloss		

Description	U.S. $	Can. $	U.K. £
Pheasant ashtray	45.00	50.00	25.00

Note: Pheasant shape 767A was used for this ashtray.

Shape 755	Duck ashtray		
Designer:	Mr. Watkin in 1939		
Issued:	1939 - 1969		
Height:	4", 10.1 cm		
Colour:	Teal green, brown and white - gloss		

Description	U.S. $	Can. $	U.K. £
Duck ashtray	45.00	50.00	25.00

Note: Duck shape 756-3 was used for this ashtray.

Shape 764	Soldier ashtray		
Designer:	Arthur Gredington in 1939		
Issued:	1939 - by 1954		
Size:	Unknown		
Colour:	Tan/brown hat and collar; green and brown bowl - gloss		

Description	U.S. $	Can. $	U.K. £
Soldier ashtray		Rare	

Shape 810	Bulldog ashtray		
Designer:	Arthur Gredington in 1940		
Issued:	1940 - by 1954		
Height:	4", 10.1 cm		
Colour:	White dog wearing a white sailor cap with a blue band, biscuit coloured base - gloss		

Description	U.S. $	Can. $	U.K. £
Bulldog ashtray	300.00	400.00	175.00

Shape 869	Five puppy ashtray
Designer:	Mr. Watkin in 1940
Issued:	1940 - 1967
Height:	2″, 5 cm
Colour:	1. Brown puppies, green ashtray - gloss
	2. Light tan puppies, green ashtray - gloss

Colour	U.S. $	Can. $	U.K. £
1. Brown	60.00	85.00	35.00
2. Light tan	60.00	85.00	35.00

Shape 916	Three puppy ashtray
Designer:	Mr. Watkin in 1941
Issued:	1941 - 1967
Height:	2″, 5.0 cm
Colour:	1. Brown puppies, green ashtray - gloss
	2. Light tan puppies, green ashtray - gloss

Colour	U.S. $	Can. $	U.K. £
1. Brown	30.00	45.00	20.00
2. Light tan	30.00	45.00	20.00

Note: Dog shape 917 was used for this ashtray.

Shape 918	Ashtray
Designer:	Mr. Watkin in 1941
Issued:	1941 - by 1954
Size:	Unknown
Colour:	1. Assorted decos, solid colours - satin matt
	2. White - matt

Colour	U.S. $	Can. $	U.K. £
1. Assorted decorations	40.00	60.00	25.00
2. White	35.00	50.00	20.00

Shape 934	Ashtray
Designer:	Mr. Watkin in 1941
Issued:	1941 - by 1954
Size:	Unknown
Colour:	1. Assorted decos, solid colours - satin matt
	2. White - matt

Colour	U.S. $	Can. $	U.K. £
1. Assorted decorations	35.00	50.00	20.00
2. White	35.00	50.00	20.00

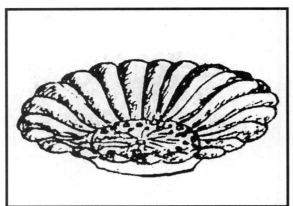

Shape 978   Ashtray

Designer:	Mr. Symcox in 1942
Issued:	1942 - by 1962
Diameter:	4", 10.1 cm
Colour:	1. Assorted decos, solid colours - satin matt
	2. White - matt

Colour	U.S. $	Can. $	U.K. £
1. Assorted decorations	40.00	60.00	25.00
2. White	35.00	50.00	20.00

Note: This ashtray later became part of the Festival Series.

Shape 1212   Three duck ashtray

Designer:	Arthur Gredington in 1951
Issued:	1. 1951 - 1965
Issued:	2. 1951 - 1970
Height:	2 ¾", 7 cm
Colour:	1. Blue - gloss
	2. Teal green, white and brown - gloss

Colour	U.S. $	Can. $	U.K. £
1. Blue	50.00	65.00	30.00
2. Teal green	50.00	65.00	30.00

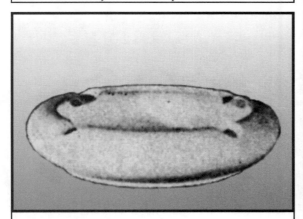

Shape 1547   Ashtray

Designer:	Albert Hallam in 1958
Issued:	1958 - 1971
Diameter:	6", 15 cm
Colour:	1. Assorted decos, solid colours - satin matt
	2. Copper lustre
	3. White or black - matt

Colour	U.S. $	Can. $	U.K. £
1. Assorted decorations	25.00	40.00	15.00
2. Copper lustre	25.00	40.00	15.00
3. White or black	20.00	30.00	10.00

Shape 1599   Trout ash-bowl

Designer:	Graham Tongue in 1959
Issued:	1959 - 1970
Height:	5", 12.7 cm
Colour:	Fish in naturalistic colours; turquoise blue bowl - gloss

Colour	U.S. $	Can. $	U.K. £
Natural, turquoise blue	200.00	300.00	125.00

Photograph not
available
at press time

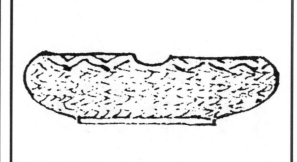

Shape 1625 Woodbine ashtray

Designer:	Albert Hallam in 1959
Issued:	1959
Size:	Unknown
Colour:	Unknown

Description	U.S. $	Can. $	U.K. £
Woodbine, ashtray	25.00	40.00	15.00

Note: Special Commission.

Shape 1722 Mexican ashtray

Designer:	Albert Hallam in 1960
Issued:	1960 - unknown
Diameter:	6", 15 cm
Colour:	Unknown

Description	U.S. $	Can. $	U.K. £
Mexican	35.00	50.00	15.00

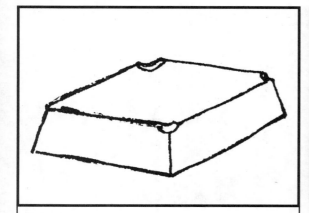

Shape 1866 Ashtray

Designer:	Albert Hallam in 1963
Issued:	1963 - unknown
Width:	3", 7.6 cm
Colours:	1. Assorted decos, solid colours - satin matt
	2. Copper - lustre
	3. White or black - matt

Colour	U.S. $	Can. $	U.K. £
1. Assorted decorations	15.00	25.00	10.00
2. Copper	15.00	25.00	10.00
3. White or black	15.00	25.00	10.00

Shape 1918 Ashbowl

Designer:	Albert Hallam in 1963
Issued:	1963 - 1971
Size:	11" x 8", 27.9 cm x 20.3 cm
Colour:	1. Blue bowl with animal - gloss
	2. Pale brown bowl with animal - gloss
	3. White or blue bowl; Babycham print

Colour	U.S. $	Can. $	U.K. £
1. Blue bowl/animal	165.00	225.00	100.00
2. Pale brown bowl/animal	100.00	150.00	65.00
3. White/blue bowl/Babycham	25.00	40.00	15.00

Shape 1932   Dachshund ashtray

Designer: Albert Hallam in 1962
Issued: 1962 - 1969
Base size: 8″ x 3″, 20.3 cm x 7.6 cm
Height :   5″, 12.7 cm
Colour: 1. Black and tan dog on charcoal base - gloss
              2. Tan dog on charcoal base - gloss

Colour	U.S. $	Can. $	U.K. £
1. Black/tan dog	100.00	150.00	65.00
2. Tan dog	100.00	150.00	65.00

Note: Dog Shape 1460 was used for this ashtray.

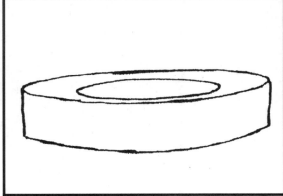

Shape 1934   Ashtray, round

Designer: Albert Hallam in 1964
Issued: 1964 - unknown
Diameter: 10″, 25.4 cm
Colour: 1. Assorted decos, solid colours - satin matt
              2. White or black - matt

Colour	U.S. $	Can. $	U.K. £
1. Assorted decorations	15.00	25.00	10.00
2. White or black	15.00	25.00	10.00

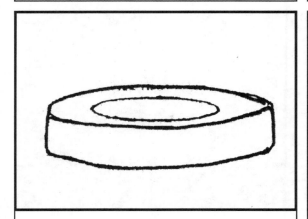

Shape 1938   Ashtray, round

Designer: Albert Hallam in 1964
Issued: 1964 - unknown
Diameter: 5″, 12.7 cm
Colour: 1. Assorted decos, solid colours - satin matt
              2. White or black - matt

Colour	U.S. $	Can. $	U.K. £
1. Assorted decorations	15.00	25.00	10.00
2. White or black	15.00	25.00	10.00

Shape 1946   Timpson's Shoemaker - ashbowl

Designer: Albert Hallam in 1964
Issued: c.1964
Height: 4 ½″, 11. 9 cm
Colour: Shoemaker wears a white apron, blue
              trousers, light green shirt, darker waistcoat;
              blue base - gloss

Colour	U.S. $	Can. $	U.K. £
Base blue	175.00	250.00	100.00

Note: Special Centenary Commission. Backstamped
"Timpson fine shoes 1865 - 1965."

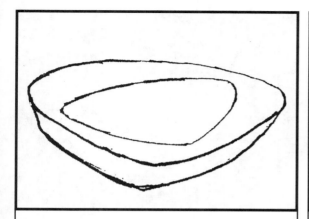

Shape 1983 Canada Dry ashtray

Designer: Mr. Murphy in 1964
Issued: c.1964
Diameter: 9", 22.9 cm
Colour: Unknown

Description	U.S. $	Can. $	U.K. £
Canada Dry	15.00	25.00	10.00

Note: Special Commission.

Shape 2001 Benson and Hedges ashtray

Designer: Mr. Murphy in 1964
Issued: c.1964
Size: 8" x 6 ½", 20.3 cm x 16.5 cm
Colour: Charcoal/bronze with gold lettering - lustre

Colour	U.S. $	Can. $	U.K. £
Charcoal/bronze	15.00	25.00	10.00

Note: Special Commission.

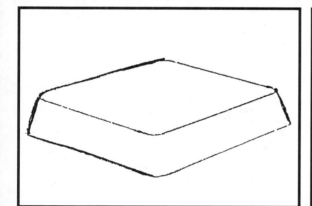

Shape 2007 Ashtray

Designer: Mr. Murphy in 1965
Issued: 1965 - unknown
Width: 8 ¾", 22.2 cm
Colour: 1. Assorted decos, solid colours - satin matt
            2. White or black - matt

Colour	U.S. $	Can. $	U.K. £
1. Assorted decorations	15.00	25.00	10.00
2. White or black	15.00	25.00	10.00

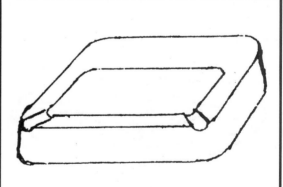

Shape 2024 Ashtray

Designer: Albert Hallam in 1965
Issued: 1965 - unknown
Size: 5 ½", 14 cm
Colour: 1. Assorted decos, solid colours - satin matt
            2. White or black - matt

Colour	U.S. $	Can. $	U.K. £
1. Assorted decorations	15.00	25.00	10.00
2. White or black	15.00	25.00	10.00

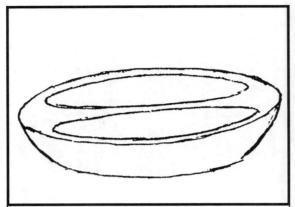

Shape 2047 Gallaher ashtray

Designer:	Albert Hallam in 1965
Issued:	c.1965
Size:	9" x 7", 22.9 cm x 17.8 cm
Colour:	Unknown

Description	U.S. $	Can. $	U.K. £
Gallaher	15.00	25.00	10.00

Note: Special commission.

Shape 2048 Les Leston ashtray

Designer:	Albert Hallam in 1965
Isuued:	c.1965
Diameter:	7 ¼", 18.4 cm
Colour:	White bowl, brown edges and silver spokes - gloss

Colour	U.S. $	Can. $	U.K. £
White, brown and silver	100.00	150.00	60.00

Note: Special commission. Les Leston was a top 500cc Formula 3 driver in the early 1950s. Later he drove for Connaught and BRM.

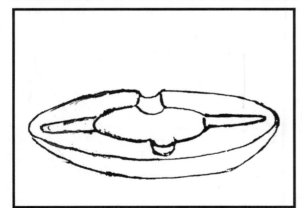

Shape 2052 Piccadilly ashtray

Designer:	Albert Hallam in 1965
Issued:	c.1965
Diameter:	8", 20.3 cm
Colour:	Unknown

Description	U.S. $	Can. $	U.K. £
Piccadilly	15.00	25.00	10.00

Note: Special commission.

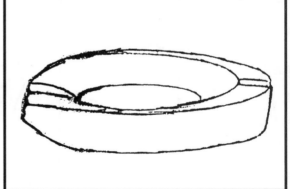

Shape 2055 Craven "A" ashtray

Designer:	Albert Hallam in 1966
Issued:	c.1966
Size:	11" x 6 ½", 27.9 x 16.5 cm
Colour:	Unknown

Description	U.S. $	Can. $	U.K £.
Craven "A"	15.00	25.00	10.00

Note: Special commission.

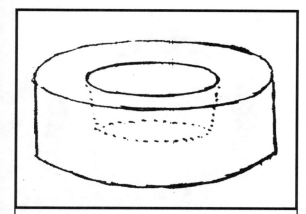

Shape 2114 Ashtray

Designer: Albert Hallam in 1967
Issued: 1967 - unknown
Size: 5" x 2", 12.7 x 5 cm
Colour: 1. Assorted decos, solid colours - satin matt
              2. Copper - lustre
              3. White or black - matt

Colour	U.S. $	Can. $	U.K. £
1. Assorted decorations	15.00	25.00	10.00
2. Copper	15.00	25.00	10.00
3. White or black	10.00	15.00	5.00

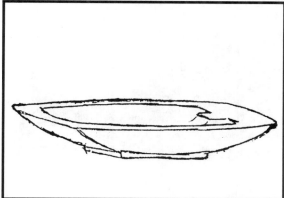

Shape 2115 Pall Mall ashtray

Designer: Albert Hallam in 1967
Issued: c.1967
Size: 9 ¾" x 4 ¾", 24.7 x 12.1 cm
Colour: Unknown

Description	U.S. $	Can. $	U.K. £
Pall Mall	15.00	25.00	10.00

Note: Special Commission.

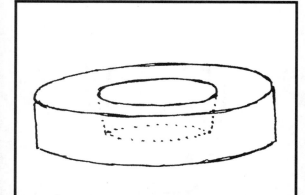

Shape 2119 Ashtray

Designer: Albert Hallam in 1967
Issued: 1967 - unknown
Size: 8" x 2", 20.3 x 5 cm
Colour: 1. Assorted decos, solid colours - satin matt
              2. Copper - lustre
              3. White or black - matt

Colour	U.S. $	Can. $	U.K. £
1. Assorted decorations	15.00	25.00	10.00
2. Copper	15.00	25.00	10.00
3. White or black	15.00	25.00	10.00

Shape 2128 Fish ashtray

Designer: Graham Tongue in 1967
Issued: 1968 - c.1970
Length: 7", 17.8 cm
Colour: Dark brown matt outer colour, turquoise
              gloss inner surface with orange spots

Colour	U.S. $	Can. $	U.K. £
Dark brown	50.00	75.00	30.00

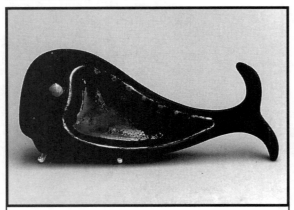

Shape 2129 Whale ashtray

Designer:	Graham Tongue in 1967
Issued:	1968 - c.1970
Length:	7 ¼", 18.4 cm
Colour:	Dark brown matt outer colour, red gloss inner surface

Colour	U.S. $	Can. $	U.K. £
Dark brown, red	50.00	75.00	30.00

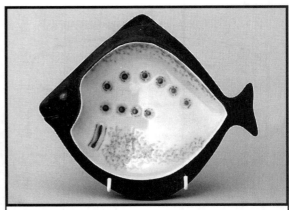

Shape 2133 Fish ashtray

Designer:	Graham Tongue in 1967
Issued:	1968 - c.1970
Length	9 ½", 24 cm
Colour:	Dark brown matt outer colour, lime green gloss inner surface

Colour	U.S. $	Can. $	U.K. £
Dark brown, lime green	50.00	75.00	30.00

Shape 2169 Sea horse ashtray

Designer:	Graham Tongue in 1967
Issued:	1968 - c.1970
Length:	10 ½", 26.7 cm
Colour:	Dark brown matt outer colour, green/blue coloured mottled gloss inner surface

Colour	U.S. $	Can. $	U.K. £
Dark brown, green/blue	50.00	75.00	30.00

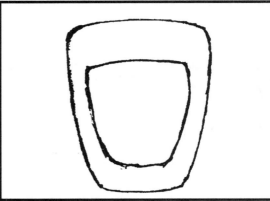

Shape 2175 Ashtray

Designer:	Graham Tongue in 1967
Issued:	1967, remodelled in 1968 - unknown
Size:	8" x 6", 20.3 x 15 cm
Colour:	1. Assorted decos, solid colours - satin matt
	2. Copper - lustre
	3. White or black - matt

Colour	U.S. $	Can. $	U.K. £
1. Assorted decorations	15.00	25.00	10.00
2. Copper	15.00	25.00	10.00
3. White or black	15.00	25.00	10.00

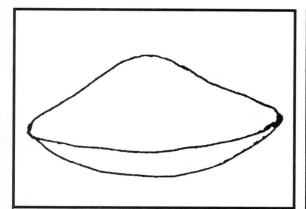

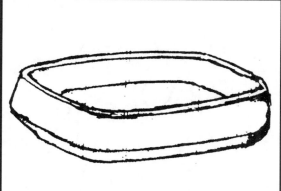

Shape 2176 Ashtray

Designer:	Graham Tongue in 1968
Issued:	1968 - unknown
Size:	5 ¾", 14.6 cm
Colour:	1. Assorted decos, solid colours - satin matt
	2. Copper - lustre
	3. White or black - matt

Colour	U.S. $	Can. $	U.K. £
1. Assorted decorations	15.00	25.00	10.00
2. Copper	15.00	25.00	10.00
3. White or black	15.00	25.00	10.00

Shape 2177 Ashtray

Designer:	Albert Hallam in 1968
Issued:	1968 - unknown
Size:	10" x 7 ½", 25.4 cm x 19.1 cm
Colour:	1. Assorted decos, solid colours - satin matt
	2. Copper - lustre
	3. White or black - matt

Colour	U.S. $	Can. $	U.K. £
1. Assorted decorations	15.00	25.00	10.00
2. Copper	15.00	25.00	10.00
3. White or black	15.00	25.00	10.00

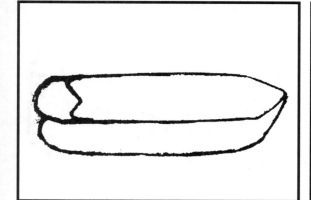

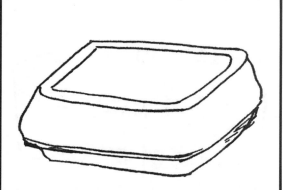

Shape 2178 Ashtray

Designer:	Albert Hallam in 1968
Issued:	1968 - unknown
Size:	10" x 7 ½", 25.4 x 19.1 cm
Colour:	1. Assorted decos, solid colours - satin matt
	2. Copper - lustre
	3. White or black - matt

Colour	U.S. $	Can. $	U.K. £
1. Assorted decorations	15.00	25.00	10.00
2. Copper	15.00	25.00	10.00
3. White or black	15.00	25.00	10.00

Shape 2192 Benson and Hedges ashtray

Designer:	Albert Hallam in 1968
Isuued:	c.1968
Width:	5", 12.7 cm
Colour:	Unknown

Description	U.S. $	Can. $	U.K. £
Benson and Hedges	15.00	25.00	10.00

Note: Special Commission.

Shape 2199 Cockerel ashtray

Designer:	Graham Tongue in 1968
Issued:	1968 - Unknown
Length:	8″, 20.3 cm
Colour:	Unknown

Description	U.S. $	Can. $	U.K. £
Cockerel	90.00	125.00	50.00

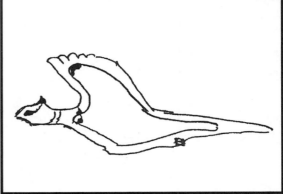

Shape 2209 Pheasant ashtray

Designer:	Graham Tongue in 1968
Issued:	1968 - Unknown
Length:	12 ¾″, 32.4 cm
Colour:	Unknown

Description	U.S. $	Can. $	U.K. £
Pheasant	100.00	150.00	60.00

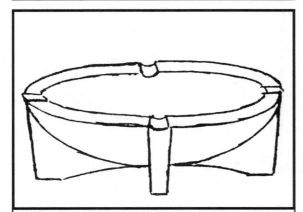

Shape 2218 Benson and Hedges orb ashtray

Designer:	Albert Hallam in 1968
Issued:	c.1968
Diameter:	7″, 17.8 cm
Colour:	Unknown

Description	U.S. $	Can. $	U.K. £
Benson and Hedges orb	15.00	25.00	10.00

Note: Special Commission.

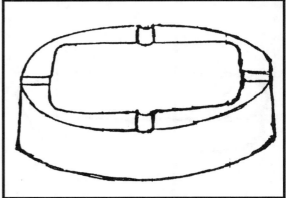

Shape 2219 Craven "A" ashtray

Designer:	Albert Hallam in 1968
Issued:	c.1968
Diameter:	8″, 20.3 cm
Colour:	Unknown

Description	U.S. $	Can. $	U.K. £
Craven "A"	15.00	25.00	10.00

Note: Special Commission.

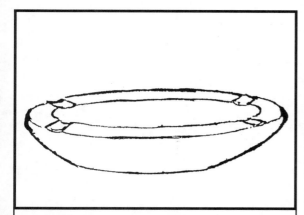

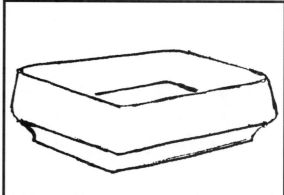

Shape 2241 Hamlet, oval ashtray

Designer:	Albert Hallam in 1968
Issued:	c.1968
Size:	7 ½" x 5", 19.1 x 12.7 cm
Colour:	Unknown

Description	U.S. $	Can. $	U.K. £
Hamlet, oval ashtray	15.00	25.00	10.00

Note: Special Commission.

Shape 2261 Hamlet Cigars ashtray

Designer:	Albert Hallam in 1969
Issued:	c.1969
Size :	6" x 6", 15.0 x 15.0 cm
Colour:	Unknown

Description	U.S. $	Can. $	U.K. £
Hamlet cigars	15.00	25.00	10.00

Note: Special Commission.

Note: Price ranges are retail market indicators of prices for models under the following conditions:
- Lower end of range = price of monochrome models
- Higher end of range = price of multicoloured models

Shape 1918 — Ashbowl

BASKETS AND BOWLS

There are a hundred and one shapes in this large group, spanning the production years from the early thirties to 1972. These shapes are mainly decorative bowls, some handled, some on feet, some large and some small. Two bulb bowls were also produced and thirteen baskets, i.e. with the handle over the top.

As can be seen here we list some members of the Festival, Elizabethan, Caprice, Rose, Chrysanthemum, Kathi Urbach, Modelle and Shell Series - a quick reference to these series is given at the beginning of this section of the book.

Note: Price ranges - the low side is an indication for an item which is white glaze, while the high end is for multicoloured models.

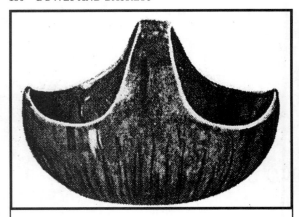

Shape 78	**Basket**
Designer:	Mr. Symcox c.1933
Issued:	c.1933 - by 1940
Length:	10 ½", 26.7 cm
Colour:	1. Assorted decorations - satin matt
	2. White - matt

Market	Range
U.S.A.	$75.00 - 125.00
Canada	$125.00 - 175.00
U.K.	£45.00 - 75.00

Shape 81	**Footed bowl**
Designer:	Mr. Symcox c.1933
Issued:	c.1933 - by 1940
Diameter:	11 ½", 29.2 cm
Colour:	1. Assorted decorations - satin matt
	2. White - matt

Market	Range
U.S.A.	$75.00 - 125.00
Canada	$125.00 - 175.00
U.K.	£45.00 - 75.00

Shape 86	**Basket**
Designer:	Mr. Symcox c.1933
Issued:	c.1933 - by 1940
Length:	7", 17.8 cm
Colour:	1. Assorted decorations - satin matt
	2. White - matt

Market	Range
U.S.A.	$45.00 - 65.00
Canada	$65.00 - 100.00
U.K.	£25.00 - 40.00

Shape 99	**Bowl**
Designer:	Mr. Symcox c.1933
Issued:	c.1933 - by 1940
Diameter:	11 ½", 29.2 cm
Colour:	1. Assorted decorations - satin matt
	2. White - matt

Market	Range
U.S.A.	$75.00 - 125.00
Canada	$125.00 - 175.00
U.K.	£45.00 - 75.00

Shape 123	Bowl
Designer:	Albert Hallam c.1933
Issued:	c.1933 - by 1959
Length:	11 ½", 29.2 cm
Colour:	1. Assorted decorations - satin matt
	2. White - matt

Market	Range
U.S.A.	$75.00 - 125.00
Canada	$125.00 - 175.00
U.K.	£45.00 - 75.00

Shape 157	Handled bowl
Designer:	Mr. Symcox c.1933
Issued:	c.1933 - by 1940
Diameter:	11", 27.9 cm
Colour:	1. Assorted decorations - satin matt
	2. White - matt

Market	Range
U.S.A.	$75.00 - 125.00
Canada	$125.00 - 175.00
U.K.	£45.00 - 75.00

Shape 199	Posy bowl
Designer:	Mr. Symcox c.1933
Issued:	c.1933 - by 1940
Size:	2 ¼" x 10", 5.7 x 25.4 cm
Colour:	1. Assorted decorations - satin matt
	2. White - matt

Market	Range
U.S.A.	$75.00 - 125.00
Canada	$125.00 - 175.00
U.K.	£45.00 - 75.00

Shape 256/1/2 Bowl Troon	
Designer:	Unknown
Issued:	c.1933 - by 1940
Size:	1. 256/1 - 10", 25.4 cm
	2. 256/2 - Unknown
Colour:	1. Assorted decorations - satin matt
	2. White - matt

Market	Range 256/1	Range 256/2
U.S.A.	$75.00 - 125.00	$125.00 - 175.00
Canada	$125.00 - 175.00	$200.00 - 250.00
U.K.	£45.00 - 75.00	£75.00 - 100.00

Shape 257   **Octagon bulb bowl**

Designer: Unknown
Issued: c.1933 - by 1940
Diameter: 8", 20.3 cm
Colour: 1. Assorted decorations - satin matt
            2. White - matt

Market	Range
U.S.A.	$75.00 - 100.00
Canada	$125.00 - 150.00
U.K.	£45.00 - 60.00

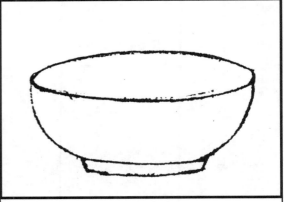

Shape 258   **Round bulb bowl**

Designer: Unknown
Issued: c.1933 - by 1940
Size: Unknown
Colour: 1. Assorted decorations - satin matt
            2. White - matt

Market	Range
U.S.A.	$75.00 - 100.00
Canada	$125.00 - 150.00
U.K.	£45.00 - 60.00

Shape 259   **Trentham bowl**

Designer: Unknown
Issued: c.1933 - by 1940
Diameter: 9", 22.9 cm
Colour: 1. Assorted decorations - satin matt
            2. White - matt

Market	Range
U.S.A.	$75.00 - 100.00
Canada	$125.00 - 150.00
U.K.	£45.00 - 6000

Shape 262   **Louis bowl, New Hall**

Designer: Unknown
Issued: c.1933 - by 1940
Diameter: 8 ¾", 22.2 cm
Colour: 1. Assorted decorations - satin matt
            2. White - matt

Market	Range
U.S.A.	$75.00 - 100.00
Canada	$125.00 - 150.00
U.K.	£45.00 - 60.00

Shape 288   Bowl

Designer:	Mr. Symcox c.1934
Issued:	c.1934 - by 1959
Length:	8″, 20.3 cm
Colour:	1. Assorted decorations - satin matt
	2. White - matt

Market	Range
U.S.A.	$75.00 - 100.00
Canada	$125.00 - 150.00
U.K.	£45.00 - 60.00

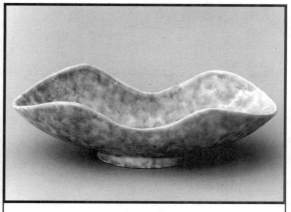

Shape 291   Bowl

Designer:	Mr. Symcox c.1934
Issued:	c.1934 - by 1940
Size:	2″ x 11″, 5.0 x 27.9 cm
Colour:	1. Assorted decorations - satin matt
	2. White - matt

Market	Range
U.S.A.	$75.00 - 125.00
Canada	$125.00 - 175.00
U.K.	£45.00 - 75.00

Shape 300   Bowl

Designer:	Mr. Symcox c.1934
Issued:	c.1934 - by 1940
Size:	9 ¾″, 24.7 cm
Colour:	1. Assorted decorations - satin matt
	2. White - matt

Market	Range
U.S.A.	$75.00 - 100.00
Canada	$125.00 - 150.00
U.K.	£45.00 - 60.00

Shape 306   Bowl

Designer:	Mr. Symcox c.1934
Issued:	1935 - by 1940
Diameter:	13″, 33 cm
Colour:	1. Assorted decorations - satin matt
	2. White - matt

Market	Range
U.S.A.	$125.00 - 175.00
Canada	$200.00 - 250.00
U.K.	£75.00 - 100.00

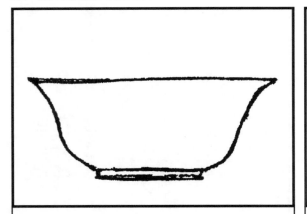

Photograph not
available
at press time

Shape 322   Bowl

Designer:	Unknown
Issued:	1935 - by 1940
Size:	Unknown
Colour:	1. Assorted decorations - satin matt
	2. White - matt

Market	Range
U.S.A.	$75.00 - 125.00
Canada	$125.00 - 175.00
U.K.	£45.00 - 75.00

Shape 342   Bowl, comport

Designer:	Mr. Symcox in 1935
Issued:	1935 - by 1940
Size:	Unknown
Colour:	1. Assorted decorations - satin matt
	2. White - matt

Market	Range
U.S.A.	$75.00 - 125.00
Canada	$125.00 - 175.00
U.K.	£45.00 - 75.00

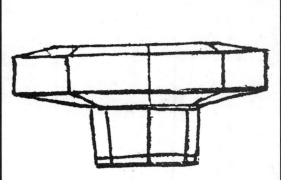

Shape 379   Bowl

Designer:	Mr. Symcox in 1936
Issued:	1936 - by 1959
Diameter:	10", 25.4 cm
Colour:	1. Assorted decorations - satin matt
	2. White - matt

Market	Range
U.S.A.	$75.00 - 125.00
Canada	$125.00 - 175.00
U.K.	£45.00 - 75.00

Shape 384   Bowl

Designer:	Mr. Symcox in 1936
Issued:	1936 - by 1940
Size:	Unknown
Colour:	1. Assorted decorations - satin matt
	2. White - matt

Market	Range
U.S.A.	$75.00 - 125.00
Canada	$125.00 - 175.00
U.K.	£45.00 - 75.00

Shape 419   Bowl

Designer: Mr. Symcox in 1936
Issued: 1936 - by 1959
Length: 12″, 30.5 cm
Colour: 1. Assorted decorations - satin matt
             2. White - matt

Market	Range
U.S.A.	$75.00 - 125.00
Canada	$125.00 - 175.00
U.K.	£45.00 - 75.00

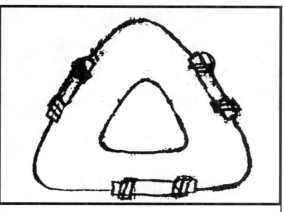

Shape 420   Bowl

Designer: Mr. Symcox in 1936
Issued: 1936 - by 1940
Size: Unknown
Colour: 1. Assorted decorations - satin matt
             2. White - matt

Market	Range
U.S.A.	$75.00 - 125.00
Canada	$125.00 - 175.00
U.K.	£45.00 - 75.00

Shape 425   Bowl

Designer: Mr. Symcox in 1936
Issued: 1936 - by 1959
Length: 11 ½″, 29.2 cm
Colour: 1. Assorted decorations - satin matt
             2. White - matt

Market	Range
U.S.A.	$75.00 - 125.00
Canada	$125.00 - 175.00
U.K.	£45.00 - 75.00

Shape 427   Bowl

Designer: Mr. Symcox in 1936
Issued: 1936 - by 1959
Length: 11 ¼″, 28.5 cm
Colour: 1. Assorted decorations - satin matt
             2. White - matt

Market	Range
U.S.A.	$75.00 - 125.00
Canada	$125.00 - 175.00
U.K.	£45.00 - 75.00

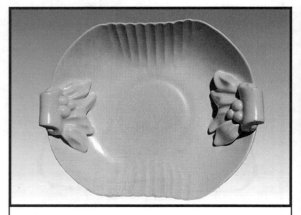

Shape 434   Bowl

Designer:	Mr. Symcox in 1936
Issued:	1936 - by 1940
Diameter:	13 ¾", 34.9cm
Colour:	1. Assorted decorations - satin matt
	2. White - matt

Market	Range
U.S.A.	$125.00 - 175.00
Canada	$200.00 - 250.00
U.K.	£75.00 - 100.00

Shape 444   Bowl

Designer:	Mr. Symcox in 1936
Issued:	1936 - by 1940
Diameter:	15", 38.1 cm
Colour:	1. Assorted decorations - satin matt
	2. White - matt

Market	Range
U.S.A.	$125.00 - 175.00
Canada	$200.00 - 250.00
U.K.	£75.00 - 100.00

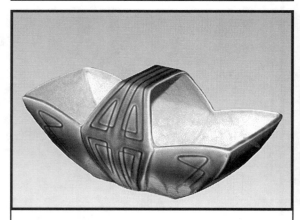

Shape 475   Basket

Designer:	Mr. Symcox in 1937
Issued:	1937 - by 1954
Length:	11", 27.9 cm
Colour:	1. Assorted decorations - satin matt
	2. White - matt

Market	Range
U.S.A.	$75.00 - 125.00
Canada	$125.00 - 175.00
U.K.	£45.00 - 75.00

Shape 476   Basket

Designer:	Mr. Symcox in 1937
Issued:	1937 - by 1940
Length:	6", 15 cm
Colour:	1. Assorted decorations - satin matt
	2. White - matt

Market	Range
U.S.A.	$65.00 - 100.00
Canada	$100.00 - 150.00
U.K.	£40.00 - 60.00

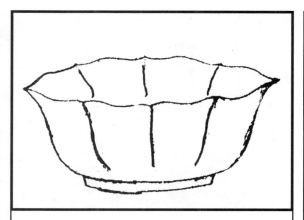

Shape 554   Bowl

Designer:	Unknown
Issued:	1937 - by 1940
Size:	Unknown
Colour:	1. Assorted decorations - satin matt
	2. White - matt

Market	Range
U.S.A.	$60.00 - 100.00
Canada	$100.00 - 150.00
U.K.	£40.00 - 60.00

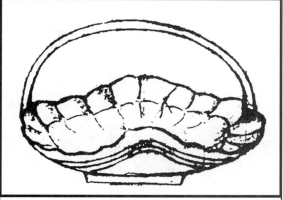

Shape 570   Basket

Designer:	Mr. Symcox in 1938
Issued:	1938 - by 1940
Size:	Unknown
Colour:	1. Assorted decorations - satin matt
	2. White - matt

Market	Range
U.S.A.	$60.00 - 100.00
Canada	$100.00 - 150.00
U.K.	£40.00 - 60.00

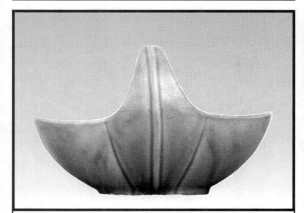

Shape 605   Basket

Designer:	Mr. Symcox in 1938
Issued:	1938 - by 1940
Size:	6 ½", 16.5 cm
Colour:	1. Assorted decorations - satin matt
	2. White - matt

Market	Range
U.S.A.	$60.00 - 100.00
Canada	$100.00 - 150.00
U.K.	£40.00 - 60.00

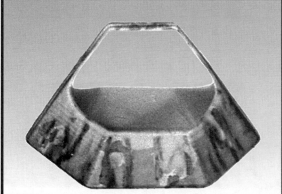

Shape 606   Basket

Designer:	Mr. Watkin in 1938
Issued:	1938 - by 1940
Length:	6 ½", 16.5 cm
Colour:	1. Assorted decorations - satin matt
	2. White - matt

Market	Range
U.S.A.	$60.00 - 100.00
Canada	$100.00 - 150.00
U.K.	£40.00 - 60.00

Shape 607   Bowl

Designer:	Mr. Symcox in 1938
Issued:	1938 - by 1940
Length:	4", 10.1 cm
Colour:	1. Assorted decorations - satin matt
	2. White - matt

Market	Range
U.S.A.	$45.00 - 65.00
Canada	$65.00 - 100.00
U.K.	£25.00 - 40.00

Shape 623   Basket

Designer:	Mr. Symcox in 1938
Issued:	1938 - by 1940
Length:	5", 12.7 cm
Colour:	1. Assorted decorations - satin matt
	2. White - matt

Market	Range
U.S.A.	$45.00 - 65.00
Canada	$65.00 - 100.00
U.K.	£25.00 - 40.00

Shape 657   Bowl, Modelle series

Designer:	Mr. Watkin in 1938
Issued:	1938 - by 1959
Size:	13 ½" x 5 ½", 34.3 x 14cm
Colour:	1. Assorted decorations - satin matt
	2. White - matt

Market	Range
U.S.A.	$125.00 - 175.00
Canada	$200.00 - 250.00
U.K.	£75.00 - 100.00

Shape 745   Bowl

Designer:	Mr. Watkin in 1939
Issued:	1939 - by 1940
Size:	Unknown
Colour:	1. Assorted decorations - satin matt
	2. White - matt

Market	Range
U.S.A.	$75.00 - 125.00
Canada	$125.00 - 175.00
U.K.	£45.00 - 75.00

Shape 758   Bowl

Designer:	Mr. Watkin in 1939
Issued:	1940 - by 1954
Size:	9 ½" x 3 ¾", 24 x 9.5 cm
Colour:	1. Assorted decorations - satin matt
	2. White - matt

Market	Range
U.S.A.	$75.00 - 100.00
Canada	$125.00 - 150.00
U.K.	£45.00 - 60.00

Shape 759   Bowl

Designer:	Mr. Watkin in 1939
Issued:	1939 - by 1959
Diameter:	12", 30.5 cm
Colour:	1. Assorted decorations - satin matt
	2. White - matt

Market	Range
U.S.A.	$75.00 - 125.00
Canada	$125.00 - 175.00
U.K.	£45.00 - 75.00

Shape 808   Bowl

Designer:	Mr. Symcox in 1940
Issued:	1940 - 1969
Height:	6 ½", 16.5 cm
Colour:	1. Assorted decorations, solid colours - satin matt
	2. Copper lustre
	3. White or black - matt

Market	Range
U.S.A.	$65.00 - 100.00
Canada	$100.00 - 150.00
U.K.	£40.00 - 60.00

Note: Price ranges are retail market indicators of prices for models under the following conditions:
- Lower end of range = price of monochrome models
- Higher end of range = price of multicoloured models

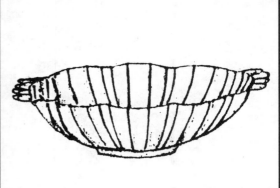

Shape 819   Basket

Designer: Mr. Watkin in 1940
Issued: 1940 - 1972
Height :   12", 30.5 cm
Colour: 1. Assorted decos, solid colours - satin matt
                   2. Copper lustre
                   3. White or black - matt

Market	Range
U.S.A.	$75.00 - 125.00
Canada	$125.00 - 175.00
U.K.	£45.00 - 75.00

Shape 835   Bowl

Designer: Mr. Symcox in 1940
Issued: 1940 - by 1969
Length: 17", 43.2 cm
Colour: 1. Assorted decos, solid colours - satin matt
                   2. Copper lustre
                   3. White or black - matt

Market	Range
U.S.A.	$125.00 - 175.00
Canada	$200.00 - 250.00
U.K.	£75.00 - 100.00

Shape 900 /1/2/3 Basket

Designer: Mr. Symcox in 1940
Issued: 1941 - by 1959
Height: 1. Shape 900/1 — 8", 20.3 cm
                   2. Shape 900/2 — 6 ¼", 15.9 cm
                   3. Shape 900/3 — 4 ½" , 11.9 cm
Colour: 1. Assorted decorations - satin matt
                   2. White - matt

Market	Range
Shape 900/1	
U.S.A.	$75.00 - 100.00
Canada	$125.00 - 150.00
U.K.	£45.00 - 60.00
Shape 900/2	
U.S.A.	$65.00 - 100.00
Canada	$100.00 - 150.00
U.K.	£40.00 - 60.00
Shape 900/3	
U.S.A.	$45.00 - 75.00
Canada	$65.00 - 100.00
U.K.	£25.00 - 45.00

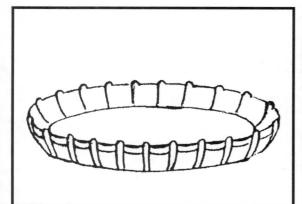

Shape 933 Bowl

Designer:	Mr. Symcox in 1941
Issued:	1941 - by 1954
Size:	Unknown
Colour:	1. Assorted decorations - satin matt
	2. White - matt

Market	Range
U.S.A.	$65.00 - 100.00
Canada	$100.00 - 150.00
U.K.	£40.00 - 60.00

Shape 979/1/2 Bowl - Festival series

Designer:	Mr. Symcox in 1941
Issued:	1942 - by 1962
Size:	1. Shape 979/1 — 8 ½", 21.6 cm
	2. Shape 979/2 — 7", 17.8 cm
Colour:	1. Assorted decorations - satin matt
	2. White - matt

Market	Range 979/1 and 979/2
U.S.A.	$75.00 - 100.00
Canada	$125.00 - 150.00
U.K.	£45.00 - 60.00

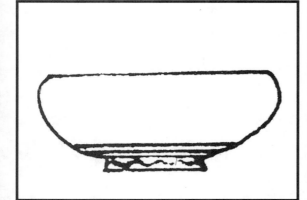

Shape 1079 Posy bowl

Designer:	Albert Hallam in 1946
Issued:	1947 - by 1959
Diameter:	4 ½", 11.9 cm
Colour:	1. Assorted decorations - satin matt
	2. White - matt

Market	Range
U.S.A.	$45.00 - 65.00
Canada	$65.00 - 100.00
U.K.	£25.00 - 45.00

Shape 1080 Posy bowl

Designer:	Albert Hallam in 1946
Issued:	1947 - 1972
Diameter:	4 ½", 11.9 cm
Colour:	1. Assorted decos, solid colours - satin matt
	2. Copper - lustre
	3. White or black - matt

Market	Range
U.S.A.	$45.00 - 65.00
Canada	$65.00 - 100.00
U.K.	£25.00 - 45.00

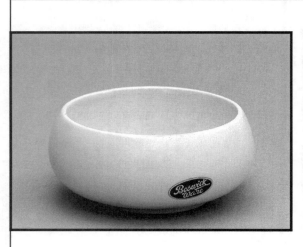

Shape 1081 Posy bowl

Designer: Albert Hallam in 1946
Issued: 1946 - 1971
Diameter: 4 ½", 11.9 cm
Colour: 1. Assorted decorations, solid colours -
  satin matt
  2. White or black - matt
  3. Copper - lustre

Market	Range
U.S.A.	$45.00 - 65.00
Canada	$65.00 - 100.00
U.K.	£25.00 - 45.00

Shape 1187/1/2/3 Handled bowl - Festival series

Designer: 1. Shape 1187/1/2 — Albert Hallam,
  James Hayward in 1950
  2. Shape 1187/2 — Albert Hallam,
  James Hayward in 1953
  3. Shape 1187/3 — Albert Hallam in 1953
Issued: 1. Shape 1187/1 — 1950 - 1972
  2. Shape 1187/2 — 1953 - 1972
  3. Shape 1187/3 — 1953 - 1972
Size: 1. Shape 1187/1 — 13", 33 cm
  2. Shape 1187/2 — 9", 22.9 cm
  3. Shape 1187/3 — 7", 17.8 cm
Colour: 1. Various decorations - satin matt
  2. White or black - matt
  3. Copper lustre

Market	Range
Shape 1187/1	
U.S.A.	$125.00 - 175.00
Canada	$200.00 - 250.00
U.K.	£75.00 - 100.00
Shape 1187/2	
U.S.A.	$75.00 - 100.00
Canada	$125.00 - 150.00
U.K.	£45.00 - 60.00
Shape 1187/3	
U.S.A.	$75.00 - 100.00
Canada	$125.00 - 150.00
U.K.	£45.00 - 60.00

Shape 1192 Low fluted bowl - Festival series

Designer:	Albert Hallam, James Hayward in 1950
Issued:	1950 - 1971
Size:	12", 30.5 cm
Colour:	1. Assorted decorations - satin matt
	2. White or black - matt
	3. Copper lustre

Market	Range
U.S.A.	$75.00 - 125.00
Canada	$125.00 - 175.00
U.K.	£45.00 - 75.00

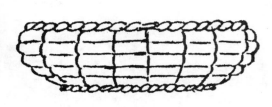

Shape 1236 Conversation piece - Festival series, bowl round wicker

Designer:	Albert Hallam, James Hayward in 1952
Issued:	1952 - 1962
Diameter:	7 ½", 19.1 cm
Colour:	1. Assorted decorations - satin matt
	2. White - matt

Market	Range
U.S.A.	$65.00 - 100.00
Canada	$100.00 - 150.00
U.K.	£40.00 - 60.00

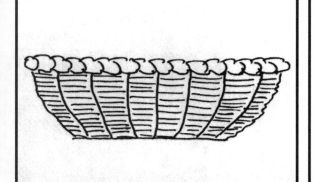

Shape 1264 Bowl, oval - Festival series

Designer:	Albert Hallam, James Hayward in 1952
Issued:	1952 - 1962
Size:	6 ½", 16.5 cm
Colour:	1. Assorted decorations - satin matt
	2. White - matt

Market	Range
U.S.A.	$65.00 - 100.00
Canada	$100.00 - 150.00
U.K.	£40.00 - 60.00

Shape 1288 Dog rose bowl - Elizabethan series

Designer:	Albert Hallam, James Hayward in 1953
Issued:	1954 - 1962
Size:	12 ½", 31.7 cm
Colour:	1. Chartreusse, holly green or maroon - gloss
	2. White - matt

Market	Range
U.S.A.	$75.00 - 125.00
Canada	$125.00 - 175.00
U.K.	£45.00 - 75.00

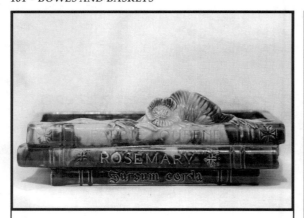

Shape 1290 Book bowl - Elizabethan series

Designer:	Albert Hallam, James Hayward in 1953
Issued:	1954 - by 1959
Size:	10" x 7", 25.4 x 17.8 cm
Colour:	1. Chartreuse, holly green or maroon - gloss
	2. White - matt

Market	Range
U.S.A.	$75.00 - 125.00
Canada	$125.00 - 175.00
U.K.	£45.00 - 75.00

Photograph not
available
at press time

Shape 1292 Leaf bowl, large - Elizabethan series

Designer:	Albert Hallam, James Hayward in 1953
Issued:	1954 - by 1962
Size:	14", 35.5 cm
Colour:	1. Chartreuse, holly green or maroon - gloss
	2. White - matt

Market	Range
U.S.A.	$125.00 - 175.00
Canada	$200.00 - 250.00
U.K.	£75.00 - 100.00

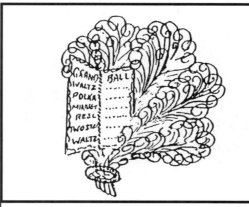

Shape 1297 Fan bowl - Elizabethan series

Designer:	Albert Hallam, James Hayward in 1953
Issued:	1954 - by 1959
Size:	14" x 12", 35.5 x 30.5 cm
Colour:	1. Chartreuse, holly green or maroon - gloss
	2. White - matt

Market	Range
U.S.A.	$125.00 - 150.00
Canada	$200.00 - 250.00
U.K.	£75.00 - 100.00

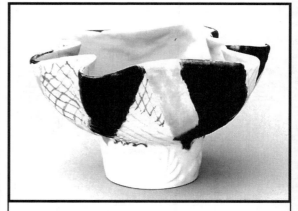

Shape 1338 Bowl

Designer:	Albert Hallam in 1954
Issued:	1954 - by 1962
Height :	4 ¾", 12.1 cm
Colour:	1. Assorted decorations - satin matt
	2. White - matt

Market	Range
U.S.A.	$45.00 - 65.00
Canada	$65.00 - 100.00
U.K.	£25.00 - 45.00

Shape 1340 Bowl

Designer:	Albert Hallam, James Hayward in 1954
Issued:	1954 - by 1962
Height :	5 ¾", 14.6 cm
Colour:	1. Assorted decorations - satin matt
	2. White - matt

Market	Range
U.S.A.	$45.00 - 65.00
Canada	$65.00 - 100.00
U.K.	£25.00 - 45.00

Shape 1346 Oval bowl

Designer:	Albert Hallam in 1954
Issued:	1954 - by 1962
Length:	14 ¼" , 36.2 cm
Height :	4 ¼", 10.8 cm
Colour:	1. Assorted decorations - satin matt
	2. White - matt

Market	Range
U.S.A.	$125.00 - 175.00
Canada	$200.00 - 250.00
U.K.	£75.00 - 100.00

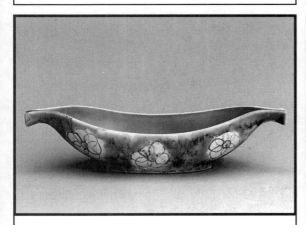

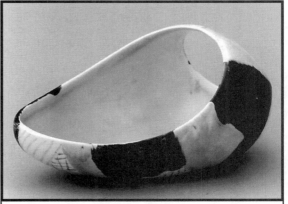

Shape 1353 Bowl

Designer:	Albert Hallam in 1954
Issued:	1954 - 1969
Size:	10 ½" x 2 ½", 26.7 x 6.4 cm
Colour:	1. Assorted decos, solid colours - satin matt
	2. Copper - lustre
	3. White or black - matt

Market	Range
U.S.A.	$75.00 - 125.00
Canada	$125.00 - 175.00
U.K.	£45.00 - 75.00

Shape 1354 Bowl

Designer:	Albert Hallam in 1954
Issued:	1954 - by 1965
Size :	5", 12.7 cm
Colour:	1. Assorted decos, solid colours - satin matt
	2. White or black - matt

Market	Range
U.S.A.	$45.00 - 65.00
Canada	$65.00 - 100.00
U.K.	£25.00 - 45.00

Shape 1358 Small oval bowl

Designer:	Albert Hallam in 1954
Issued:	1954 - by 1962
Size:	6″ x 2 ½″, 15.0 x 6.4 cm
Colour:	1. Assorted decorations - satin matt
	2. White - matt
	3. Copper lustre

Market	Range
U.S.A.	$65.00 - 100.00
Canada	$100.00 - 150.00
U.K.	£40.00 - 60.00

Shape 1387 Bowl on three feet

Designer:	Albert Hallam in 1955
Issued:	1955 - by 1962
Height:	4 ½″, 11.9 cm
Colour:	1. Assorted decorations - satin matt
	2. White - matt

Market	Range
U.S.A.	$45.00 - 65.00
Canada	$65.00 - 100.00
U.K.	£25.00 - 45.00

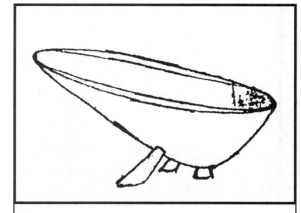

Shape 1388 Bowl on three feet

Designer:	Albert Hallam in 1955
Issued:	1955 - by 1962
Height :	3 ¾″, 9.5 cm
Colour:	1. Assorted decorations - satin matt
	2. White - matt

Market	Range
U.S.A.	$45.00 - 65.00
Canada	$65.00 - 100.00
U.K.	£25.00 - 45.00

Shape 1458 Bowl

Designer:	Albert Hallam in 1956
Issued:	1957 - by 1962
Size :	3 ¼″ x 9″, 8.3 x 22.9 cm
Colour:	1. Assorted decorations - satin matt
	2. White - matt

Market	Range
U.S.A.	$75.00 - 100.00
Canada	$125.00 - 150.00
U.K.	£45.00 - 60.00

Shape 1497 Bowl, round, on foot with two handles

Designer: Albert Hallam in 1957
Issued: 1957 - by 1966
Size: 10" x 6", 25.4 x 15cm
Colour: 1. Assorted decos, solid colours - satin matt
            2. Copper - lustre
            3. White or black - matt

Market	Range
U.S.A.	$75.00 - 125.00
Canada	$125.00 - 175.00
U.K.	£45.00 - 75.00

Shape 1498/1/2 Bowl, footed, oval

Designer: Albert Hallam in 1957
Issued: 1. Shape 1498/1 — 1957 - 1971
            2. Shape 1498/2 — 1957 - 1972
Size: 1. Shape 1498/1 — 16" x 7", 41.9 x 17.8 cm
            2. Shape 1498/2 — 13" x 6", 33 x 15cm
Colour: 1. Assorted decorations - satin matt
            2. White or black - matt
            3. Copper - lustre

Market	Range
Shape 1498/1	
U.S.A.	$75.00 - 125.00
Canada	$125.00 - 175.00
U.K.	£45.00 - 75.00
Shape 1498/2	
U.S.A.	$75.00 - 125.00
Canada	$125.00 - 175.00
U.K.	£45.00 - 75.00

Note: Introduced in 1968 Caprice Series (size 2 only)
            Colours: Orange, turquoise or yellow

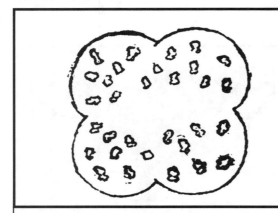

Shape 1589 Bowl

Designer: Kathi Urbach
Modeller: Albert Hallam in 1959
Issued: 1959 - 1965
Size: 8", 20.3 cm
Colour: Various colours incl. black with green/blue
                or white - gloss

Market	Range
U.S.A.	$75.00 - 100.00
Canada	$125.00 - 150.00
U.K.	£45.00 - 60.00

Shape 1593A   Oval fluted bowl footed

Designer: Kathi Urbach
Modeller: Albert Hallam in 1959
Issued: 1959 - 1965
Length: 12" x 5", 30.5 x 12.7 cm
Colour: Black with green/blue or white - gloss

Description	U.S. $	Can. $	U.K. £
Oval fluted bowl	100.00	150.00	55.00

Shape 1593B   Oval fluted bowl footed

Designer: Kathi Urbach
Modeller: Albert Hallam in 1959
Reissued: 1966 - 1968
Size: 12" x 5", 30.5 x 12.7 cm
Colour: See Below

Description	U.S. $	Can. $	U.K. £
1. Assorted decos - satin matt	125.00	175.00	75.00
2. Black - matt	75.00	125.00	45.00
3. Copper - lustre	100.00	150.00	55.00
4. White - matt	75.00	125.00	45.00

Shape 1603   Chrysanthemum, bowl

Designer: Albert Hallam in 1959
Issued: 1959 - by 1963
Size: 14", 35.5 cm
Colour: Coloured flowers on white
                background - gloss

Description	U.S. $	Can. $	U.K. £
Chrysanthemum bowl	100.00	150.00	60.00

Shape 1620 Bowl footed

Designer:	Albert Hallam in 1959
Issued:	1959 - 1968
Size:	12 ½″ x 5 ½″, 31.7 x 14 cm
Colour:	1. Assorted decos; solid colours - satin matt
	2. Copper - lustre
	3. White or black - matt

Market	Range
U.S.A.	$75.00 - 100.00
Canada	$125.00 - 150.00
U.K.	£45.00 - 60.00

Shape 1650 Basket

Designer:	Albert Hallam in 1959
Issued:	1959 - 1968
Length:	11 ¼″, 28.5 cm
Colour:	1. Assorted decos; solid colours - satin matt
	2. Copper - lustre
	3. White or black - matt

Market	Range
U.S.A.	$75.00 - 125.00
Canada	$125.00 - 175.00
U.K.	£45.00 - 75.00

Shape 1659 Rose, basket

Designer:	Albert Hallam in 1959
Issued:	1959 - 1965
Size:	11 ¼″, 28.5 cm
Colour:	Rose, green leaves on cream background - satin matt

Description	U.S.$	Can.$	U.K.£
Rose basket	125.00	175.00	75.00

Shape 1668 Chrysanthemum, basket

Designer:	Albert Hallam in 1960
Issued:	1960 - by 1963
Size:	Unknown
Colour:	Coloured flowers on a white background - gloss

Description	U.S.$	Can.$	U.K.£
Chrysanthemum basket	125.00	175.00	75.00

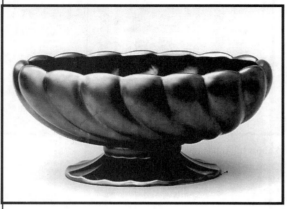

Shape 1683/1/2 Bowl

Designer:	Albert Hallam in 1960
Issued:	1. Shape 1683/1 — 1960 - 1968
	2. Shape 1683/2 — 1960 - 1971
Size:	1. Shape 1683/1 — 14 ¾" x 6 ½", 37.5 x 16.5 cm
	2. Shape 1683/2 — 10" x 5", 25.4 x 12.7 cm
Colour:	1. Assorted decorations; solid colours - satin matt
	2. Copper - lustre
	3. White or black - matt

Market	Range
Shape 1683/1	
U.S.A.	$125.00 - 175.00
Canada	$200.00 - 250.00
U.K.	£75.00 - 100.00
Shape 1683/2	
U.S.A.	$75.00 - 125.00
Canada	$125.00 - 175.00
U.K.	£45.00 - 75.00

Shape 1721 Oval bowl

Designer:	Albert Hallam in 1960
Issued:	1960 - 1971
Size:	4 ½", 11.9 cm
Colour:	1. Assorted decos; solid colours - satin matt
	2. White or black - matt
	3. Copper - lustre

Market	Range
U.S.A.	$45.00 - 65.00
Canada	$65.00 - 100.00
U.K.	£25.00 - 45.00

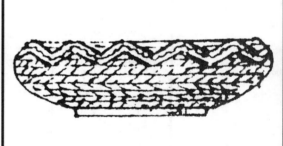

Shape 1735 Mexican flower bowl

Designer:	Albert Hallam in 1961
Issued:	Unknown
Height:	5", 12.7 cm
Colour:	1. Assorted decorations - satin matt
	2. White - matt

Market	Range
U.S.A.	$45.00 - 65.00
Canada	$65.00 - 100.00
U.K.	£25.00 - 45.00

Shape 1788 Bowl on pedestal

Designer: Albert Hallam in 1961
Issued: 1961 - 1972
Size: 6 ½", 16.5 cm
Colour: 1. Assorted decorations - satin matt
             2. Copper - lustre
             3. White or black - matt

Market	Range
U.S.A.	$65.00 - 100.00
Canada	$100.00 - 150.00
U.K.	£40.00 - 60.00

Shape 1789 Shell bowl

Designer: Albert Hallam in 1961
Issued: 1961 - 1971
Size: 7" x 4 ¼", 17.8 x 10.8 cm
Colour: 1. Assorted decos; solid colours - satin matt
             2. Copper - lustre
             3. White or black - matt

Market	Range
U.S.A.	$65.00 - 100.00
Canada	$100.00 - 150.00
U.K.	£40.00 - 60.00

Shape 1790 Shell bowl on pedestal

Designer: Albert Hallam in 1961
Issued: 1961 - 1969
Height :   6 ½", 16.5 cm
Colour: 1. Assorted decos; solid colours - satin matt
             2. Copper - lustre
             3. White or black - matt

Market	Range
U.S.A.	$65.00 - 100.00
Canada	$100.00 - 150.00
U.K.	£40.00 - 60.00

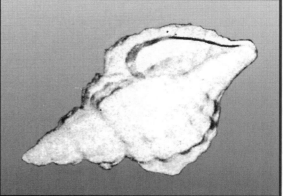

Shape 1794 Shell bowl, large

Designer: Albert Hallam in 1961
Issued: 1961 - 1970
Size: 10" x 5 ¾", 25.4 x 14.6 cm
Colour: 1. Assorted decos; solid colours - satin matt
             2. Copper - lustre
             3. White or black - matt

Market	Range
U.S.A.	$75.00 - 125.00
Canada	$125.00 - 175.00
U.K.	£45.00 - 75.00

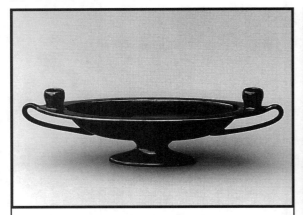

Shape 1798 Bowl, with or without candle holders and snuffers

Designer: Albert Hallam in 1962
Issued: 1962 - 1969
Length: 15", 38.1 cm
Colour: 1. Assorted decos; solid colours - satin matt
           2. Copper - lustre 3. White or black - matt

Market	Range
U.S.A.	$125.00 - 175.00
Canada	$200.00 - 250.00
U.K.	£75.00 - 100.00

Shape 1800 Pineapple comport

Designer: Albert Hallam in 1962
Issued: 1962 - 1968
Height: 9", 22.9 cm
Colour: 1. Assorted decos; solid colours - satin matt
           2. Copper - lustre
           3. White or black - matt

Market	Range
U.S.A.	$75.00 - 100.00
Canada	$125.00 - 150.00
U.K.	£45.00 - 60.00

Shape 1860 Bowl on pedestal

Designer: Albert Hallam in 1963
Issued: 1963 - 1971
Height :   7", 17.8 cm
Colour: 1. Assorted decos; solid colours - satin matt
           2. Copper - lustre
           3. White or black - matt

Market	Range
U.S.A.	$65.00 - 100.00
Canada	$100.00 - 150.00
U.K.	£40.00 - 60.00

Shape 1861 Bowl

Designer: Albert Hallam in 1962
Issued: 1963 - 1972
Size: 16 ½" x 7 ½, 41.9 x 19.1 cm
Colour: 1. Assorted decos, sold colours - satin matt
           2. Copper - lustre
           3. White or black - matt

Market	Range
U.S.A.	$125.00 - 175.00
Canada	$200.00 - 250.00
U.K.	£75.00 - 100.00

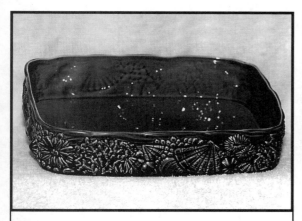

Shape 1996 Bowl, Shell series

Designer: Albert Hallam in 1964
Issued: 1965 - 1968
Size: 10 ½" x 7 ½, 26.7 x 19.1 cm
Colour: Soft variegated pastel colours - gloss

Description	U.S. $	Can. $	U.K. £
Bowl, Shell series	125.00	175.00	75.00

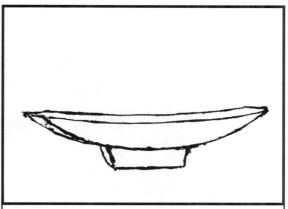

Shape 2142 Bowl

Designer: Graham Tongue in 1967
Issued: 1968 - 1970
Length: 11 ¼", 28.5 cm
Colour: 1. Assorted decos; solid colours - satin matt
2. Copper - lustre
3. White or black - matt

Market	Range
U.S.A.	$75.00 - 125.00
Canada	$125.00 - 175.00
U.K.	£45.00 - 75.00

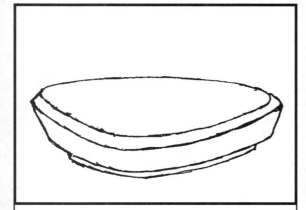

Shape 2143 Bowl

Designer: Albert Hallam in 1967
Issued: 1968 - 1970
Length: 13 ½", 34.3 cm
Colour: 1. Assorted decos; solid colours - satin matt
2. Copper - lustre
3. White or black - matt

Market	Range
U.S.A.	$125.00 - 175.00
Canada	$200.00 - 250.00
U.K.	£75.00 - 100.00

Shape 2144 Bowl

Designer: Graham Tongue in 1967
Issued: 1968 - 1970
Size: 8" x 4", 20.3 x 10.1cm
Colour: 1. Assorted decos; solid colours - satin matt
2. Copper - lustre
3. White or black - matt

Market	Range
U.S.A.	$75.00 - 100.00
Canada	$125.00 - 150.00
U.K.	£45.00 - 60.00

Shape 2145 Bowl

Designer:	Graham Tongue in 1967
Issued:	1968 - 1970
Size:	5" x 2 ½", 12.7 x 6.4 cm
Colour:	1. Assorted decos; solid colours - satin matt
	2. Copper - lustre
	3. White or black - matt

Market	Range
U.S.A.	$45.00 - 65.00
Canada	$65.00 - 100.00
U.K.	£25.00 - 45.00

Shape 2146 Bowl

Designer:	Graham Tongue in 1967
Issued:	1968 - 1970
Diameter:	10 ½", 26.7 cm
Colour:	1. Assorted decos; solid colours - satin matt
	2. Copper - lustre
	3. White or black - matt

Market	Range
U.S.A.	$75.00 - 125.00
Canada	$125.00 - 175.00
U.K.	£45.00 - 75.00

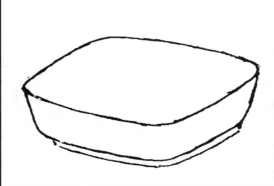

Shape 2147 Oval bowl

Designer:	Albert Hallam in 1967
Issued:	1968 - 1970
Size	10 ½" x 4 ¾", 26.7 x 12.1 cm
Colour:	1. Assorted decos; solid colours - satin matt
	2. Copper - lustre
	3. White or black - matt

Market	Range
U.S.A.	$75.00 - 125.00
Canada	$125.00 - 175.00
U.K.	£45.00 - 75.00

Shape 2148 Bowl

Designer:	Graham Tongue in 1967
Issued:	1968 - 1970
Size:	7 ½" x 1 ½", 19.1 x 3.1 cm
Colour:	1. Assorted decos; solid colours - satin matt
	2. Copper - lustre
	3. White or black - matt

Market	Range
U.S.A.	$75.00 - 100.00
Canada	$125.00 - 150.00
U.K.	£45.00 - 60.00

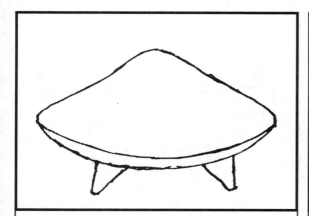

Shape 2149 Bowl

Designer:	Graham Tongue in 1967
Issued:	1968 - 1970
Width:	9 ½″, 24.0 cm
Colour:	1. Assorted decos; solid colours - satin matt
	2. Copper - lustre
	3. White or black - matt

Market	Range
U.S.A.	$75.00 - 100.00
Canada	$125.00 - 150.00
U.K.	£45.00 - 60.00

Shape 2150 Bowl with candleholder

Designer:	Albert Hallam in 1967
Issued:	1968 - 1970
Size:	12 ¼″ x 5 ¼″, 31.1 x 13.3 cm
Colour:	1. Assorted decos; solid colours - satin matt
	2. Copper - lustre
	3. White or black - matt

Market	Range
U.S.A.	$75.00 - 125.00
Canada	$125.00 - 175.00
U.K.	£45.00 - 75.00

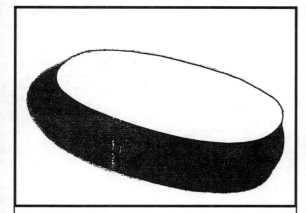

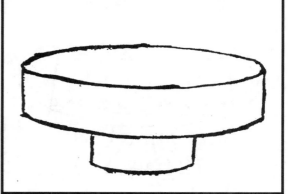

Shape 2153 Oval bowl

Designer:	Graham Tongue in 1967
Issued:	1968 - 1972
Size:	13 ½″ x 3 ½″, 34.3 x 8.9 cm
Colour:	1. Assorted decos; solid colours - satin matt
	2. Copper - lustre
	3. White or black - matt

Market	Range
U.S.A.	$125.00 - 175.00
Canada	$200.00 - 250.00
U.K.	£75.00 - 100.00

Shape 2168 Bowl

Designer:	Albert Hallam in 1967
Issued:	1968 - 1970
Size:	7″ x 3″, 17.8 x 7.6 cm
Colour:	1. Assorted decos; solid colours - satin matt
	2. Copper - lustre
	3. White or black - matt

Market	Range
U.S.A.	$65.00 - 100.00
Canada	$100.00 - 150.00
U.K.	£40.00 - 60.00

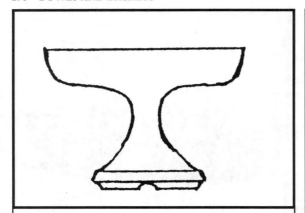

Shape 2278 Bowl, comport

Designer: Albert Hallam in 1969
Issued: 1969 - 1970
Height: 4″, 10.1 cm
Colour: 1. Assorted decos; solid colours - satin matt
2. Copper - lustre
3. White or black - matt

Market	Range
U.S.A.	$45.00 - 65.00
Canada	$65.00 - 100.00
U.K.	£25.00 - 45.00

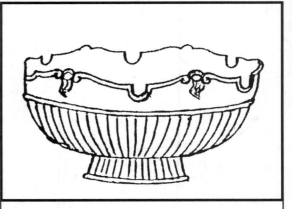

Shape 2374 Bowl, round

Designer: Graham Tongue in 1971
Issued: 1971 - 1972
Size: 10″ x 5 ½″, 25.4 x 14.0 cm
Colour: 1. Assorted decos; solid colours - satin matt
2. Copper - lustre
3. White or black - matt

Market	Range
U.S.A.	$125.00 - 175.00
Canada	$200.00 - 250.00
U.K.	£75.00 - 100.00

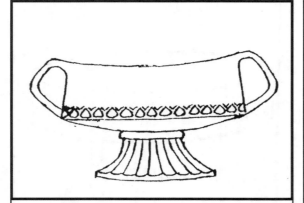

Shape 2380 Bowl, oval handled

Designer: Graham Tongue in 1971
Issued: 1971 - 1972
Size : 14″ x 6 ¼″, 35.5 x 15.9 cm
Colour: 1. Assorted decos; solid colours - satin matt
2. Copper - lustre
3. White or black - matt

Market	Range
U.S.A.	125.00 - 175.00
Canada	$200.00 - 250.00
U.K.	£75.00 - 100.00

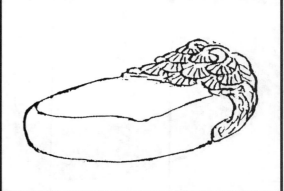

Shape 2396 Bowl

Designer: Graham Tongue in 1971
Issued: 1972 only
Size: 7 ½″ x 3 ¾″, 19.1 x 9.5 cm
Colour: 1. Pewteramic - satin matt
2. White - matt

Market	Range
U.S.A.	$75.00 - 125.00
Canada	$125.00 - 175.00
U.K.	£45.00 - 75.00

CANDLEHOLDERS

Thirty-one candleholders were designed over the years spanning the early 1930s to the late 1960s. One represented three ducks (shape 370) and another was in the shape of a pig (shape 2294).

Mostly they were produced in the matt glaze (satin matt) finish with an enormous variety of subtle colour combinations. Later, dark colours were introduced, which included pewter, black matt and copper lustre. Some were handled and one, shape 1798 in the form of a long bowl, even had candle snuffers.

Shape 23   **Candlestick**

Designer: Unknown
Issued: c.1932 - by 1954
Size: Unknown
Colour: 1. Assorted decos; solid colours - satin matt
            2. White - matt

Market	Range
U.S.A.	$25.00 - 40.00
Canada	$35.00 - 60.00
U.K.	£15.00 - 25.00

Shape 48   **Aladdin's lamp candleholder**

Designer: Mr. Symcox c.1933
Issued: c.1933 - by 1954
Length: 8", 20.3 cm
Colour: 1. Assorted decos; solid colours - satin matt
            2. White - matt

Market	Range
U.S.A.	$25.00 - 40.00
Canada	$35.00 - 60.00
U.K.	£15.00 -25.00

Shape 82   **Candleholder with handle**

Designer: Mr. Symcox c.1933
Issued: c.1933 - by 1954
Size: 5 ½" x 2", 14 x 5 cm
Colour: 1. Assorted decos; solid colours - satin matt
            2. White - matt

Market	Range
U.S.A.	$25.00 - 40.00
Canada	$35.00 - 60.00
U.K.	£15.00 - 25.00

Shape 85   **Candleholder with handle**

Designer: Mr. Symcox c.1933
Issued: c.1933 - by 1954
Size: 4" x 2 ½", 10.1 x 6.4 cm
Colour: 1. Assorted decos; solid colours - satin matt
            2. White - matt

Market	Range
U.S.A.	$25.00 - 40.00
Canada	$35.00 - 60.00
U.K.	£15.00 - 25.00

Shape 156   Candleholder with handle

Designer: Mr. Symcox c.1933
Issued: c.1933 - by 1954
Size: Unknown
Colour: 1. Assorted decos; solid colours - satin matt
             2. White - matt

Market	Range
U.S.A.	$25.00 - 40.00
Canada	$35.00 - 60.00
U.K.	£15.00 - 25.00

Shape 160   Candleholder with match box holder

Designer: Unknown c.1933
Issued: c.1933 - by 1954
Height: 7", 17.8 cm
Colour: 1. Assorted decos; solid colours - satin matt
             2. White - matt

Market	Range
U.S.A.	$25.00 - 40.00
Canada	$35.00 - 60.00
U.K.	£15.00 - 25.00

Shape 203   Candlestick

Designer: Mr. Symcox c.1933
Issued: 1933 - by 1954
Height: 9 ½", 24 cm
Colour: 1. Assorted decos; solid colours - satin matt
             2. White - matt

Market	Range
U.S.A.	$25.00 - 40.00
Canada	$35.00 - 60.00
U.K.	£15.00 - 25.00

Note: Price per stick.

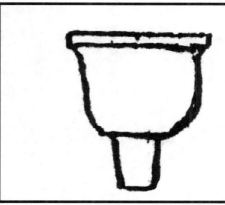

Shape 295   Candleholder

Designer: Mr. Symcox in 1935
Issued: 1935 - by 1954
Diameter: 2", 5 cm Height: 2 ¼", 5.7 cm
Colour: 1. Assorted decos; solid colours - satin matt
             2. White - matt

Market	Range
U.S.A.	$15.00 - 25.00
Canada	$25.00 - 40.00
U.K.	£10.00 - 15.00

Note: Made to slide into the posy troughs (eg. shape 294).

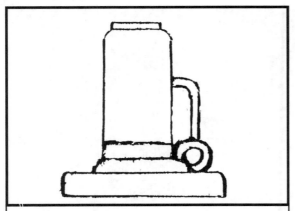

Shape 304   Candleholder

Designer:	Mr. Symcox in 1935
Issued:	1935 - by 1954
Size:	Unknown
Colour:	1. Assorted decos; solid colours - satin matt
	2. White - matt

Market	Range
U.S.A.	$25.00 - 40.00
Canada	$35.00 - 60.00
U.K.	£15.00 - 25.00

Shape 354   Candlestick

Designer:	Mr. Symcox in 1935
Issued:	1935 - by 1954
Size:	4 ¾", 12.1 cm
Colour:	1. Assorted decos; solid colours - satin matt
	2. White - matt

Market	Range
U.S.A.	$25.00 - 40.00
Canada	$35.00 - 60.00
U.K.	£15.00 - 25.00

Shape 370   Ducks, candleholder

Designer:	James Hayward in 1935
Issued:	1935 - by 1954
Height:	3 ½", 8.9 cm
Colours:	1. Assorted decos; solid colours - satin matt
	2. White - matt

Colourway	U.S. $	Can. $	U.K. £
1. Assorted decos - satin matt	75.00	100.00	45.00
2. Solid colours - satin matt	40.00	60.00	25.00
3. White - matt	40.00	60.00	25.00

Shape 422   Candleholder

Designer:	Mr. Symcox in 1936
Issued:	1936 - by 1954
Size:	Unknown
Colour:	1. Assorted decos; solid colour - satin matt
	2. White - matt

Market	Range
U.S.A.	$25.00 - 40.00
Canada	$35.00 - 60.00
U.K.	£15.00 - 25.00

Shape 423   Candleholder

Designer:	Mr. Symcox in 1936
Issued:	1936 - by 1963
Height:	5", 12.7 cm
Colour:	1. Assorted decos; solid colours - satin matt
	2. White - matt

Market	Range
U.S.A.	$35.00 - 60.00
Canada	$50.00 - 90.00
U.K.	£20.00 - 35.00

Shape 435   Candleholder and match holder

Designer:	Mr. Owen in 1936
Issued:	1936 - by 1954
Length:	3 ¾", 9.5 cm
Colour:	1. Assorted decos; solid colours - satin matt
	2. White - matt

Market	Range
U.S.A.	$35.00 - 60.00
Canada	$50.00 - 90.00
U.K.	£20.00 - 35.00

Shape 447   Candleholder

Designer:	Mr. Symcox in 1936
Issued:	1936 - by 1963
Height:	6 ¼", 15.9 cm
Length:	11", 27.9 cm
Colour:	1. Assorted decos; solid colours - satin matt
	2. White - matt

Market	Range
U.S.A.	$40.00 - 65.00
Canada	$60.00 - 10000
U.K.	£25.00 - 40.00

Shape 502   Candlestick

Designer:	Mr. Symcox in 1937
Issued:	1938 - by 1963
Height:	2 ½", 6.4 cm
Colour:	1. Assorted decos; solid colour - satin matt
	2. White - matt

Market	Range
U.S.A.	$25.00 - 40.00
Canada	$35.00 - 60.00
U.K.	£15.00 - 25.00

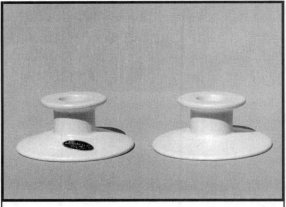

Shape 549	Candleholder
Designer:	Mr. Symcox in 1937
Issued:	1938 - by 1954
Height:	6 ¼", 15.9 cm
Length:	8 ½", 21.6 cm
Colour:	1. Assorted decos; solid colours - satin matt
	2. White - matt

Market	Range
U.S.A.	$40.00 - 65.00
Canada	$60.00 - 100.00
U.K.	£25.00 - 40.00

Shape 611	Candlestick
Designer:	Mr. Symcox in 1938
Issued:	1938 - by 1954
Diameter:	3 ¾", 9.5 cm
Colour:	1. Assorted decos; solid colour - satin matt
	2. White - matt

Market	Range
U.S.A.	$25.00 - 40.00
Canada	$35.00 - 60.00
U.K.	£15.00 - 25.00

Photograph not
available
at press time

Shape 712	Candleholder
Designer:	Mr. Symcox in 1939
Issued:	1939 - by 1954
Base Size:	10 ½" x 4 ¾", 26.7 cm x 12.1 cm
Height:	6 ¾", 17.2 cm
Colour:	1. Assorted decos; solid colours - satin matt
	2. White - matt

Market	Range
U.S.A.	$40.00 - 65.00
Canada	$60.00 - 100.00
U.K.	£25.00 - 40.00

Shape 748	Candleholder
Designer:	Mr. Symcox in 1939
Issued:	1939 - by 1954
Size:	Unknown
Colour:	1. Assorted decos; solid colour - satin matt
	2. White - matt

Market	Range
U.S.A.	$35.00 - 65.00
Canada	$50.00 - 100.00
U.K.	£20.00 - 40.00

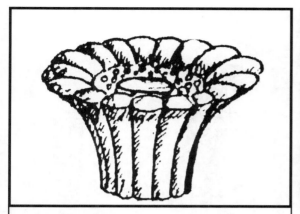

Shape 977   Candlestick

Designer:	Mr. Symcox in 1942
Issued:	1942 - by 1963
Size:	Unknown
Colour:	1. Assorted decos; solid colours - satin matt
	2. White - matt

Market	Range
U.S.A.	$25.00 - 40.00
Canada	$35.00 - 60.00
U.K.	£15.00 - 25.00

Note: This shape later became part of the Festival series.

Shape 1237 Candlestick

Designer:	James Hayward and Albert Hallam in 1952
Issued:	1952 - by 1963
Size:	3″ x 2″, 7.6 cm x 5 cm
Height:	2 ¼″, 5.7 cm
Colour:	1. Assorted decos; solid colours - satin matt
	2. White - matt

Market	Range
U.S.A.	$25.00 - 35.00
Canada	$35.00 - 50.00
U.K.	£15.00 - 20.00

Shape 1798   Bowl with two candle holders (1798C)
        Bowl with candle holders and snuffers (1798CS)

Designer:	Albert Hallam in 1962
Issued:	1962 - 1969
Length:	15″, 38.1 cm
Colour:	1. Assorted decos; solid colours - satin matt
	2. White or black - matt
	3. Copper lustre

Market	Range
U.S.A.	$125.00 - 175.00
Canada	$200.00 - 250.00
U.K.	£75.00 - 100.00

Note: Also listed in Bowls and Basket section on page 171.

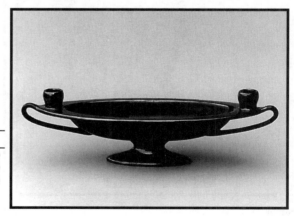

Note: Price ranges are retail market indicators of prices for models under the following conditions:
- Lower end of range = price of monochrome models
- Higher end of range = price of multicoloured models

Shape 2072/2080 Candlestick

Designer:	Graham Tongue in 1966
Issued:	1967 - 1972
Height:	1. Shape 2072 — 7", 17.8
	2. Shape 2080 — 9", 22.9 cm
Colour:	1. Pink pearl or pewter - satin matt
	2. Copper - lustre
	3. White or black - matt

Market	Range
Shape 2072	
U.S.A.	$40.00 - 65.00
Canada	$60.00 - 100.00
U.K.	£25.00 - 40.00
Shape 2080	
U.S.A.	$50.00 - 75.00
Canada	$75.00 - 115.00
U.K.	£30.00 - 45.00

Shape 2141 Candlestick

Designer:	Albert Hallam in 1967
Issued:	1968 - 1970
Height:	4 ½", 11.9 cm
Colour:	1. Assorted decos; solid colours - satin matt
	2. Copper - lustre
	3. White or black - matt

Market	Range
U.S.A.	$25.00 - 35.00
Canada	$35.00 -50.00
U.K.	£15.00 - 20.00

Shape 2203 Candleholder

Designer:	Graham Tongue in 1968
Issued:	1970 - 1972
Height:	2 ½", 6.4 cm
Colour:	1. Black - matt
	2. Opaque white or green glaze - gloss

Market	Range
U.S.A.	$15.00 - 25.00
Canada	$25.00 - 40.00
U.K.	£10.00 - 15.00

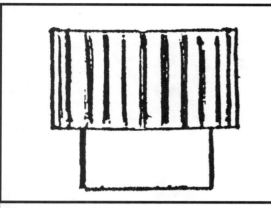

Shape 2204 Candleholder

Designer:	Graham Tongue in 1968
Issued:	1970 only
Height :	2 ½", 6.4 cm
Colour:	1. Black - matt
	2. Opaque white or green glaze - gloss

Market	Range
U.S.A.	$15.00 - 25.00
Canada	$25.00 - 40.00
U.K.	£10.00 - 15.00

Shape 2246 Candlestick

Designer:	Graham Tongue in 1968
Issued:	1970 only
Height:	2 ½", 6.4 cm
Colour:	1. Black - matt
	2. Opaque white or green glaze - gloss

Market	Range
U.S.A.	$15.00 - 25.00
Canada	$25.00 - 40.00
U.K.	£10.00 - 15.00

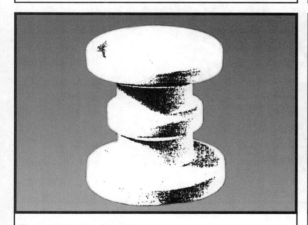

Shape 2247 Candlestick

Designer:	Albert Hallam in 1968
Issued:	1970 - 1972
Height:	3 ¼", 8.3 cm
Colour:	1. Black - matt
	2. Opaque white or green glaze - gloss

Market	Range
U.S.A.	$15.00 - 25.00
Canada	$25.00 - 40.00
U.K.	£10.00 - 15.00

Shape 2294 Piglet candleholder

Designer:	Harry Sales in 1969
Issued:	1970 - 1972
Size:	11" x 3 ½", 27.9 cm x 8.9 cm
Colour:	1. Blue and white gloss
	2. Brown gloss

Colourway	U.S. $	Can. $	U.K. £
1. Blue/white	95.00	135.00	60.00
2. Brown	70.00	100.00	45.00

Note: This shape has four candle holders.

Shape 423 Candleholder

Shape 418 Vase   Shape 934 Ashtray   Shape 509 Vase

DECORATIVE DISHES AND TRAYS

In this list there are forty-one shapes, most of which belong to the attractive "Afternoon Tea" style, used in the days when four o'clock tea was one of the main traditions and a highlight of the day. These dishes could have been purchased boxed, for use as gifts, complete with a decorative knife, (Shape 598) or spoon, (Shape 599). An additional spoon was Shape 730.

Shapes 1907 to 1912 and shape 1916 can be found on pages 24 and 25 in the Heather and Gorse chapter. Shape 1689, a three-sectioned Mexican Hat, can be found on page 33 in the Hors-d'oeuvre chapter.

Other decorative dishes can also be found in the Tableware section. These dishes belong to the individual groups and conform to the style and decorations mentioned in that section.

Shape 343   Dish/Dessert plate

Designer:	Mr. Symcox in 1935
Issued:	1935 - by 1940
Diameter:	8 ¼", 21 cm
Colour:	1. Assorted decorations - satin matt
	2. White - matt

Market	Range
U.S.A.	$35.00 - 65.00
Canada	$50.00 - 100.00
U.K.	£20.00 - 40.00

Shape 344   Nut tray

Designer:	Mr. Symcox in 1935
Issued:	1935 - by 1940
Diameter:	8", 20.3 cm
Colour:	1. Assorted decorations - satin matt
	2. White - matt

Market	Range
U.S.A.	$35.00 - 65.00
Canada	$50.00 - 100.00
U.K.	£20.00 - 40.00

Shape 359   Nut tray

Designer:	Mr. Symcox in 1935
Issued:	1935 - by 1963
Length:	10 ¼", 26 cm
Colour:	1. Assorted decorations - satin matt
	2. White - matt

Market	Range
U.S.A.	$50.00 - 85.00
Canada	$75.00 - 125.00
U.K.	£30.00 - 50.00

Shape 591   Buttercup and apricot double tray

Designer:	Mr. White in 1938
Issued:	1938 - by 1963
Length:	4 ¼" x 8 ¼", 10.8 x 21.0 cm
Colour:	Shades of yellow with green - gloss

Description	U.S. $	Can. $	U.K. £
Double tray	40.00	60.00	25.00

Note: Could be purchased separately, or boxed with a knife and spoon or with one knife or one spoon.

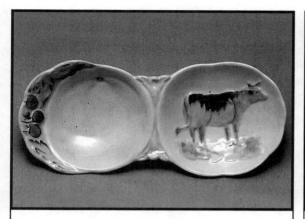

Shape 592 Cow and apple double tray

Designer: Mr. White in 1938
Issued: 1938 - by 1963
Length: 7 ¾", 19.7 cm
Colour: Green, yellow, brown and mauve - gloss

Description	U.S. $	Can. $	U.K. £
Double tray	40.00	60.00	25.00

Note: Could be purchased separately, or boxed with a knife and spoon or with one knife or one spoon.

Shape 593 Pansies triple tray

Designer: Mr. White in 1938
Issued: 1938 - by 1963
Size: 7 ½", 19.1 cm triangular
Colour: 1. Yellow flowers with green - gloss
             2. White - matt

Market	Range
U.S.A.	$25.00 - 50.00
Canada	$40.00 - 75.00
U.K.	£15.00 - 30.00

Shape 594 Butterfly tray

Designer: Mr. White in 1938
Issued: 1938 - by 1954
Size: 6 ¾" x 5 ½", 17.2 x 14 cm
Colour: Green, yellow, orange and black - gloss

Description	U.S. $	Can. $	U.K. £
Butterfly tray	40.00	60.00	25.00

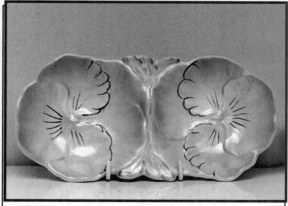

Shape 595 Pansies double tray

Designer: Mr. White in 1938
Issued: 1938 - by 1963
Length: 7 ¾", 19.7 cm
Colour: Pink, yellow and mauve with green - gloss or lustre

Description	U.S. $	Can. $	U.K. £
Pansies double tray	35.00	50.00	20.00

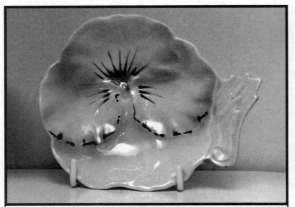

Shape 600   Pansy dish

Designer: Mr. White in 1938
Issued: 1938 - by 1963
Size: 5", 12.7 cm
Colour: Yellow and oranges with green - gloss

Description	U.S. $	Can. $	U.K. £
Pansy dish	25.00	40.00	15.00

Note: Could be purchased separately, or boxed with one
            knife or one spoon.

Shape 601   Apricot dish

Designer: Mr. White in 1938
Issued: 1938 - by 1963
Size: 5", 12.7 cm
Colour: Shades of yellow - gloss

Description	U.S. $	Can. $	U.K. £
Apricot dish	25.00	40.00	15.00

Note: Could be purchased separately, or boxed with one
            knife or one spoon.

Shape 602   Buttercup dish

Designer;   Mr. White in 1938
Issued: 1938 - by 1963
Size: 5", 12.7 cm
Colour: Yellow, green, with orange centre -
              gloss or lustre

Description	U.S. $	Can. $	U.K. £
Buttercup dish	25.00	40.00	15.00

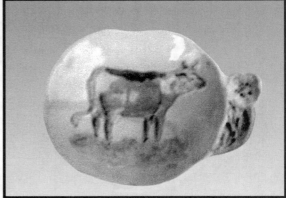

Shape 603   Cow dish

Designer: Mr. White in 1938
Issued: 1938 - by 1963
Size: 5", 12.7 cm
Colour: Yellow, brown with green grass - gloss

Description	U.S. $	Can. $	U.K. £
Cow dish	25.00	40.00	15.00

Note: Could be purchased separately, or boxed with one
            knife or one spoon.

Shape 604 Apple dish

Designer:	Mr. White in 1938
Issued:	1938 - 1963
Size:	5", 12.7 cm
Colour:	Pink, green and yellow/orange - gloss or lustre

Description	U.S. $	Can. $	U.K. £
Apple dish	25.00	40.00	15.00

Note: Could be purchased separately or boxed with one knife or one spoon.

Shape 627 Dish tray

Designer:	Mr. Symcox in 1938
Issued:	1938 - by 1954
Size:	9" x 6 ½", 23.1 x 16.5 cm
Colour:	1. Assorted decorations - satin matt
	2. White - matt

Market	Range
U.S.A.	$35.00 - 65.00
Canada	$50.00 - 100.00
U.K.	£20.00 - 40.00

Shape 628 Daisy sweet dish

Designer:	Mr. Watkin in 1938
Issued:	1938 - by 1963
Diameter:	6 ¼", 15.9 cm
Colour:	Pink and green with pink, yellow, green or white centre - gloss

Description	U.S. $	Can. $	U.K. £
Daisy sweet dish	25.00	40.00	15.00

Note: Could be purchased separately, or boxed with a knife.

Shape 629 Chrysanthemum sweet dish

Designer:	Mr. Watkin in 1938
Issued:	1938 - by 1963
Size:	6 ¼" x 4 ¾", 15.9 x 12.1 cm
Colour:	Pink and yellow flowers with green - gloss

Description	U.S. $	Can. $	U.K. £
Chrysanthemum sweet dish	25.00	40.00	15.00

Note: Could be purchased separately, or boxed with a knife.

Shape 659   **Narcissus sweet dish**

Designer:	Unknown
Issued:	1938 - by 1963
Size:	9 ¼" x 5.3/4", 23.5 x 14.6 cm
Colour:	White and yellow, with green - gloss

Description	U.S. $	Can. $	U.K. £
Narcissus sweet dish	25.00	40.00	15.00

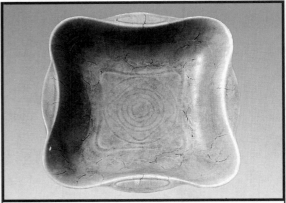

Shape 660   **Dish**

Designer:	Mr. Symcox in 1938
Issued:	1938 - by 1940
Width:	10 ½", 26.7 cm
Colour:	1. Assorted decorations - satin matt
	2. White - matt

Market	Range
U.S.A.	$50.00 - 85.00
Canada	$75.00 - 125.00
U.K.	£30.00 - 50.00

Shape 716   **Daisy butter pat dish**

Designer:	Mr. Hayward in 1939
Issued:	1939 - by 1963
Diameter:	3 ½", 8.9 cm
Colour:	Assorted decorations - satin matt

Market	Range
U.S.A.	$16.00 - 25.00
Canada	$25.00 - 40.00
U.K.	£10.00 - 15.00

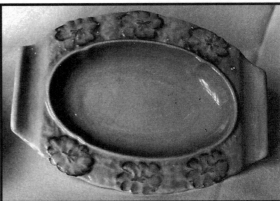

Shape 722   **Love in a mist, sweet dish**

Designer:	Mr. Watkin in 1939
Issued:	1939 - by 1963
Size:	6" x 4 ¾", 15.0 x 12.1 cm
Colour:	Green and pink with green, pink, yellow or white centre - gloss

Market	Range
U.S.A.	$25.00 - 50.00
Canada	$40.00 - 75.00
U.K.	£15.00 - 30.00

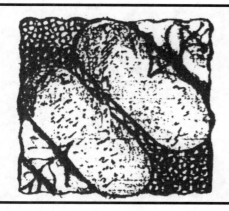

Shape 727	**Forget-me-not sweet dish**
Designer:	Mr. Watkin in 1939
Issued:	1939 - by 1963
Width:	5 ¼", 13.3 cm
Colour:	Assorted shades of green, pink, yellow or white - gloss

Market	Range
U.S.A.	$16.00 - 35.00
Canada	$25.00 - 50.00
U.K.	£10.00 - 20.00

Shape 932	**Leaf dish**
Designer:	Mr. Watkin in 1941
Issued:	1941 - by 1954
Size:	Unknown
Colour:	1. Assorted decorations - satin matt
	2. White - matt

Market	Range
U.S.A.	$16.00 - 35.00
Canada	$25.00 - 50.00
U.K.	£10.00 - 20.00

Photograph not
available
at press time

Photograph not
available
at press time

Shape 1253	**Elizabeth II Coronation tray, large**
Designer:	Albert Hallam, James Hayward in 1952
Issued:	1953 - 1953
Size:	Unknown
Colour:	Assorted colours on white background - gloss

Description	U.S. $	Can. $	U.K. £
Coronation tray, large	60.00	90.00	35.00

Shape 1254	**Elizabeth II Coronation tray, small**
Designer:	Albert Hallam, James Hayward in 1952
Issued:	1953 - 1953
Size:	Unknown
Colour:	Assorted colours on white background - gloss

Description	U.S. $	Can. $	U.K. £
Coronation tray, small	50.00	75.00	30.00

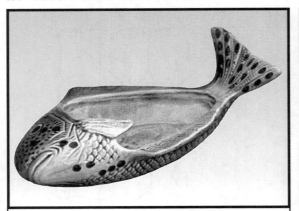

Shape 1304 Fish tray/trinket dish

Designer: Arthur Gredington in 1953
Issued: 1953 - 1966
Length: 5", 12.7 cm
Colour: Blues, yellow, browns and pink
with black - gloss

Description	U.S. $	Can. $	U.K. £
Fish tray/trinket dish	100.00	150.00	50.00

Shape 1537 Dish

Designer: Albert Hallam in 1958
Issued: 1958 - by 1965
Size: 5 ¾" x 3 ½", 14.6 x 8.9 cm
Colour: 1. Assorted decorations - satin matt
2. White - matt

Market	Range
U.S.A.	$16.00 - 35.00
Canada	$25.00 - 50.00
U.K.	£10.00 - 20.00

Note: Also shown in Tableware, page 268.

Shape 1538 Dish

Designer: Albert Hallam in 1958
Issued: 1958 - by 1965
Size: 5", 12.7 cm
Colour: 1. Assorted decorations - satin matt
2. White - matt

Market	Range
U.S.A.	$16.00 - 35.00
Canada	$25.00 - 50.00
U.K.	£10.00 - 20.00

Note: Also shown in Tableware, page 268.

Shape 1635 Dish, rectangular

Designer: Albert Hallam in 1959
Issued: 1960 - by 1963
Size: 7 ¾" x 5 ¼", 19.7 x 13.3 cm
Colour: 1. Assorted decorations - satin matt
2. White - matt

Market	Range
U.S.A.	$35.00 - 65.00
Canada	$50.00 - 100.00
U.K.	£20.00 - 40.00

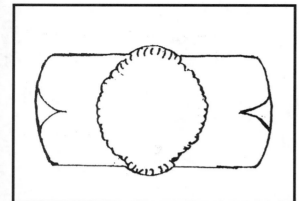

Shape 1690 Dish, rectangular

Designer: Albert Hallam in 1960
Issued: 1960 - by 1962
Length: 14", 35.5 cm
Colour: 1. Assorted decorations - satin matt
            2. White - matt

Market	Range
U.S.A.	$65.00 - 100.00
Canada	$100.00 - 150.00
U.K.	£40.00 - 60.00

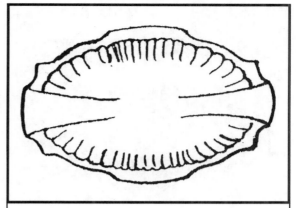

Shape 1691 Dish, oval

Designer: Albert Hallam in 1960
Issued: 1960 - by 1962
Length: 12", 30.5 cm
Colour: 1. Assorted decorations - satin matt
            2. White - matt

Market	Range
U.S.A.	$65.00 - 100.00
Canada	$100.00 - 150.00
U.K.	£40.00 - 60.00

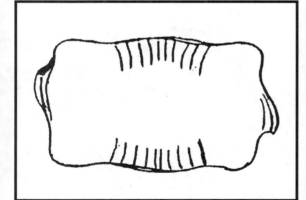

Shape 1692 Dish, rectangular

Designer: Albert Hallam in 1960
Issued: 1960 - by 1962
Length: 12 ½", 31.7 cm
Colour: 1. Assorted decorations - satin matt
            2. White - matt

Market	Range
U.S.A.	$65.00 - 100.00
Canada	$100.00 - 150.00
U.K.	£40.00 - 60.00

Shape 1693 Dish, kidney shape

Designer: Albert Hallam in 1960
Issued: 1960 - by 1963
Size: 9 ½" x 4 ½", 24 x 11.9 cm
Colour: 1. Assorted decorations - satin matt
            2. White - matt

Market	Range
U.S.A.	$50.00 - 85.00
Canada	$75.00 - 125.00
U.K.	£30.00 - 50.00

Photograph not
available
at press time

Shape 1701 Dish, Mexican hat (four sections)

Designer:	Albert Hallam in 1960
Issued:	1960 - by 1963
Size:	8 ¼" x 3 ½", 21 x 8.9 cm
Colour:	Yellow hat with blue, white and brown trim - gloss

Description	U.S. $	Can. $	U.K. £
Dish, Mexican hat	65.00	100.00	40.00

Shape 1856 Double Diamond dish

Designer:	Unknown
Issued:	1962
Size:	Unknown
Colour:	1. Assorted solid colours - matt
	2. White - matt

Market	Range
U.S.A.	$25.00 - 40.00
Canada	$40.00 - 60.00
U.K.	£15.00 - 25.00

Note: Special Commission.

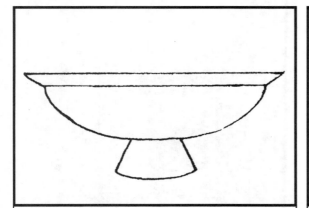

Shape 1889 Dish on foot

Designer:	Albert Hallam in 1963
Issued:	1963 - by 1965
Length:	12" x 4 ¾", 30.5 x 12.1 cm
Colour:	1. Assorted decorations - satin matt
	2. White - matt

Market	Range
U.S.A.	$65.00 - 100.00
Canada	$100.00 - 150.00
U.K.	£40.00 - 60.00

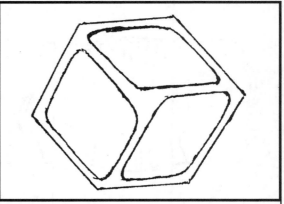

Shape 2013 Dish in three sections

Designer:	Mr. Murphy in 1964
Issued:	1964 - unknown
Size:	Unknown
Colour:	1. Assorted decos; solid colours - satin matt
	2. White or black - matt

Market	Range
U.S.A.	$25.00 - 50.00
Canada	$40.00 - 75.00
U.K.	£15.00 - 30.00

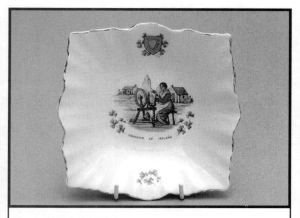

Shape 2113-2116 Dish

Designer:	Albert Hallam in 1967
Issued:	1967 - 1969
Size:	Shape 2113 — 5 ½", 14.0 cm
	Shape 2116 — 6 ½", 16.5 cm
Colours:	Assorted decorations - gloss

Description	U.S. $	Can. $	U.K. £
Dish	8.00	12.00	5.00

Note: This model makes a set of four with Shapes 2117 and 2120 (see Tableware section, page 284).

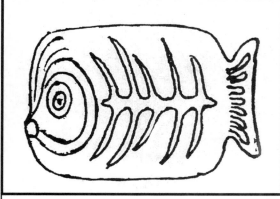

Shape 2167 Fish dish

Designer:	Albert Hallam in 1967
Issued:	1967 - 1969
Size:	7 ½" x 6", 19.1 x 15 cm
Colour:	Assorted decorations, solid colours - gloss

Market	Range
U.S.A.	$25.00 - 50.00
Canada	$40.00 - 75.00
U.K.	£15.00 - 30.00

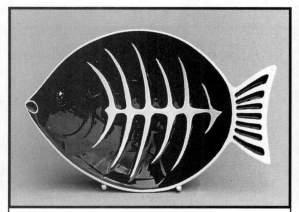

Shape 2170 Fish dish

Designer:	Albert Hallam in 1967
Issued:	1967 - 1969
Size:	7 ½" x 5 ½", 19.1 x 14 cm
Colour:	Assorted decorations, solid colours - gloss

Market	Range
U.S.A.	$25.00 - 50.00
Canada	$40.00 - 75.00
U.K.	£15.00 - 30.00

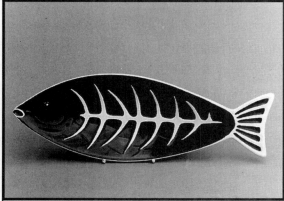

Shape 2171 Fish dish

Designer:	Albert Hallam in 1967
Issued:	1967 - 1969
Size:	12" x 4", 30.5 x 10.1 cm
Colour:	Assorted decorations, solid colours - gloss

Market	Range
U.S.A.	$50.00 - 85.00
Canada	$75.00 - 125.00
U.K.	£30.00 - 50.00

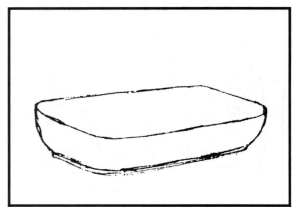

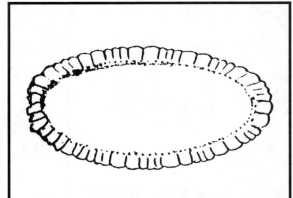

Shape 2277 Dish

Designer:	Albert Hallam in 1969
Issued:	1969 - 1970
Size:	9 ½" x 7 ¼", 24 x 18.4 cm
Colour:	1. Assorted decos; solid colours - satin matt
	2. Copper - lustre
	3. White or black - matt

Market	Range
U.S.A.	$50.00 - 85.00
Canada	$75.00 - 125.00
U.K.	£30.00 - 50.00

Shape 2291 Oval tray, pair with shape 2292

Designer:	Graham Tongue in 1969
Issued:	1969 - unknown
Size:	5 ½" x 8 ½", 14 x 21.6 cm
Colour:	1. Assorted decos; solid colours - satin matt
	2. Copper - lustre
	3. White or black - matt

Market	Range
U.S.A.	$16.00 - 35.00
Canada	$25.00 - 50.00
U.K.	£10.00 - 20.00

Shape 2292 Sweet dish

Designer:	Graham Tongue in 1969
Issued:	1969 - unknown
Diameter:	5", 12.7 cm
Colour:	1. Assorted decos; solid colours - satin matt
	2. Copper - lustre
	3. White or black - matt

Market	Range
U.S.A.	$16.00 - 35.00
Canada	$25.00 - 50.00
U.K.	£10.00 - 20.00

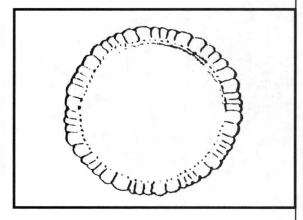

Note: Price ranges are retail market indicators of prices for models under the following conditions:
- Lower end of range = price of monochrome models
- Higher end of range = price of multicoloured models

JUGS

There are one hundred shapes listed in this section, most of which could be called "jug-vases," since they appear to have been designed for use as flower holders, or simply for ornamental purposes only. Because of this, they have been listed separately from the jugs which form part of named series or small sets, for example, milk or cream jugs, which are to be found listed with the appropriate named series or in the Tableware Section.

The early assorted decorations used for these jugs varied considerably - ranging from the soft blended colours with subtle shading of the matt glazes, (satin matt), to dynamic Art deco styles (often backstamped - "Handpainted"). Very detailed decorations were used on the four Shakespeare Jugs, which were embossed and decorated with many colours. Other jugs were quite plain, yet still very striking, such as the copper lustre finish with black gloss inners. There are also some very interesting shapes to note, eg. Shape 94 with a spout pourer, and even a jug with feet! Quite a selection?

Shape 22   **Jug**

Designer: Mr. Symcox in 1933
Issued: 1933 - by 1954
Height: 12", 30.5 cm
Colour: 1. Assorted decorations - satin matt
   2. White - matt

Market	Range
U.S.A.	$100.00 - 135.00
Canada	$150.00 - 225.00
U.K.	£60.00 - 85.00

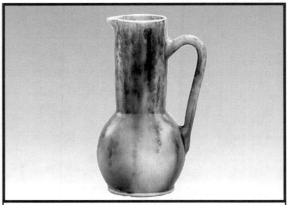

Shape 26   **Jug**

Designer: Mr. Symcox in 1933
Issued: 1933 - by 1954
Height :   10 ½", 26.7 cm
Colour: 1. Assorted decorations - satin matt
   2. White - matt

Market	Range
U.S.A.	$100.00 - 135.00
Canada	$150.00 - 225.00
U.K.	£60.00 - 85.00

Shape 28   **Jug**

Designer: Mr. Symcox in 1933
Issued: 1933 - by 1959
Height: 9 ½", 24 cm
Colour: 1. Assorted decorations - satin matt
   2. White - matt

Market	Range
U.S.A.	$100.00 - 135.00
Canada	$150.00 - 225.00
U.K.	£60.00 - 85.00

Shape 72   **Ruth jug**

Designer: Unknown
Issued: 1932 - by 1954
Height :   10 ¼", 26 cm
Colour: 1. Assorted decorations - satin matt
   2. White - matt

Market	Range
U.S.A.	$125.00 - 175.00
Canada	$200.00 - 250.00
U.K.	£75.00 - 100.00

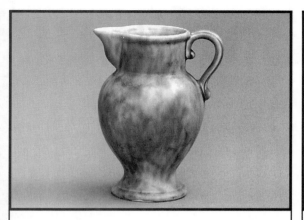

Shape 91   Jug

Designer: Mr. Symcox in 1933
Issued: 1933 - by 1954
Height: 8″, 20.3 cm
Colour: 1. Assorted decorations - satin matt
             2. White - matt

Market	Range
U.S.A.	$75.00 - 125.00
Canada	$125.00 - 175.00
U.K.	£45.00 - 75.00

Shape 92   Jug

Designer: Mr. Symcox in 1933
Issued: 1933 - by 1954
Height :   6 ½″, 16.5 cm
Colour: 1. Assorted decorations - satin matt
             2. White - matt

Market	Range
U.S.A.	$75.00 - 100.00
Canada	$125.00 - 150.00
U.K.	£45.00 - 60.00

Shape 94   Jug

Designer: Mr. Symcox in 1933
Issued: 1933 - by 1954
Height: 9″, 22.9 cm
Colour: 1. Assorted decorations - satin matt
             2. White - matt

Market	Range
U.S.A.	$75.00 - 125.00
Canada	$125.00 - 175.00
U.K.	£45.00 - 75.00

Shape 98/1/2 Jug

Designer: Mr. Symcox in 1933
Issued: 1933 - by 1954
Height :   1. Shape 98/1 — 10″, 25.4 cm
             2. Shape 98/2 — Unknown
Colour: 1. Assorted decorations - satin matt
             2. White - matt

Market	Range
U.S.A.	$75.00 - 125.00
Canada	$125.00 - 175.00
U.K.	£45.00 - 75.00

Shape 119   Jug

Designer: Mr. Symcox in 1933
Issued: 1934 - by 1954
Height: 11", 27.9 cm
Colour: 1. Assorted decorations - satin matt
        2. White - matt

Market	Range
U.S.A.	$100.00 - 135.00
Canada	$150.00 - 225.00
U.K.	£60.00 - 85.00

Shape 125   Jug

Designer: Mr. Owen in 1934
Issued: 1934 - by 1954
Height :   7 ¼", 18.4 cm
Colour: 1. Assorted decorations - satin matt
        2. White - matt

Market	Range
U.S.A.	$75.00 - 125.00
Canada	$125.00 - 175.00
U.K.	£45.00 - 75.00

Shape 129/1/2 Jug

Designer: Mr. Symcox in 1933
Issued: 1934 - by 1954
Size :   1. 129/1 - 10", 25.4 cm
       2. 129/2 - 9 ½", 24.0 cm
Colour: 1. Assorted decorations - satin matt
        2. White - matt

Market	Range 129/1	Range 129/2
U.S.A.	$100.00 - 135.00	$75.00 - 125.00
Canada	$150.00 - 225.00	$125.00 - 175.00
U.K.	£60.00 - 85.00	£45.00 - 75.00

Shape 131   Jug

Designer: Mr. Symcox in 1933
Issued: 1934 - by 1963
Height :   6 ¼", 15.9 cm
Colour: 1. Assorted decorations - satin matt
        2. White - matt

Market	Range
U.S.A.	$65.00 - 100.00
Canada	$100.00 - 150.00
U.K.	£40.00 - 60.00

Shape 136 Jug

Designer:	Mr. Symcox in 1933
Issued:	1934 - by 1954
Height:	4 ½", 11.9 cm
Colour:	1. Assorted decorations - satin matt
	2. White - matt

Market	Range
U.S.A.	$45.00 - 65.00
Canada	$65.00 - 100.00
U.K.	£25.00 - 45.00

Shape 137 Jug

Designer:	Mr. Symcox in 1933
Issued:	1934 - by 1963
Height :	4 ½", 11.9 cm
Colour:	1. Assorted decorations - satin matt
	2. White - matt

Market	Range
U.S.A.	$45.00 - 65.00
Canada	$65.00 - 100.00
U.K.	£25.00 - 45.00

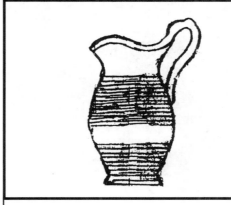

Shape 140 Jug

Designer:	Mr. Symcox in 1933
Issued:	1934 - by 1954
Size :	Unknown
Colour:	1. Assorted decorations - satin matt
	2. White - matt

Market	Range
U.S.A.	$100.00 - 135.00
Canada	$150.00 - 225.00
U.K.	£60.00 - 85.00

Shape 141 Jug

Designer:	Mr. Symcox in 1933
Issued:	1934 - by 1954
Height :	11", 27.9 cm
Colour:	1. Assorted decorations - satin matt
	2. White - matt

Market	Range
U.S.A.	$100.00 - 135.00
Canada	$150.00 - 225.00
U.K.	£60.00 - 85.00

Shape 146   Jug

Designer: Mr. Symcox in 1933
Issued: 1934 - by 1954
Height: 9 ½", 24.0 cm
Colour: 1. Assorted decorations - satin matt
             2. White - matt

Market	Range
U.S.A.	$75.00 - 125.00
Canada	$125.00 - 175.00
U.K.	£45.00 - 75.00

Shape 148   Jug

Designer: Mr. Symcox in 1933
Issued: 1934 - by 1962
Height :   9 ¼", 23.5 cm
Colour: 1. Assorted decorations - satin matt
             2. White - matt

Market	Range
U.S.A.	$75.00 - 125.00
Canada	$125.00 - 175.00
U.K.	£45.00 - 75.00

Shape 150   Jug

Designer: Mr. Symcox in 1933
Issued: 1934 - by 1954
Height: 7 ¾", 19.7 cm
Colour: 1. Assorted decorations - satin matt
             2. White - matt

Market	Range
U.S.A.	$75.00 - 125.00
Canada	$125.00 - 175.00
U.K.	£45.00 - 75.00

Shape 151   Jug

Designer: Mr. Symcox in 1933
Issued: 1934 - by 1954
Height :   10 ½", 26.7 cm
Colour: 1. Assorted decorations - satin matt
             2. White - matt

Market	Range
U.S.A.	$100.00 - 135.00
Canada	$150.00 - 225.00
U.K.	£60.00 - 85.00

Shape 155   Jug

Designer: Mr. Owen in 1933
Issued: 1934 - by 1954
Height: 5 ½", 14 cm
Colour: 1. Assorted decorations - satin matt
              2. White - matt

Market	Range
U.S.A.	$45.00 - 65.00
Canada	$65.00 - 100.00
U.K.	£25.00 - 45.00

Shape 162   Jug

Designer: Mr. Symcox in 1933
Issued: 1934 - by 1963
Height :   11 ¼", 28.5
Colour: 1. Assorted decorations - satin matt
              2. White - matt

Market	Range
U.S.A.	$100.00 - 135.00
Canada	$150.00 - 225.00
U.K.	£60.00 - 85.00

Shape 163   Jug

Designer: Mr. Symcox in 1933
Issued: 1934 - by 1954
Size :   Unknown
Colour: 1. Assorted decorations - satin matt
              2. White - matt

Market	Range
U.S.A.	$100.00 - 135.00
Canada	$150.00 - 225.00
U.K.	£60.00 - 85.00

Shape 173   Jug

Designer: Mr. Symcox in 1933
Issued: 1934 - by 1954
Height :   9", 22.9 cm
Colour: 1. Assorted decorations - satin matt
              2. White - matt

Market	Range
U.S.A.	$75.00 - 125.00
Canada	$125.00 - 175.00
U.K.	£45.00 - 75.00

Shape 174   Jug

Designer:	Mr. Owen in 1934
Issued:	1934 - by 1954
Height:	8", 20.3 cm
Colour:	1. Assorted decorations - satin matt
	2. White - matt

Market	Range
U.S.A.	$75.00 - 125.00
Canada	$125.00 - 175.00
U.K.	£45.00 - 75.00

Shape 175   Jug

Designer:	Mr. Symcox in 1933
Issued:	1934 - by 1954
Height :	11", 27.9 cm
Colour:	1. Assorted decorations - satin matt
	2. White - matt

Market	Range
U.S.A.	$100.00 - 135.00
Canada	$150.00 - 225.00
U.K.	£60.00 - 85.00

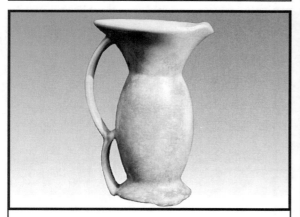

Shape 176   Jug

Designer:	Mr. Symcox in 1933
Issued:	1934 - by 1954
Height:	8", 20.3 cm
Colour:	1. Assorted decorations - satin matt
	2. White - matt

Market	Range
U.S.A.	$75.00 - 125.00
Canada	$125.00 - 175.00
U.K.	£45.00 - 75.00

Shape 177/1/2 Jug

Designer:	Mr. Symcox in 1933
Issued:	1934 - by 1954
Height :	1. Shape 177/1 — 10 ½", 26.7 cm
	2. Shape 177/2 — 9 ", 22.9 cm
Colour:	1. Assorted decorations - satin matt
	2. White - matt

Market	Range 177/1	Range 177/2
U.S.A.	$100.00 - 135.00	$75.00 - 125.00
Canada	$150.00 - 225.00	$125.00 - 175.00
U.K.	£60.00 - 85.00	£45.00 - 75.00

Shape 178	Jug
Designer:	Mr. Symcox in 1933
Issued:	1934 - by 1954
Height:	8 ½", 21.6 cm
Colour:	1. Assorted decorations - satin matt
	2. White - matt

Market	Range
U.S.A.	$75.00 - 125.00
Canada	$125.00 - 175.00
U.K.	£45.00 - 75.00

Shape 179	Jug
Designer:	Mr. Symcox in 1933
Issued:	1934 - by 1954
Size:	7", 17.8 cm
Colour:	1. Assorted decorations - satin matt
	2. White - matt

Market	Range
U.S.A.	$75.00 - 125.00
Canada	$125.00 - 175.00
U.K.	£45.00 - 75.00

Shape 260/1/2/3 Jug

Designer:	Albert Hallam in 1933
Issued:	1934 - by 1954
Height:	1. Shape 260/1 — 7 ¾", 19.7 cm
	2. Shape 260/2 — 6 ½", 16.5 cm
	3. Shape 260/3 — 5 ½", 14 cm
Colour:	1. Assorted decorations - satin matt
	2. White - matt

Market	Range
Shape 260/1	
U.S.A.	$75.00 - 125.00
Canada	$125.00 - 175.00
U.K.	£45.00 - 75.00
Shape 260/2	
U.S.A.	$65.00 - 100.00
Canada	$100.00 - 150.00
U.K.	£40.00 - 60.00
Shape 260/3	
U.S.A.	$45.00 - 65.00
Canada	$65.00 - 100.00
U.K.	£25.00 - 45.00

Shape 261/1/2/3 Jug "Zenith"

Designer:	Mr. Symcox in 1934
Issued:	1934 - by 1954
Height :	1. 261/1 - Unknown
	2. 261/2 - 7 ¾", 19.7 cm
	3/261/3 - 6 ¾", 17.2 cm
Colour:	1. Assorted decorations - satin matt
	2. White - matt

Market	261/1	261/2	261/3
U.S.A.	$75.00-125.00	$75.00-125.00	$65.00-100.00
Canada	$125.00-175.00	$125.00-175.00	$100.00-150.00
U.K.	£45.00-75.00	£45.00-75.00	£40.00-60.00

Shape 265/1/2/3 Jug in three sizes

Designer:	Unknown
Issued:	1934 - by 1959
Reissued:	1962 - by 1970
Height:	See below
Colour:	1. Assorted decorations - satin matt
	2. White - matt

Shape No.	Height	Colour	U.S. $	Can. $	U.K. £
265/1	5", 12.7 cm	Assorted	40.00	60.00	25.00
265/1	5", 12.7 cm	White	25.00	40.00	15.00
265/2	4 ½", 11.9 cm	Assorted	35.00	50.00	20.00
265/2	4 ½", 11.9 cm	White	30.00	20.00	12.00
265/3	4", 10.1 cm	Assorted	25.00	40.00	15.00
265/3	4", 10.1 cm	White	15.00	25.00	10.00

Note: First issued in 1934 with a plain design, this jug was reissued in 1962 with a ribbed design.

Shape 266   Wolstan jug

Designer: Unknown
Issued: 1933 - by 1954
Height :   6 ½", 16.5 cm
Colour: 1   Assorted decorations - satin matt
             2. White - matt

Market	Range
U.S.A.	$75.00 - 125.00
Canada	$125.00 - 175.00
U.K.	£45.00 - 75.00

Shape 292   Jug

Designer: Mr. Symcox in 1934
Issued: 1935 - by 1954
Height: 4 ½", 11.9 cm
Colour: 1. Assorted decorations - satin matt
             2. White - matt

Market	Range
U.S.A.	$45.00 - 65.00
Canada	$65.00 - 100.00
U.K.	£25.00 - 45.00

Shape 293   Jug

Designer: Mr. Symcox in 1934
Issued: 1935 - by 1954
Size: 6 ½", 16.5 cm
Colour: 1. Assorted decorations - satin matt
             2. White - matt

Market	Range
U.S.A.	$65.00 - 100.00
Canada	$100.00 - 150.00
U.K.	£40.00 - 60.00

Shape 346   Jug

Designer: Mr. Symcox in 1934
Issued: 1935 - by 1954
Height: 5 ½",14 cm
Colour: 1. Assorted decorations - satin matt
             2. White - matt

Market	Range
U.S.A.	$65.00 - 100.00
Canada	$100.00 - 150.00
U.K.	£40.00 - 60.00

Shape 348   Jug

Designer: Mr. Symcox in 1934
Issued: 1935 - by 1954
Height :   7 ¾", 19.7 cm
Colour: 1. Assorted decorations - satin matt
             2. White - matt

Market	Range
U.S.A.	$75.00 - 125.00
Canada	$125.00 - 175.00
U.K.	£45.00 - 75.00

Shape 349   Jug

Designer: Mr. Symcox in 1934
Issued: 1935 - by 1954
Size :   5 ½", 14.0 cm
Colour: 1. Assorted decorations - satin matt
             2. White - matt

Market	Range
U.S.A.	$75.00 - 125.00
Canada	$125.00 - 175.00
U.K.	£45.00 - 75.00

Shape 350   Jug

Designer: Mr. Symcox in 1935
Issued: 1935 - by 1965
Height :   8 ½", 21.6 cm
Colour: 1. Assorted decorations, solid colours -
                satin matt
             2. White or black - matt

Market	Range
U.S.A.	$75.00 - 125.00
Canada	$125.00 - 175.00
U.K.	£45.00 - 75.00

Shape 355   Jug

Designer: Mr. Symcox in 1935
Issued: 1935 - by 1954
Height: 10", 25.4 cm
Colour: 1. Assorted decorations - satin matt
             2. White - matt

Market	Range
U.S.A.	$100.00 - 135.00
Canada	$150.00 - 225.00
U.K.	£60.00 - 85.00

Shape 356 **Jug**

Designer: Mr. Symcox in 1935
Issued: 1935 - by 1954
Height : 10", 25.4 cm
Colour: 1. Assorted decorations - satin matt
2. White - matt

Market	Range
U.S.A.	$100.00 - 135.00
Canada	$150.00 - 225.00
U.K.	£60.00 - 85.00

Shape 387 **Jug**

Designer: Mr. Symcox in 1936
Issued: 1936 - by 1954
Size : 7", 17.8 cm
Colour: 1. Assorted decorations - satin matt
2. White - matt

Market	Range
U.S.A.	$75.00 - 125.00
Canada	$125.00 - 175.00
U.K.	£45.00 - 75.00

Shape 394/1/2 Jug

Designer: Mr. Symcox in 1936
Issued: 1936 - by 1959
Height: 1. Shape 394/1 — 10", 25.4 cm
2. Shape 394/2 — 8", 20.3 cm
Colour: 1. Assorted decorations - satin matt
2. White - matt

Market	Range 394/1	Range 394/2
U.S.A.	$100.00 - 135.00	$75.00 - 125.00
Canada	$150.00 - 225.00	$125.00 - 175.00
U.K.	£60.00 - 85.00	£45.00 - 75.00

Shape 421 **Jug**

Designer: Mr. Symcox in 1936
Issued: 1936 - by 1954
Size: 7 ½", 19.1 cm
Colour: 1. Assorted decorations - satin matt
2. White - matt

Market	Range
U.S.A.	$75.00 - 125.00
Canada	$125.00 - 175.00
U.K.	£45.00 - 75.00

Shape 424   Jug

Designer:	Mr. Owen in 1936
Issued:	1936 - by 1954
Height :	9 ¼", 23.5 cm
Colour:	1. Assorted decorations - satin matt
	2. White - matt

Market	Range
U.S.A.	$75.00 - 125.00
Canada	$125.00 - 175.00
U.K.	£45.00 - 75.00

Shape 426   Jug

Designer:	Mr. Owen in 1936
Issued:	1936 - by 1954
Height:	7 ½", 19.1 cm
Colour:	1. Assorted decorations - satin matt
	2. White - matt

Market	Range
U.S.A.	$75.00 - 125.00
Canada	$125.00 - 175.00
U.K.	£45.00 - 75.00

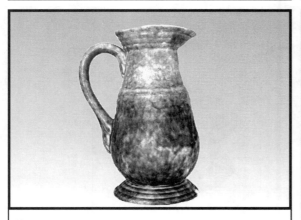

Shape 430   Jug

Designer:	Mr. Symcox in 1936
Issued:	1936 - by 1954
Size:	12", 30.5 cm
Colour:	1. Assorted decorations - satin matt
	2. White - matt

Market	Range
U.S.A.	$100.00 - 135.00
Canada	$150.00 - 225.00
U.K.	£60.00 - 85.00

Shape 448   Jug

Designer:	Mr. Symcox in 1936
Issued:	1936 - by 1954
Height:	12", 30.5 cm
Colour:	1. Assorted decorations - satin matt
	2. White - matt

Market	Range
U.S.A.	$100.00 - 135.00
Canada	$150.00 - 225.00
U.K.	£60.00 - 85.00

Shape 478 Jug

Designer: Mr. Symcox in 1937
Issued: 1937 - by 1962
Height :   6", 15 cm
Colour: 1. Assorted decorations - satin matt
            2. White - matt

Market	Range
U.S.A.	$65.00 - 100.00
Canada	$100.00 - 150.00
U.K.	£40.00 - 60.00

Shape 480 Jug

Designer: Mr. Symcox in 1937
Issued: 1937 - by 1954
Size :   8 ½", 21.6 cm
Colour: 1. Assorted decorations - satin matt
            2. White - matt

Market	Range
U.S.A.	$75.00 - 125.00
Canada	$125.00 - 175.00
U.K.	£45.00 - 75.00

Shape 488 Jug

Designer: Mr. Symcox in 1937
Issued: 1937 - by 1954
Height: 10", 25.4 cm
Colour: 1. Assorted decorations - satin matt
            2. White - matt

Market	Range
U.S.A.	$100.00 - 135.00
Canada	$150.00 - 225.00
U.K.	£60.00 - 65.00

Shape 493 Jug

Designer: Mr. Owen in 1937
Issued: 1937 - by 1954
Size :   9", 22.9 cm
Colour: 1. Assorted decorations - satin matt
            2. White - matt

Market	Range
U.S.A.	$75.00 - 125.00
Canada	$125.00 - 175.00
U.K.	£45.00 - 75.00

Photograph not
available
at press time

Shape 505   Jug

Designer: Mr. Owen in 1937
Issued: 1937 - by 1962
Height :   10", 25.4 cm
Colour: 1. Assorted decorations - satin matt
           2. White - matt

Market	Range
U.S.A.	$100.00 - 135.00
Canada	$150.00 - 225.00
U.K.	£60.00 - 85.00

Shape 510   Jug

Designer: Mr. Symcox in 1937
Issued: 1937 - by 1954
Height: 10", 25.4 cm
Colour: 1. Assorted decorations - satin matt
           2. White - matt

Market	Range
U.S.A.	$100.00 - 135.00
Canada	$150.00 - 225.00
U.K.	£60.00 - 85.00

Shape 544   Jug

Designer: Mr. Symcox in 1937
Issued: 1938 - by 1954
Size: 10", 25.4 cm
Colour: 1. Assorted decorations - satin matt
           2. White - matt

Market	Range
U.S.A.	$75.00 - 125.00
Canada	$125.00 - 175.00
U.K.	£45.00 - 75.00

Shape 547   Jug

Designer: Mr. Symcox in 1937
Issued: 1938 - by 1954
Size :   9", 23.0 cm
Colour: 1. Assorted decorations - satin matt
           2. White - matt

Market	Range
U.S.A.	$75.00 - 125.00
Canada	$125.00 - 175.00
U.K.	£45.00 - 75.00

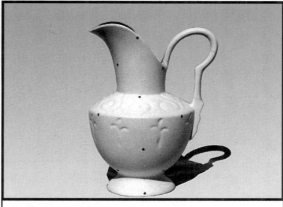

Shape 550	Jug
Designer:	Mr. Symcox in 1937
Issued:	1938 - by 1954
Size:	7 ½", 19.1 cm
Colour:	1. Assorted decorations - satin matt
	2. White - matt

Market	Range
U.S.A.	$75.00 - 125.00
Canada	$125.00 - 175.00
U.K.	£45.00 - 75.00

Shape 555	Jug
Designer:	Mr. Symcox in 1937
Issued:	1938 - by 1954
Size::	9", 22.9 cm
Colour:	1. Assorted decorations - satin matt
	2. White - matt

Market	Range
U.S.A.	$75.00 - 125.00
Canada	$125.00 - 175.00
U.K.	£45.00 - 75.00

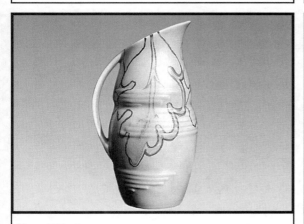

Shape 561	Jug
Designer:	Mr. Owen in 1937
Issued:	1938 - by 1962
Height :	11", 27.9 cm
Colour:	1. Assorted decorations - satin matt
	2. White - matt

Market	Range
U.S.A.	$100.00 - 135.00
Canada	$150.00 - 225.00
U.K.	£60.00 - 65.00

Shape 567	Jug
Designer:	Mr. Owen in 1937
Issued:	1938 - by 1954
Height:	8", 20.3 cm
Colour:	1. Assorted decorations - satin matt
	2. White - matt

Market	Range
U.S.A.	$75.00 - 125.00
Canada	$125.00 - 175.00
U.K.	£45.00 - 75.00

Shape 578   Jug

Designer: Mr. Newman in 1938
Issued: 1938 - by 1954
Size: 9 ¾", 24.7 cm
Colour: 1. Assorted decorations - satin matt
             2. White - matt

Market	Range
U.S.A.	$75.00 - 125.00
Canada	$125.00 - 175.00
U.K.	£45.00 - 75.00

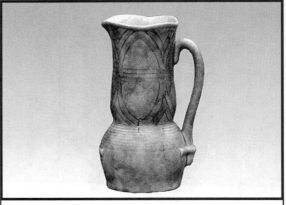

Shape 616   Jug

Designer: Mr. Symcox in 1938
Issued: 1938 - by 1954
Height: 8", 20.3 cm
Colour: 1. Assorted decorations - satin matt
             2. White - matt

Market	Range
U.S.A.	$75.00 - 125.00
Canada	$125.00 - 175.00
U.K.	£45.00 - 75.00

Shape 652   Jug

Designer: Mr. Symcox in 1938
Issued: 1938 - by 1954
Height :   9", 22.9 cm
Colour: 1. Assorted decorations - satin matt
             2. White - matt

Market	Range
U.S.A.	$75.00 - 125.00
Canada	$125.00 - 175.00
U.K.	£45.00 - 75.00

Shape 653   Jug, Modelle Series

Designer: Mr. Watkin in 1938
Issued: 1939 - by 1962
Size: 8 ½", 21.6 cm
Colour: 1. Assorted decorations - satin matt
             2. White - matt

Market	Range
U.S.A.	$75.00 - 125.00
Canada	$125.00 - 175.00
U.K.	£45.00 - 75.00

Shape 654   Jug, Modelle Series

Designer: James Hayward 1938
Issued: 1939 - by 1962
Size: 10", 25.4 cm
Colour: 1. Assorted decorations- satin matt
             2. White - matt

Market	Range
U.S.A.	$100.00 - 135.00
Canada	$150.00 - 225.00
U.K.	£60.00 - 85.00

Shape 662   Jug

Designer: Mr. Symcox in 1938
Issued: 1939 - by 1954
Size :   Unknown
Colour: 1. Assorted decorations - satin matt
             2. White - matt

Market	Range
U.S.A.	$100.00 - 135.00
Canada	$150.00 - 225.00
U.K.	£60.00 - 85.00

Shape 667   Jug

Designer: Mr. Symcox in 1938
Issued: 1939 - by 1962
Height :   4 ½", 11.9 cm
Colour: 1. Assorted decorations - satin matt
             2. White - matt

Market	Range
U.S.A.	$45.00 - 65.00
Canada	$65.00 - 100.00
U.K.	£25.00 - 45.00

Shape 676   Jug, Modelle Series

Designer: Mr. Watkin in 1939
Issued: 1939 - by 1962
Size: 10", 25.4 cm
Colour: 1. Assorted decorations - satin matt
             2. White - matt

Market	Range
U.S.A.	$100.00 - 135.00
Canada	$150.00 - 225.00
U.K.	£60.00 - 85.00

Shape 679   Jug, Modelle Series

Designer: Mr. Watkin in 1939
Issued: 1939 - by 1962
Size: 8", 20.3 cm
Colour: 1. Assorted decorations - satin matt
            2. White - matt

Market	Range
U.S.A.	$75.00 - 125.00
Canada	$125.00 - 175.00
U.K.	£45.00 - 75.00

Shape 694   Jug, Modelle Series

Designer: Mr. Watkin in 1939
Issued: 1939 - by 1962
Size: 9 ¾", 24.7 cm
Colour: 1. Assorted decorations - satin matt
            2. White - matt

Market	Range
U.S.A.	$75.00 - 125.00
Canada	$125.00 - 175.00
U.K.	£45.00 - 75.00

Shape 717   Jug

Designer: Mr. Watkin in 1939
Issued: 1939 - by 1954
Height :   10", 25.4 cm
Colour: 1. Assorted decorations - satin matt
            2. White - matt

Market	Range
U.S.A.	$100.00 - 135.00
Canada	$150.00 - 225.00
U.K.	£60.00 - 85.00

Shape 718   Jug

Designer: Mr. Watkin in 1939
Issued: 1939 - by 1954
Height: 7 ½", 19.1 cm
Colour: 1. Assorted decorations - satin matt
            2. White - matt

Market	Range
U.S.A.	$75.00 - 125.00
Canada	$125.00 - 175.00
U.K.	£45.00 - 75.00

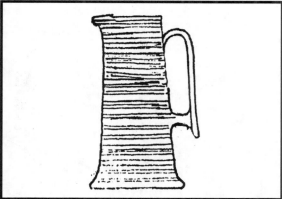

Shape 734   **Jug**

Designer: Mr. Symcox in 1939
Issued: 1939 - by 1962
Height :   12", 30.5 cm
Colour: 1. Assorted decorations - satin matt
            2. White - matt

Market	Range
U.S.A.	$100.00 - 135.00
Canada	$150.00 - 225.00
U.K.	£60.00 - 85.00

Shape 955   **Jug**

Designer: Albert Hallam in 1941
Issued: 1941 - by 1954
Size :   Unknown
Colour: 1. Assorted decorations - satin matt
            2. White - matt

Market	Range
U.S.A.	$100.00 - 135.00
Canada	$150.00 - 225.00
U.K.	£60.00 - 85.00

Note: Jug is pair with tankard shape 956, see page 244.

Shape 957/1/2 Soup Jugs

Designer: Albert Hallam in 1941
Issued: 1941 - by 1954
Size: Unknown
Colour: 1. Assorted decorations - satin matt
            2. White - matt

Market	Range
U.S.A.	$75.00 - 125.00
Canada	$125.00 - 175.00
U.K.	£45.00 - 75.00

Note: Set with shapes 958 (soup bowl)
            and shape 959 (soup saucer).

Shape 1045/1/2 Robert Burns, jug

Designer:	Unknown 1946
Issued:	1947 - 1966
Height :	1. Shape 1045/1 — 10", 25.4 cm
	2. Shape 1045/2 — 8", 20.3 cm
Colour:	1. Multicoloured on embossed white background - gloss
	2. Plain white, embossed - gloss

Description	U.S. $	Can. $	U.K. £
Shape 1045/1			
1. Multicoloured	325.00	425.00	135.00
2. White	200.00	300.00	110.00
Shape 1045/2			
1. Multicoloured	300.00	400.00	120.00
2. White	175.00	275.00	95.00

Shape 1126 Falstaff jug, Shakespeare Series

Designer:	Albert Hallam, Arthur Gredington in 1948
Issued:	1948 - 1972
Hight:	8", 20.3 cm
Colour:	Maroon, black, yellow and green - gloss

Description	U.S.$	Can.$	U.K.£
Falstaff jug	300.00	300.00	100.00

Note: Set of four with jugs no. 1146,1214 and 1366.

Shape 1146 Hamlet jug, Shakespeare Series

Designer:	Arthur Gredington in 1949
Issued:	1949 - 1972
Hight:	8 ¼", 21 cm
Colour:	Black, yellow and maroon - gloss

Description	U.S.$	Can.$	U.K.£
Hamlet jug	250.00	300.00	100.00

Note: Set of four with jugs no. 1126,1214 and 1366.

Shape 1176 Jug, Festival Series

Designer:	Albert Hallam in 1949
Issued:	1950 - by 1954
Height :	7 ½", 19.1 cm
Colour:	1. Assorted decorations - satin matt
	2. White - matt

Market	Range
U.S.A.	$75.00 - 125.00
Canada	$125.00 - 175.00
U.K.	£45.00 - 75.00

Shape 1177 Jug

Designer:	Albert Hallam in 1949
Issued:	1950 - by 1954
Size :	6 ¼", 15.9 cm
Colour:	1. Assorted decorations - satin matt
	2. White - matt

Market	Range
U.S.A.	$65.00 - 100.00
Canada	$100.00 - 150.00
U.K.	£40.00 - 60.00

Shape 1214 Juliet jug, Shakespeare Series

Designer:	Albert Hallam, Arthur Gredington in 1951
Issued:	1951 - 1972
Height:	8 ¼", 21 cm
Colour:	Maroon, blue, brown and green - gloss

Description	U.S.$	Can.$	U.K.£
Juliet jug	300.00	300.00	100.00

Shape 1366 Midsummer Nights Dream jug, Shakespeare Series

Designer:	Albert Hallam, Mr. Orwell in 1955
Issued:	1955 - 1972
Height:	8", 20.3 cm
Colour:	Light blue, yellow, brown and black - gloss

Description	U.S.$	Can.$	U.K.£
Midsummer Nights Dream jug	400.00	500.00	125.00

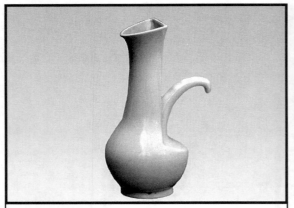

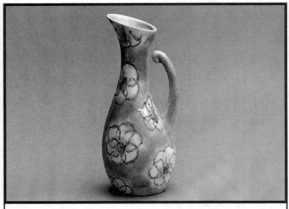

Shape 1367 Jug

Designer:	Albert Hallam in 1955
Issued:	1955 - by 1962
Height:	10 ½", 26.7 cm
Colour:	1. Assorted decorations - satin matt
	2. White - matt

Market	Range
U.S.A.	$100.00 - 135.00
Canada	$150.00 - 225.00
U.K.	£60.00 - 85.00

Shape 1372 Jug, with handle not joined at the top

Designer:	Albert Hallam in 1955
Issued:	1955 - 1973
Height :	6", 15 cm
Colour:	1. Assorted decorations - satin matt
	2. White - matt

Market	Range
U.S.A.	$65.00 - 100.00
Canada	$100.00 - 150.00
U.K.	£40.00 - 60.00

Shape 1441 Cutty Sark, jug

Designer:	Albert Hallam in 1956
Issued:	c.1956
Size:	Unknown
Colour:	Unknown

Market	Range
U.S.A.	$65.00 - 100.00
Canada	$100.00 - 150.00
U.K.	£40.00 - 60.00

Note: Special Commission. For the Contemporary shape see Tableware section page 265.

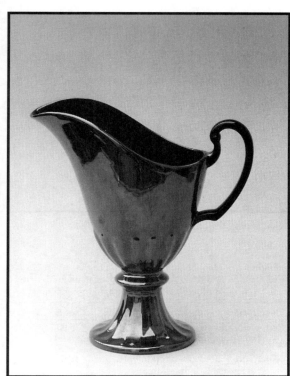

Shape 1550/1/2/3 Jugs

Designer: Albert Hallam in 1958
Issued: 1958 - 1967
Height: 1. Shape 1550/1 — 11", 27.9 cm
      2. Shape 1550/2 — 9", 22.9 cm
      3. Shape 1550/3 — 7", 17.8 cm
Colour: 1. Assorted decorations, solid colours -
        satin matt
      2. Copper - lustre
      3. White or black - matt

Market	Range
Shape 1550/1	
U.S.A.	$75.00-125.00
Canada	$125.00-175.00
U.K.	£45.00-75.00
Shape 1550/2	
U.S.A.	$75.00-100.00
Canada	$125.00-150.00
U.K.	£45.00-60.00
Shape 1550/3	
U.S.A.	$65.00-100.00
Canada	$100.00-150.00
U.K.	£40.00-60.00

Shape 1553/1/2/3 Jugs

Designer: Albert Hallam in 1958
Issued: 1958 - 1971
Height: 1. Shape 1553/1 — 5", 12.7 cm
      2. Shape 1553/2 — 5 ½", 14 cm
      3. Shape 1553/3 — 4", 10.1 cm
Colour: 1. Assorted decorations, solid colours -
        satin matt
      2. Copper - lustre
      3. White or black - matt

Market	Range
Shape 1553/1	
U.S.A.	$45.00-65.00
Canada	$65.00-100.00
U.K.	£25.00-45.00
Shape 1553/2	
U.S.A.	$30.00-60.00
Canada	$50.00-90.00
U.K.	£20.00-40.00
Shape 1553/3	
U.S.A.	$15.00-50.00
Canada	$25.00-75.00
U.K.	£10.00-30.00

Shape 1672/1/2 Double Diamond, jug

Designer:	Albert Hallam in 1960
Issued:	1960 - 1965
Size:	6 ½", 16.5 cm
Colour:	Black hat and jacket, white shirt, green tie - gloss

Description	U.S. $	Can. $	U.K. £
Black, white and green	250.00	375.00	150.00

Shape 1741   Lord Mayor, water jug

Designer:	Albert Hallam in 1961
Issued:	1962 - 1967
Height:	8 ½", 21.6 cm
Colour:	Red robe, black jacket and hat, with gold chain of office; red top to bottle - gloss

Description	U.S. $	Can. $	U.K. £
Red, black and gold	125.00	175.00	75.00

Note: Re-issued green top to bottle 1986 - 1987. Special Commission.

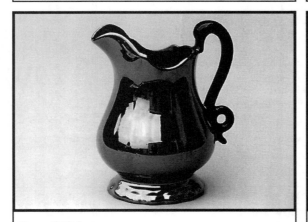

Shape 1859   Jug

Designer:	Albert Hallam in 1963
Issued:	1963 - 1971
Height :	8", 20.3 cm
Colour:	1. Assorted decos, solid colours - satin matt
	2. Copper - lustre
	3. White or black - matt

Market	Range
U.S.A.	$75.00 - 100.00
Canada	$125.00 - 150.00
U.K.	£45.00 - 60.00

Shape 2027   Soup jug

Designer:	Albert Hallam in 1965
Issued:	c. 1965
Height:	7 ¼", 18.4 cm
Colour:	1. Assorted decos, solid colours - satin matt
	2. White or black - matt

Market	Range
U.S.A.	$75.00 - 100.00
Canada	$125.00 - 150.00
U.K.	£45.00 - 60.00

Note: Pair with soup cup shape 2028 see page 283.

Shape 2053 Gallaher jug

Designer: Albert Hallam in 1965
Issued: c.1965
Height : 5 ½", 14 cm
Colour: Unknown

Description	U.S. $	Can. $	U.K. £
Gallagher jug	60.00	90.00	35.00

Note: Special Commission.

Shape 2118 Lemonade jug

Designer: Graham Tongue in 1967
Issued: c.1967
Height: 9 ½", 24 cm
Colour: 1. Assorted decos, solid colours - satin matt
 2. Copper - lustre
 3. White or black - matt

Market	Range
U.S.A.	$75.00 - 100.00
Canada	$125.00 - 150.00
U.K.	£45.00 - 60.00

Shape 2127 Ale jug

Designer: Albert Hallam in 1967
Issued: 1968 - 1972
Height : 8 ¼", 21 cm
Colour: 1. Assorted decorations - satin matt
 2. Copper - lustre
 3. White or black - matt
 4. Pewter

Market	Range
U.S.A.	$75.00 - 100.00
Canada	$125.00 - 150.00
U.K.	£45.00 - 60.00

Shape 2172/2173/2174 Jug

Designer: Mr. Garbet in 1967
Issued: 1967 - 1972
Height : 9 ¾", 5 ½", 4 ½", 24.7, 14.0, 11.9 cm
Colour: 1. Various decorations - satin matt
2. White or black - matt
3 Copper - lustre

Market	2172	2173	2174
U.S.A.	$75.00-125.00	$45.00-65.00	$45.00-65.00
Canada	$125.00-175.00	$65.00-100.00	$65.00-100.00
U.K.	£45.00-75.00	£25.00-45.00	£25.00-45.00

Shape 2280 Cockerel jug, Chante Clair

Designer: Unknown
Issued: Unknown
Height: 9 ¾", 24.7 cm
Colour: Greens and browns, with red crest
and comb - gloss

Description	U.S. $	Can. $	U.K. £
Cockerel jug	275.00	400.00	165.00

Shape 2506 Jug, Minton ewer, Bass Charrington

Designer: Mr. Plant in 1976
Issued: c.1976
Height : 6 ¾", 17.2 cm
Colour: Logo with red triangle, and garland of pale
green leaves with pale ochre flowers on white
background - gloss

Description	U.S. $	Can. $	U.K. £
Jug, Minton ewer	60.00	90.00	35.00

Note: Special Commission.

LAMPS AND LAMP BASES

There are only twenty-eight shapes in this section, of which the best known is the Peter Rabbit Tree Lamp Base (No. 1531). It is an attractive base and although the Beatrix Potter models, being the obvious choice, were supplied with it, of course, the owner could have added any figure or animal model of his or her choice.

Strangely, in our experience, over the many years that we have been involved with Beswick, lamps and lamp bases appear to be very elusive and have just not come to light! ... if they have, where are they hiding?

Six shapes were Special Commissions for the tobacco and brewing companies and due to lack of information at the present time, sadly we cannot indicate the colours for these items.

Shape 47   Lamp base/vase

Designer: Mr. Symcox c.1933
Issued: 1933 - by 1940
Size: Unknown
Colour: 1. Assorted decorations - satin matt
             2. White - matt

Market	Range
U.S.A.	$35.00 - 60.00
Canada	$50.00 - 90.00
U.K.	£20.00 - 35.00

Shape 75   Lamp base/vase

Designer: Mr. Symcox c.1933
Issued: 1933 - by 1940
Height :   6 ½", 16.5 cm
Colour: 1. Assorted decorations - satin matt or gloss
             2. White - matt

Market	Range
U.S.A.	$35.00 - 60.00
Canada	$50.00 - 90.00
U.K.	£20.00 - 35.00

Shape 116   Lamp base/vase

Designer: Mr. Symcox c.1933
Issued: c.1934 - by 1940
Size: 7", 17.8 cm
Colour: 1. Assorted decorations - satin matt
             2. White - matt

Market	Range
U.S.A.	$35.00 - 60.00
Canada	$50.00 - 90.00
U.K.	£20.00 - 35.00

Shape 135   Lamp base/vase

Designer: Unknown
Issued: c.1934 - by 1940
Height :   5 ½", 14 cm
Colour: 1. Assorted decorations - satin matt
             2 White - matt

Market	Range
U.S.A.	$35.00 - 60.00
Canada	$50.00 - 90.00
U.K.	£20.00 - 35.00

Shape 143   Lamp base/vase

Designer:	Albert Hallam c.1934
Issued:	c.1934 - by 1940
Height:	9", 22.9 cm
Colour:	1. Assorted decorations - satin matt
	2. White - matt

Market	Range
U.S.A.	$60.00 - 80.00
Canada	$90.00 - 125.00
U.K.	£35.00 - 50.00

Shape 144   Lamp base/vase

Designer:	Albert Hallam c.1934
Issued:	c.1934 - by 1940
Height :	10 ¾", 27.8 cm
Colour:	1. Assorted decorations - satin matt
	2. White - matt

Market	Range
U.S.A.	$60.00 - 80.00
Canada	$90.00 - 125.00
U.K.	£35.00 - 50.00

Shape 272   Lamp base with clock

Designer:	Mr. Symcox c.1934
Issued:	c.1934 - by 1940
Height:	8 ¾", 22.2 cm
Colour:	1. Assorted decorations - satin matt
	2. White - matt

Market	Range
U.S.A.	$125.00 - 165.00
Canada	$175.00 - 250.00
U.K.	£75.00 - 100.00

Shape 275   Lamp

Designer:	Mr. Symcox c.1934
Issued:	c.1934 - by 1940
Size:	Unknown
Colour:	1. Assorted decorations - satin matt
	2. White - matt

Market	Range
U.S.A.	$60.00 - 80.00
Canada	$90.00 - 125.00
U.K.	£35.00 - 50.00

Shape 276 **Lamp**

Designer:	Mr. Symcox c.1934
Issued:	c.1934 - by 1940
Size:	7 ¼", 18.4 cm
Colour:	1. Assorted decorations - satin matt
	2. White - matt

Market	Range
U.S.A.	$45.00 - 75.00
Canada	$60.00 - 100.00
U.K.	£25.00 - 45.00

Shape 477 **Lamp**

Designer:	Mr. Symcox in 1937
Issued:	1937 - by 1940
Size:	Unknown
Colour:	1. Assorted decorations - satin matt
	2. White - matt

Market	Range
U.S.A.	$35.00 - 60.00
Canada	$50.00 - 90.00
U.K.	£20.00 - 35.00

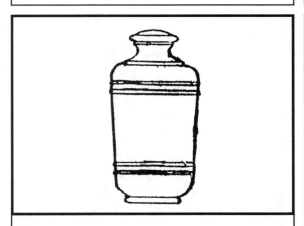

Shape 666 **Lamp**

Designer:	Mr. Symcox in 1938
Issued:	1938 - by 1940
Size:	Unknown
Colour:	1. Assorted decorations - satin matt
	2. White - matt

Market	Range
U.S.A.	$35.00 - 60.00
Canada	$50.00 - 90.00
U.K.	£20.00 - 35.00

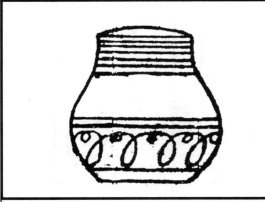

Shape 703 **Lamp base/vase**

Designer:	Albert Hallam in 1939
Issued:	1939 - by 1940
Size:	Unknown
Colour:	1. Assorted decorations - satin matt
	2. White - matt

Market	Range
U.S.A.	$35.00 - 60.00
Canada	$50.00 - 90.00
U.K.	£20.00 - 35.00

Shape 1158 Lamp base

Designer: Albert Hallam, JamesHayward in 1949
Issued: 1949 - by 1954
Size: Unknown
Colour: 1. Assorted decorations - satin matt
              2. White - matt

Market	Range
U.S.A.	$50.00 - 80.00
Canada	$75.00 - 125.00
U.K.	£30.00 - 50.00

Shape 1231 Etched lamp base

Designer: Albert Hallam, JamesHayward in 1952
Issued: 1952 - 1954
Size: Unknown
Colour: 1. Assorted decorations - satin matt
              2. White - matt

Market	Range
U.S.A.	$50.00 - 80.00
Canada	$75.00 - 125.00
U.K.	£30.00 - 50.00

Shape 1459/1/2 Lamp

Designer: Albert Hallam in 1956
Issued: 1957 - by 1963
Size: Unknown
Colour: 1. Assorted decorations - satin matt
              2. White - matt

Market	Range
U.S.A.	$35.00 - 60.00
Canada	$50.00 - 90.00
U.K.	£20.00 - 35.00

Note: Lamp was taken from vase shape 1432.

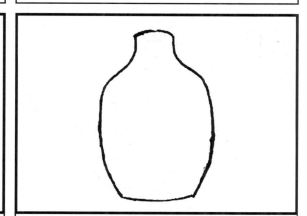

Shape 1509 Lamp

Designer: Colin Melbourne in 1956
Issued: 1957 - by 1963
Height: 6 ½″, 16.5 cm
Colour: 1. Assorted decorations - satin matt
              2. White - matt

Market	Range
U.S.A.	$35.00 - 60.00
Canada	$50.00 - 90.00
U.K.	£20.00 - 35.00

Note: Lamp converted from CM Series shape 1399.

Shape 1531 Peter Rabbit tree-lamp base

Designer: Albert Hallam, James Hayward in 1958
Issued: 1958 - 1969
Height :   7", 17.8 cm
Colour: Browns and greens - gloss

Description	U.S. $	Can. $	U.K. £
Peter Rabbit base	100.00	160.00	65.00

Note: This item was supplied with or without a Beatrix
Potter figure attached at the base of the tree trunk.

**Shape 1544 Lamp - barrel with tap
(sherry, port or whisky)**

Designer: Albert Hallam in 1958
Issued: 1958 - by 1962
Height: 4 ½", 11.9 cm
Colour: Red or green on white background - gloss

Description	U.S. $	Can. $	U.K. £
Barrel lamp	60.00	90.00	35.00

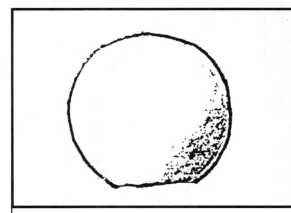

Shape 1808 Lamp

Designer: Albert Hallam in 1962
Issued: 1962 - unknown
Size: Unknown
Colour: 1. Assorted decorations - satin matt
             2. White - matt

Market	Range
U.S.A.	$15.00 - 30.00
Canada	$25.00 - 50.00
U.K.	£10.00 - 20.00

Shape 1850 Double Diamond lamp

Designer: Albert Hallam in 1962
Issued: Unknown
Size: 6", 15 cm
Colour: Unknown - gloss

Description	U.S. $	Can. $	U.K. £
Double Diamond	60.00	90.00	35.00

Note: Special commission.

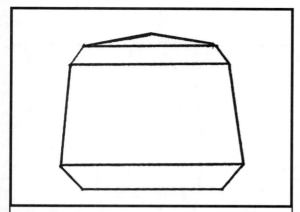

Shape 1984 Rothmans lamp

Designer: Albert Hallam in 1962
Issued: Unknown
Size: 4 ½", 11.9 cm
Colour: Unknown - gloss

Description	U.S. $	Can. $	U.K. £
Rothmans	50.00	75.00	30.00

Note: Special commission.

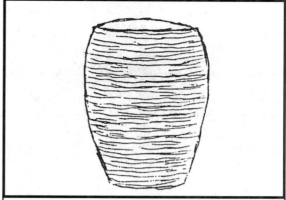

Shape 2009 Skol lamp

Designer: Albert Hallam in 1965
Issued: Unknown
Size: 6", 15 cm
Colour: Unknown - gloss

Description	U.S. $	Can. $	U.K. £
Skol	50.00	75.00	30.00

Note: Special commission.

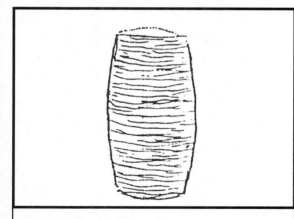

Shape 2010 Double Diamond lamp

Designer: Albert Hallam in 1965
Issued: Unknown
Size: 5 ½", 14 cm
Colour: Unknown - gloss

Description	U.S. $	Can. $	U.K. £
Double Diamond	50.00	75.00	30.00

Note: Special commission.

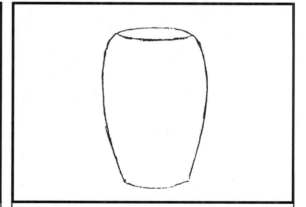

Shape 2011 Skol lamp

Designer: Albert Hallam in 1965
Issued: Unknown
Size: 6", 15 cm
Colour: Unknown - gloss

Description	U.S. $	Can. $	U.K. £
Skol	50.00	75.00	30.00

Note: Special commission.

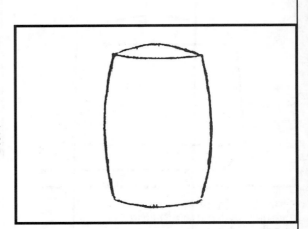

Shape 2018 Double Diamond lamp

Designer:	Albert Hallam in 1965
Issued:	Unknown
Size:	5 ½", 14 cm
Colour:	Unknown - gloss

Description	U.S. $	Can. $	U.K. £
Double Diamond	50.00	75.00	30.00

Note: Special commission.

Note: Price ranges are retail market indicators of prices for models under the following conditions:
- Lower end of range = price of monochrome models
- Higher end of range = price of multicoloured models

LIQUOR FLASKS AND CONTAINERS

The use of earthenware and china items to promote their products has long been the practice of the brewing, distilling and tobacco trades, and Beswick supplied a variety of items for this purpose during a period of over twenty years. Nineteen of them, mainly whisky flasks are listed here. In addition Beswick produced many other whisky containers, in the shape of animals and birds, and information on these can be obtained from *The Charlton Standard Catalogue of Beswick Animals*.

Other Beswick products used as promotional lines appear elsewhere in this book, and are listed in the appropriate sections.

Shape 1517 Double Diamond man container

Designer: Albert Hallam, James Hayward in 1958
Issued: c.1958
Height: 8", 20.3 cm
Colour: Black hat and suit, white shirt and green tie, striped trousers - gloss

Colour	U.S. $	Can. $	U.K. £
Black, white and green	300.00	450.00	175.00

Note: The hat is attached by a cork. Special commission.

Shape 1587 Barrel, container for port

Designer: Albert Hallam in 1959
Issued: 1959 - unknown
Size: 4 ¼", 10.8 cm
Colour: 1. Green and white - gloss
2. Maroon and white - gloss

Colour	U.S. $	Can. $	U.K. £
1. Green and white	40.00	60.00	25.00
2. Maroon and white	40.00	60.00	25.00

Note: Also available with "Sherry" or "Whisky."

Shape 1598 Barrel, container for sherry

Designer: Albert Hallam in 1959
Issued: 1959 - unknown
Width: 5 ¼" x 5 ¼", 13.3 x 13.3 cm
Colour: 1. Green and white - gloss
2 Maroon and white - gloss

Colour	U.S. $	Can. $	U.K. £
1. Green and white	40.00	60.00	25.00
2. Maroon and white	40.00	60.00	25.00

Note: Also available with "Port" or "Whisky."

Shape 1820 Barrel, Beneagles scotch whisky

Designer: Albert Hallam in 1962
Issued: 1962 - 1986
Height: 2", 5 cm
Colour: Brown - gloss

Colour	U.S. $	Can. $	U.K. £
Brown	8.00	15.00	5.00

Note: Special commission for Peter Thompson (Perth) Ltd.

Shape 1829 The Sportsman's,
Catto's scotch whisky flask

Designer: Mr. Folkard in 1962
Height: 11 ½", 29.2 cm
Colour: Green jacket and maroon waistcoat with
            yellow stripes, white trousers - gloss

Colour	U.S. $	Can. $	U.K. £
Green, maroon, yellow	300.00	450.00	175.00

Note: Special commission.

Shape 2033 Fisherman's Beneagles scotch whisky flask

Designer: Albert Hallam in 1965
Issued: c.1965
Height: 3 ¾", 9.5 cm
Colour: Blue - gloss

Colour	U.S. $	Can. $	U.K. £
Blue	25.00	35.00	15.00

Note: Special commission for Peter Thompson (Perth) Ltd.

Shape 2056 Pheasant, Beneagles scotch whisky flask

Designer: Albert Hallam in 1966
Issued: c.1966
Height: 3 ½", 8.9 cm
Colour: Blue - gloss

Colour	U.S. $	Can. $	U.K. £
Blue	25.00	35.00	15.00

Note: Replaced by shape 2208 in 1968. Special
commission for Peter Thompson (Perth) Ltd.

Shape 2057 Pike, Beneagles scotch whisky flask

Designer:	Albert Hallam in 1966
Issued:	c.1966
Height::	3 ½", 8.9 cm
Colour:	Unknown - gloss

Colour	U.S. $	Can. $	U.K. £
Unknown	25.00	35.00	15.00

Note: Replaced by Shape 2207 in 1968. Special commission for Peter Thompson (Perth) Ltd.

Shape 2058 Deer, Beneagles scotch whisky flask

Designer:	Albert Hallam in 1966
Issued:	c.1966
Height:	3 ½", 8.9 cm
Colour:	Green - gloss

Colour	U.S. $	Can. $	U.K. £
Green	25.00	35.00	15.00

Note: Replaced by Shape 2206 in 1968. Special commission for Peter Thompson (Perth) Ltd.

Shape 2076 Robert Burns cottage, Beneagles scotch whisky flask

Designer	Albert Hallam in 1966
Issued:	c.1966
Length:	3 ½", 8.9 cm
Colour:	Blue-grey - gloss

Colour	U.S. $	Can. $	U.K. £
Blue-grey	25.00	35.00	15.00

Note: Special commission for Peter Thompson (Perth) Ltd.

Shape 2077 Edinburgh Castle, Beneagles scotch whisky flask

Designer:	Albert Hallam in 1966
Isued:	c.1956
Length:	3 ½", 8.9 cm
Colour:	Olive-green - gloss

Colour	U.S. $	Can. $	U.K. £
Olive-green	25.00	35.00	15.00

Note: Special commission for Peter Thompson (Perth) Ltd.

Shape 2180 Tower Bridge,
 Beneagles scotch whisky flask

Designer: Albert Hallam in 1968
Issued: c.1968
Length: 3 ½", 8.9 cm
Colour: Blue - gloss

Colour	U.S. $	Can. $	U.K. £
Blue	25.00	35.00	15.00

Note: Special commission for Peter Thompson (Perth) Ltd.

Shape 2185 Arundel castle flask

Designer: Albert Hallam in 1968
Issued: c.1968
Height: 4 ½", 11.9 cm
Colour: Unknown

Colour	U.S. $	Can. $	U.K. £
Unknown	25.00	35.00	15.00

Note: Special commission for Merrydown Cider.

Shape 2206 Deer flask, Beneagles scotch whisky

Designer: Albert Hallam in 1966. Re-modelled
             by Graham Tongue in 1968
Issued: c.1968
Height: 3", 7.6 cm
Colour: Green - gloss

Colour	U.S. $	Can. $	U.K. £
Green	25.00	35.00	15.00

Note: Replaced shape 2058. Special commission for
 Peter Thompson (Perth) Ltd.

Shape 2207 Trout flask, Beneagles scotch whisky

Designer: Albert Hallam in 1966. Re-modelled by
             Graham Tongue in 1968
Issued: c.1968
Height: 3", 7.6 cm
Colour: Blue - gloss

Colour	U.S. $	Can. $	U.K. £
Blue	25.00	35.00	15.00

Note: Replaced shape 2057. Special commission for
 Peter Thompson (Perth) Ltd.

Shape 2208 Pheasant flask, Beneagles scotch whisky

Designer:	Albert Hallam in 1966. Re-modelled by Graham Tongue in 1968
Issued:	c.1968
Height:	3", 7.6 cm
Colour:	Blue - gloss

Colour	U.S. $	Can. $	U.K. £
Blue	25.00	35.00	15.00

Note: Replaced shape 2056. Special commission for Peter Thompson (Perth) Ltd.

Shape 2318 Golf ball, Beneagles scotch whisky flask

Designer:	Graham Tongue in 1970
Issued:	c.1970
Diameter:	1 ¼", 3.1 cm
Colour:	White with red lettering - gloss

Colour	U.S. $	Can. $	U.K. £
White with red lettering	25.00	35.00	15.00

Note: Special commission for Peter Thompson (Perth) Ltd.

Shape 2349 Robert Burns,
Beneagles scotch whisky flask

Designer:	Albert Hallam in 1970
Issued:	c.1970
Height :	4", 10.1 cm
Colour:	Unknown

Colour	U.S. $	Can. $	U.K. £
Robert Burns flask	150.00	200.00	85.00

Note: Special commission for Peter Thompson (Perth) Ltd.

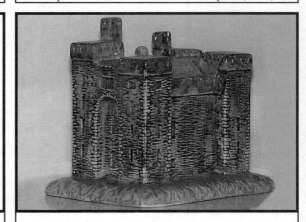

Shape 2670 Bunratty castle, flask

Designer:	Mr. Lyttleton in 1980
Issued:	c.1980
Height:	6", 15 cm
Colour:	Grey castle with green grass - gloss

Colour	U.S. $	Can. $	U.K. £
Grey and green	40.00	60.00	25.00

MUGS, BEAKERS AND TANKARDS

Forty-three shapes make up this group, which were produced between about 1933 and 1970.

Eight were Royal Commemoratives and although Edward's Coronation did not take place, surprisingly some shapes have been found. The twelve Christmas Carol Tankards are the most detailed in this group both in the modelling and the decoration, where many colours were used to illustrate the scenes from the book by Charles Dickens.

The three wartime mugs (numbers 735, 736 and 737) are very unusual and are also very rare. The Nursery Ware with coloured transfer prints are very attractive and we have listed the whole series at the beginning of the Tableware Section.

Shape 205   Beaker

Designer: Albert Hallam c.1933
Issued: c.1933 - by 1954
Size: Unknown
Colour: 1. Assorted decorations - satin matt
             2. White - matt

Colour	U.S. $	Can. $	U.K. £
1. Assorted decorations	15.00	25.00	10.00
2. White	10.00	15.00	5.00

Shape 445   Edward VIII Musical Coronation tankard

Designer: Mr. Roscoe in 1936
Issued: Not issued
Size: 5", 12.7 cm
Colour: Ivory glaze embossed

Description	U.S. $	Can. $	U.K. £
Musical jug		Not issued.	

Note: Although not issued, several pieces are known.

Shape 446   Edward VIII Coronation mug

Designer: Mr. Owen in 1936
Issued: Not issued
Size: 3 ½", 8.9 cm
Colour: Ivory glaze embossed

Description	U.S. $	Can. $	U.K. £
Edward VIII Coronation mug		Not issued	

Note: Although not issued, several pieces are known.

Photograph not
available
at press time

Shape 461   George VI Musical Coronation tankard

Designer: Unknown in 1937
Issued: 1937 - 1937
Size: 5", 12.7 cm
Colour: Ivory glaze embossed

Description	U.S. $	Can. $	U.K. £
Musical jug	165.00	250.00	100.00

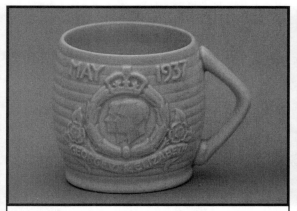

Shape 462   George VI Coronation mug

Designer: Unknown in 1937
Issued: 1937 - 1937
Size: 3 ½", 8.9 cm
Colour: Ivory glaze embossed

Description	U.S. $	Can. $	U.K. £
George VI Coronation mug	50.00	75.00	30.00

Shape 735   Army "Old Bill," mug

Designer: Mr. Watkin in 1939
Issued: 1939 - by 1954
Size: 5", 12.7 cm
Colour: Flesh tones, khaki cap - gloss

Description	U.S. $	Can. $	U.K. £
"Old Bill" mug	550.00	675.00	250.00

Note: Set of three with shape nos 736 and 737.

Shape 736   Navy "HMS Wink," mug

Designer: Mr. Watkin in 1939
Issued: 1939 - by 1954
Size: 5", 12.7 cm
Colour: Flesh tones, brown hair, blue and white
             hat - gloss

Description	U.S. $	Can. $	U.K. £
"HMS Wink" mug	500.00	650.00	250.00

Note: Set of three with shape nos. 735 and 737.

Shape 737   Air Force, mug

Designer: Mr. Watkin in 1939
Issued: 1939 - by 1954
Size   5", 12.7 cm
Colour: Flesh tones, dark brown hair, blue hat - gloss

Description	U.S. $	Can. $	U.K. £
Air Force mug	450.00	500.00	250.00

Note: Set of three with shape nos. 735 and 736.

Shape 956/1/2/3 Tankard

Designer:	Albert Hallam in 1941
Issued:	1939 - by 1954
Size :	Unknown
Colour:	1. Assorted decorations - satin matt
	2. White - matt

Colour	U.S. $	Can. $	U.K. £
1. Assorted decorations	25.00	35.00	15.00
2. White	15.00	25.00	10.00

Note: Tankard is pair with jug shape 955, see page 219.

First Version

Second Version

Shape 987/1 Tankard

Designer:	Unknown in 1942
Issued:	1942 - by 1954
Re-issued:	1966 - by 1971
Size:	1. 18 oz — 4", 10.1 cm
	2. 12 oz — 3 ½", 8.9 cm
Colour:	1. Transfer print on white - gloss
	2. Assorted decorations - matt glaze
	3. Copper - lustre

Description	U.S. $	Can. $	U.K. £
1. 18 oz	25.00	35.00	15.00
2. 12 oz	15.00	25.00	10.00

Shape 987/3 Queen Elizabeth Coronation tankard

Designer:	Unknown in 1942
Issued:	1953 - 1953
Height:	3 ¾", 9.5 cm
Colour:	Transfer print on white

Description	U.S. $	Can. $	U.K. £
Coronation tankard	30.00	50.00	20.00

Shape 988 Mug, Newhall

Designer:	Unknown
Issued:	1942 - by 1954
Height:	Unknown
Colour:	1. Assorted decorations - satin matt
	2. White - matt

Colour	U.S. $	Can. $	U.K. £
1. Assorted decorations	15.00	25.00	10.00
2. White	8.00	12.00	5.00

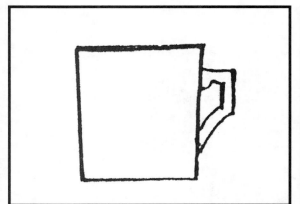

Shape 1056 Mug

Designer:	Unknown
Issued:	1946
Size:	Unknown
Colour:	Unknown - gloss

Colour	U.S. $	Can. $	U.K. £
Unknown	15.00	25.00	10.00

Note: Special commission for The Ministry of Works in 1946.

Shape 1127 Falstaff mug

Designer:	Arthur Gredington, Albert Hallam in 1948
Issued:	1948 - 1972
Size:	4", 10.1 cm
Colour:	Green, orange and blue - gloss
Series:	Shakespeare

Description	U.S. $	Can. $	U.K. £
Falstaff mug	90.00	90.00	45.00

Note: Set of four with shape nos. 1147, 1215, 1368.

Shape 1147 Hamlet mug			
Designer:	Arthur Gredington in 1949		
Issued:	1949 - 1972		
Size:	4 ¼", 10.8 cm		
Colour:	Browns, greens, black and yellow - gloss		
Series:	Shakespeare		

Description	U.S. $	Can. $	U.K. £
Hamlet mug	100.00	100.00	45.00

Note: Set of four with shape nos. 1127, 1215, 1368.

Shape 1215 Juliet mug			
Designer:	Arthur Gredington, Albert Hallam in 1951		
Issued:	1951 - 1972		
Size:	4", 10.1 cm		
Colour:	Browns, greens, maroon and blue - gloss		
Series:	Shakespeare		

Description	U.S. $	Can. $	U.K. £
Juliet mug	90.00	90.00	45.00

Note: Set of four with shape nos. 1127, 1215, 1368.

Shape 1250 Elizabeth II Federation Coronation mug			
Designer:	Unknown in 1952		
Issued:	1953 - 1953		
Height:	3 ¼", 8.3 cm		
Colour:	Colour transfer on white background - gloss		

Description	U.S. $	Can. $	U.K. £
Coronation mug	25.00	35.00	15.00

Shape 1251 Elizabeth II Federation Coronation beaker			
Designer:	Unknown in 1952		
Issued:	1953 - 1953		
Height :	4 ¼", 10.8 cm		
Colour:	Colour transfer on white background - gloss		

Description	U.S. $	Can. $	U.K. £
Coronation beaker	25.00	35.00	15.00

Shape 1252 Elizabeth II Coronation beaker

Designer:	Albert Hallam, James Hayward in 1952
Issued:	1953 - 1953
Height:	3 ½", 8.9 cm
Colour:	Ivory glaze embossed

Description	U.S. $	Can. $	U.K. £
Coronation beaker	25.00	35.00	15.00

Shape 1286 Baby mug with one handle

Shape 1286T Baby mug with two handles

Shape 1286   Baby mug with one handle
Shape 1286T   Baby mug with two handles

Designer:	Albert Hallam in 1953
Issued:	See below
Height:	Unknown
Colour:	Transfer print on white background - gloss

Shape No.	Description	Issued	U.S. $	Can. $	U.K. £
1286/1a	Disney image, Bambi	1954 - 1959	30.00	50.00	20.00
1286/1b	Disney image, Thumper	1954 - 1959	30.00	50.00	20.00
1286/2	Nursery rhyme images	1960 - 1963	15.00	25.00	10.00
1286/3	Jack and Jill comic series	1964 - 1970	15.00	25.00	10.00
1286T/1a	Disney image, Bambi	1954 - 1959	30.00	50.00	20.00
1286T/1b	Disney image, Thumper	1954 - 1959	30.00	50.00	20.00
1286T/2	Nursery rhyme images	1960 - 1963	15.00	25.00	10.00
1286T/3	Jack and Jill comic series	1964 - 1970	15.00	25.00	10.00

Shape 1368 Midsummer Night's Dream mug

Designer:	Albert Hallam, Mr. Orwell in 1955
Issued:	1951 - 1972
Size:	4 ¼", 10.8 cm
Colour:	Greens, browns, blue and maroon - gloss
Series:	Shakespeare

Description	U.S. $	Can. $	U.K. £
Midsummer Night's Dream mug	150.00	175.00	75.00

Note: Set of four with shape nos. 1127, 1147, 1215.

Shape 1596 Robert Burns, Mug

Designer:	Albert Hallam, James Hayward in 1959
Issued:	1959 - 1966
Height:	4 ½", 11.9 cm
Colour:	1. Multi-coloured - gloss
	2. White - gloss

Colour	U.S. $	Can. $	U.K. £
1. Multi-coloured	200.00	200.00	95.00
2. White	150.00	150.00	75.00

Shape 1669 Nursery ware beaker

Designer:	Albert Hallam in 1960
Issued:	1. 1960 - 1963 2. 1964 - by 1966
Size:	Unknown
Colour:	1. Transfer print of nursery rhyme character on white background - gloss
	2. Transfer print of Jack and Jill comic character on white background - gloss

Description	U.S. $	Can. $	U.K. £
1. Nursery rhyme character	25.00	45.00	15.00
2. Jack and Jill comic series	25.00	45.00	15.00

Shape 1670 Nursery ware mug

Designer:	Albert Hallam in 1960
Issued:	1. 1960 - 1963 2. 1964 - 1970
Size:	Unknown
Colour:	1. Transfer print of nursery rhyme character on white background - gloss
	2. Transfer print of Jack and Jill comic character on white background - gloss

Description	U.S. $	Can. $	U.K. £
1. Nursery rhyme character	25.00	45.00	15.00
2. Jack and Jill comic series	25.00	45.00	15.00

Shape 1821 Tankard, one pint

Designer: Harry Sales in 1962
Issued: 1963 - 1971
Height :   5 ¼", 13.3 cm
Colour: 1. Solid colours - gloss
          2. White or black - matt
          3. Copper - lustre

Colour	U.S. $	Can. $	U.K. £
1. Solid colours	15.00	20.00	10.00
2. White or black	15.00	20.00	10.00
3. Copper	15.00	20.00	10.00

Shape 1979 Beaker

Designer: Albert Hallam in 1964
Issued: 1964 - 1970
Size: 3 ¾", 9.5 cm
Colour :   1. Transfer of characters from Jack and
             Jill comic - gloss
          2. Trendsetter series - gloss (illustrated)

Description	U.S. $	Can. $	U.K. £
1. Jack and Jill series	15.00	20.00	10.00
2. Trendsetter series	15.00	20.00	10.00

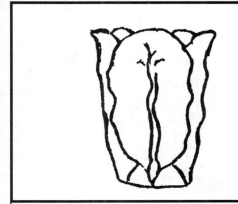

Shape 2044 Beaker

Designer: Albert Hallam in 1965
Issued: Unknown
Height: 4", 10.1 cm
Colour: 1. Solid colours - gloss
          2. White or black - matt
          3. Copper - lustre

Colour	U.S. $	Can. $	U.K. £
1. Solid colours	15.00	20.00	10.00
2. White or black	15.00	20.00	10.00
3. Copper	15.00	20.00	10.00

Shape 2073 Tankard

Designer: Graham Tongue in 1966
Issued: 1967 - 1972
Height :   5 ½", 14 cm
Colour: 1. Solid colours - gloss
          2. White or black - matt
          3. Copper - lustre

Colour	U.S. $	Can. $	U.K. £
1. Solid colours	15.00	20.00	10.00
2. White or black	15.00	20.00	10.00
3. Copper	15.00	20.00	10.00

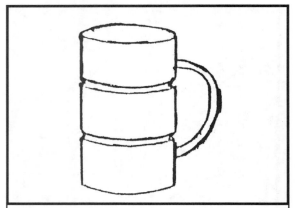

Shape 2125/ Pint tankard
Shape 2126 Half-pint tankard

Designer:	Graham Tongue in 1967
Issued:	c.1967
Height:	1. Shape 2125 — 5 ½", 14.0 cm
	2. Shape 2126 — 4 ½", 11.9 cm
Colour:	1. Solid colours - glosss
	2. White or black - matt
	3. Copper - lustre

Description	U.S. $	Can. $	U.K. £
Pint tankard	15.00	20.00	10.00
Half-pint tankard	15.00	20.00	10.00

Shape 2165/ Pint tankard
Shape 2166 Half-pint tankard

Designer:	Graham Tongue in 1967
Issued:	c.1967
Height:	1. Shape 2165 — 5", 12.7 cm
	2. Shape 2166 — 4 ½", 11.9 cm
Colour:	1. Solid colours - gloss
	2. White or black - matt
	3. Copper - lustre

Description	U.S. $	Can. $	U.K. £
Pint tankard	15.00	20.00	10.00
Half-pint tankard	15.00	20.00	10.00

Shape 2310 Shaving mug

Designer:	Graham Tongue in 1970
Issued:	c.1970
Height:	3 ½", 8.9 cm
Colour:	1. Solid colours - gloss
	2. White or black - matt
	3. Copper - lustre

Colour	U.S. $	Can. $	U.K. £
1. Solid colours	15.00	20.00	10.00
2. White or black	15.00	20.00	10.00
3. Copper	15.00	20.00	10.00

Shape 2351 Yule 1971, Latama Tankard
"Bob Cratchit and Scrooge"

Designer:	Graham Tongue in 1971
Issued:	1971 - 1971
Height:	5", 12.7 cm
Colour:	Multi-coloured - gloss
Series:	Christmas Carol Tankards

Description	U.S.$	Can. $	U.K.£
Yule 1971	60.00	100.00	40.00

Shape 2375 Yule 1972 - Latama Tankard
"The Carol Singers"

Designer:	Albert Hallam in 1971
Issued:	1972 - 1972
Height:	5", 12.7 cm
Colour:	Multi-coloured - gloss
Series:	Christmas Carol Tankards

Description	U.S.$	Can.$	U.K.£
Yule 1972	60.00	100.00	40.00

Shape 2423 Yule 1973 - Latama Tankard, "Solicitation"

Designer:	Albert Hallam in 1972
Issued:	1973 - 1973
Height :	5", 12.7 cm
Colour:	Multi-coloured - gloss
Series:	Christmas Carol Tankards

Description	U.S.$	Can.$	U.K.£
Yule 1973	60.00	100.00	40.00

Shape 2445 Yule 1974 - Latama Tankard
"The Ghost of Marley"

Designer:	Albert Hallam in 1973
Issued:	1974 - 1974
Height:	5", 12.7 cm
Colour:	Multi-coloured - gloss
Series:	Christmas Carol Tankards

Description	U.S.$	Can.$	U.K.£
Yule 1974	60.00	100.00	40.00

Shape 2523 Yule 1975 - Latama Tankard
"The Ghost of Christmas Past"

Designer:	Graham Tongue in 1974
Issued:	1975 - 1975
Height :	5", 12.7 cm
Colour:	Multi-coloured - gloss
Series:	Christmas Carol Tankards

Description	U.S.$	Can.$	U.K.£
Yule 1975	60.00	100.00	40.00

**Shape 2539 Yule 1976, Latama Tankard
            "The Ghost of Christmas Present"**

Designer:	Mr. Plant, Mr. Lyttleton in 1975
Issued:	1976 - 1976
Height:	5", 12.7 cm
Colour:	Multi-coloured - gloss
Series:	Christmas Carol Tankards

Description	U.S.$	Can.$	U.K.£
Yule 1976	60.00	100.00	40.00

**Shape 2568 Yule 1977, Latama Tankard
            "The Ghost of Christmas Present"**

Designer:	Mr. Plant, Mr. Lyttleton,
	Graham Tongue in 1976
Issued:	1977 - 1977
Height :	5", 12.7 cm
Colour:	Multi-coloured - gloss
Series:	Christmas Carol Tankards

Description	U.S.$	Can.$	U.K.£
Yule 1977	60.00	100.00	40.00

**Shape 2599 Yule 1978, Latama Tankard
            "The Ghost of Christmas Present"**

Designer:	Mr. Lyttleton in 1977
Issued:	1978 - 1978
Height:	5", 12.7 cm
Colour:	Multi-coloured - gloss
Series:	Christmas Carol Tankards

Description	U.S.$	Can.$	U.K.£
Yule 1978	60.00	100.00	40.00

**Shape 2624 Yule 1979, Latama Tankard
            "The Ghost of Christmas Future"**

Designer:	Mr. Lyttleton in 1978
Issued:	1979 - 1979
Height:	5", 12.7 cm
Colour:	Multi-coloured - gloss
Series:	Christmas Carol Tankards

Description	U.S.$	Can.$	U.K.£
Yule 1979	60.00	100.00	40.00

**Shape 2657 Yule 1980, Latama Tankard
"Scrooge sees his own Grave"**

Designer:	Mr. Lyttleton in 1979
Issued:	1980 - 1980
Height:	5", 12.7 cm
Colour:	Multi-coloured - gloss
Series:	Christmas Carol Tankards

Desription	U.S.$	Can.$	U.K.£
Yule 1980	60.00	100.00	40.00

**Shape 2692 Yule 1981, Latama Tankard
"Scrooge goes to Church"**

Designer:	Mr. Lyttleton in 1980
Issued:	1981 - 1981
Height :	5", 12.7 cm
Colour:	Multi-coloured - gloss
Series:	Christmas Carol Tankards

Description	U.S.$	Can.$	U.K.£
Yule 1981	60.00	100.00	40.00

Photograph not
available
at press time

**Shape 2764 Yule 1982 - Latama Tankard
"Christmas with Bob Cratchit"**

Designer:	Mr. Lyttleton in 1981
Issued:	1982 - 1982
Height:	5", 12.7 cm
Colour:	Multi-coloured - gloss
Series:	Christmas Carol Tankards

Description	U.S.$	Can.$	U.K.£
Yule 1982	100.00	150.00	60.00

Shape 1273 — Teapot

Shape 1273 — Tea Cup

TABLEWARE

Tableware was produced over many years in the Marie, Eton, Contemporary and Orbit shapes with the decorations often overlapping the shapes. Often the same decoration was applied to two shapes e.g. Contemporary and Orbit, and even in some cases, to all four shapes. We have used the decoration title in the listing to denote the patterns and colours used for the decorations, which in all cases had a gloss finish.

Beswick also produced Souvenir Ware e.g. Souvenir of Scotland with a Piper (see shape 2120 on page 284), Souvenir of Ireland with an Irish Harp and/or a Spinning Wheel and Present from Morecombe with sailing ships.

In addition to the shapes listed in this section there were two mugs (shape 1286 on page 247 and shape 1670 on page 248) and one beaker (shape 1669 on page 248), details of these are in the Mugs, Beakers and Tankards Section, but included here is the Childrens Tea Set (Shape 1273).

The following shapes have not been included in the listing as it is possible that they were never put into full commercial production - 1619 (Butter), 1621 (Covered Scallop), 1622 (Gravy Boat), 1679 (Mustard), 1698 (Salt), 1699 (Pepper), 1920 (Gravy Boat), 1921 (Sugar), 1961 (Sugar) and 1971 (Cheese).

GILT EDGES

The transfer decorations mostly had gilt edges, although examples have been found with silver or coloured rims, and some with no rim colouring at all. They included:

A cottage scene	Hazelnut
Red rose pattern	Poppies
Yellow rose pattern	Blue flowers
Blue rose pattern	Crinoline ladies
Yellow flowers	Ladies in long dresses
Red and white flowers	Ballerinas
Fruit pattern (e.g. oranges and lemons)	Dogs

NURSERY WARE

Nursery ware, as the name suggests, was for the use of children. This ware consisted of three groups all in a light ivory coloured background and gloss finish:

Walt Disney	Coloured transfer prints of Disney characters. Issued 1954 - 1959.
Nursery	Coloured transfer prints of Nursery Rhyme characters. Issued 1960 - 1963.
Jack and Jill	Coloured transfer prints of characters from the comic Jack and Jill. Issued 1964 - 1970.

TRANSFER DESIGNS

The Contemporary shaped tableware was decorated with "transfer designs" on a white background (with two exceptions), brief descriptions of the patterns are:

Ballet	Blue and pink dress, cream background
Circus	Blue horse with bare-back rider
Dancing Days/Frolic	Boy and girl dancing to the music of a barrel organ complete with monkey. Multicoloured scene on a white or cream background.
Dawn Chorus	Birds are blue, black and pink
Greenfingers	Willow tree, multi-coloured scene
Happy Morn	Yellow sun with multicoloured scene
Hors d'Oeuvre	Multicoloured decoration - see Section 1 Series Ware (Hors D'Oeuvres) for details.
Horses	Grey and black horses. Rims red or grey
Mexican Madness	Yellow hat with coloured flowers
Moonlight	Blue bulrushes
Pavlova	Blue and pink dress
Picnic	Oranges on tree, multi-coloured scene

A boxed set was made up of Shape No.1445 together with two of Shape No.1446 and two of Shape No.1447.

THE TREND-SETTERS

"Trend-Setters" was the advertising slogan used for the series of tableware, which included the decorations known as Apollo, Lunar, Metric and Verona. These sets had their shapes in common, had transfer prints on to a white background and were in a gloss finish, but, of course, the design for each set was individual. They were issued 1966 - 1970.

Apollo	Blue design with mustard foliage on brown stems with lids and bases in solid blue.
Lunar	The shape in this series had a brown and mustard design with lids and bases in solid brown or green.
Metric	As the name suggests this was a geometric design and the colours were two shades of brown with mustard. The lids and bases were solid brown.
Verona	A foliage pattern with mustard and brown flowers, green leaves and solid brown or green lids and bases. This decoration has also been seen with a bird incorporated in the design.

PLAIN COLOURS

The shapes used for the "trend-setters" series were also produced in plain colours - green, blue, mink and calypso.

REGAL FLUTED WARE

The sketch shown is of shape 1130 which serves as a guide to the style. Unfortunately, at this time we have no further information on these shapes.

Listed below are the shapes which occur in Regal Fluted ware without prices as all pieces must be considered extremely rare.

Shape 1130 Tall cup

Designer: Albert Hallam
Issued: 1948 - 1952
Colours: Unknown

Shape	Description	Shape	Description
Shape 1130	Tall cup and saucer	Shape 1140	Coffee sugar
Shape 1131	Low cup	Shape 1141	Coffee cream
Shape 1132	Coffee cup and saucer	Shape 1142	Fruit bowl
Shape 1133	Muffin, 4"	Shape 1143	Fruit saucer/oatmeal
Shape 1134	Muffin, 5"	Shape 1144	Sweet dish
Shape 1135	Muffin, 6"	Shape 1174	Teapot
Shape 1136	Muffin, 7"	Shape 1175	Coffee pot
Shape 1137	Bread and butter plate	Shape 1181	Dish
Shape 1138	Sugar	Shape 1213	Oatmeal, small
Shape 1139	Cream	Shape 1229	Bread and butter plate

MARIE

Shape 1161 Tea cup and saucer, Gilt edge design

Shape1165 Plate, Nursery Ware design

Shape 1169 Sugar, Gilt edge design

Shape1170 Cream, Gilt edge design

Shape 1228 Marie bread and butter plate

Shape 2019 Marie plate with flat, wide rim

Shape 2034 Marie plate, large size

Shape 2035 Marie plate, medium size

Designer: Albert Hallam in 1949
except 1208 in 1950, 1228 in 1951,
2019 in 1964, 2034, 2035, 2036 in 1965
Issued: See below
Size: See below

Design: Gilt edge — shapes 1161, 1162, 1163, 1164,
1165, 1166, 1167, 1169, 1170, 1171, 1172, 1173,
1208, 2019, 2034, 2035, 1036
Nursery Ware — shape 1165
Trend-setters and Transfer Designs —
shapes 2019, 2034, 2035, 2036

Shape	Name	Issued	Size	U.S. $	Can. $	U.K.£
1161	Tea cup and saucer	1949 - 1970	Cup — 3", 7.6 cm	10.00	15.00	7.00
			Saucer — 5 ½", 14.0 cm			
1162	Breakfast cup and saucer	1949 - 1970	3 ½", 8.9 cm	15.00	20.00	10.00
1163	Coffee cup and saucer	1949 - unknown	Unknown	15.00	20.00	10.00
1164	Plate	1949 - 1961	6", 15.0 cm	7.50	10.00	5.00
1165	Plate (gilt edge)	1949 - 1961	6 ¾", 17.2 cm	7.50	10.00	5.00
1165	Plate (nursery ware)	1954 - 1963	6 ¾", 17.2 cm	25.00	35.00	15.00
1166	Plate	1949 - 1961	8 ¾", 22.2 cm	10.00	15.00	7.50
1167	Plate	1949 - 1961	9 ¾", 24.7 cm	15.00	20.00	10.00
1169	Sugar bowl	1949 - by 1959	3", 11.9 cm	10.00	15.00	7.50
1170	Cream jug	1949 - by 1959	3 ¼", 8.3 cm	10.00	15.00	7.50
1171	Fruit bowl	1949 - by 1959	Unknown	30.00	45.00	15.00
1172	Fruit saucer/oatmeal	1949 - by 1959	7", 17.8 cm	10.00	15.00	7.50
1173	Oval dish	1949 - by 1959	Unknown	20.00	30.00	10.00
1208	Oatmeal, small	1951 - by 1959	6", 12.7 cm	10.00	15.00	7.50
1228	Bread and butter plate	1952 - by 1959	9 ¾", 24.7 cm	20.00	30.00	10.00
2019	Plate with flat, wide rim	1964 - 1970	9 ¾", 24.7 cm	20.00	30.00	10.00
2034	Plate with flat, wide rim	1965 - 1970	8 ¾", 22.2 cm	20.00	30.00	10.00
2035	Plate with flat, wide rim	1965 - 1970	7 ¾", 19.7 cm	15.00	20.00	8.00
2036	Plate with flat, wide rim	1965 - 1970	6 ¾", 17.2 cm	12.00	15.00	6.00

SHAPE 1273
CHILDREN'S TEA SET

| Designer: | Albert Hallam in 1952 | | Size: | See below | | |
| Issued: | 1953 - 1959 | | Design: | Nursery ware (© Walt Disney) | | |

Shape	Description	Height	Diameter	U.S. $	Can. $	U.K.£
1273	Teapot	3 ¾", 9.5 cm	3 ½", 8.9 cm	80.00	125.00	50.00
1273	Cream	2", 5.0 cm	1 ¾", 4.4 cm	15.00	25.00	10.00
1273	Sugar	1 ½", 3.8 cm	2 ½", 6.4 cm	15.00	25.00	10.00
1273	Cup	1 ¾", 4.4 cm	2", 5.0 cm	12.00	15.00	8.00
1273	Saucer		4 ½", 11.9 cm	12.00	15.00	7.00
1273	Plate		4 ½", 11.9 cm	12.00	15.00	7.00

Note: The first version cup and cream had supported handles.
In 1954 the cup was replaced by shape 1317, and the cream was replaced by shape 1318.

Photograph not
available
at press time

Shape 1285 Baby plate

Designer:	Albert Hallam in 1953
Issued:	1954 - 1970
Diameter:	6 ½", 16.5 cm
Design:	Nursery ware

Description	U.S. $	Can. $	U.K. £
Baby plate	60.00	90.00	35.00

Shape 1303 Baby cup

Designer:	Albert Hallam in 1953
Issued:	1954 - 1970
Size:	Unknown
Design:	Nursery ware

Description	U.S. $	Can. $	U.K. £
Baby cup	12.00	15.00	7.50

Shape 1317 Toy cup

Designer:	Albert Hallam in 1953
Issued:	1954 - 1959
Size:	Unknown
Design:	Nursery ware

Description	U.S. $	Can. $	U.K. £
Toy cup	12.00	15.00	7.00

Note: Shape 1317 replaced the cup in set 1273.

Shape 1318 Toy cream

Designer:	Albert Hallam in 1953
Issued:	1954 - 1959
Size:	Unknown
Design:	Nursery ware

Description	U.S. $	Can. $	U.K. £
Toy cream	12.00	15.00	7.00

Note: Shape 1318 replaced the cream in set 1273.

Shape 1423 Contemporary sugar bowl

Designer: Albert Hallam in 1956
Issued: 1956 - 1961
Diameter: 5", 12.7 cm
Design: Transfer designs

Description	U.S. $	Can. $	U.K. £
Sugar bowl	10.00	15.00	8.00

Shape 1424 Contemporary cream jug

Designer: Albert Hallam in 1956
Issued: 1956 - 1961
Height: 3 ½", 8.9 cm
Design: Transfer designs

Description	U.S. $	Can. $	U.K. £
Cream jug	10.00	15.00	8.00

Shape 1425/A/B Contemporary cup and saucer

Designer: Albert Hallam in 1956
Issued: 1956 - by 1962
Height: 2 ¾", 7.0 cm
Design: Transfer designs

Description	U.S. $	Can. $	U.K. £
1. Angled handle on cup	10.00	15.00	8.00
2. Rounded handle on cup	10.00	15.00	8.00

Note: The bottom of the cup is square.

Shape 1426 Contemporary plate, small size

Designer: Albert Hallam in 1956
Issued: 1956 - 1961
Size: 6 ¾", 17.2 cm
Design: Transfer designs

Description	U.S. $	Can. $	U.K. £
Plate, small	10.00	15.00	6.00

Shape 1427 Contemporary bread and butter plate

Designer: Albert Hallam in 1956
Issued: 1956 - 1961
Diameter: 9 ½", 24 cm
Design: Transfer designs

Description	U.S. $	Can. $	U.K. £
Bread/butter plate	10.00	15.00	8.00

Shape 1428 Contemporary fruit bowl

Designer: Albert Hallam in 1956
Issued: 1956 - 1961
Diameter: 9", 22.9cm
Design: Transfer designs

Description	U.S. $	Can. $	U.K. £
Fruit bowl	15.00	20.00	10.00

Shape 1429 Contemporary fruit saucer

Designer: Albert Hallam in 1956
Issued: 1956 - 1961
Diameter: 6 ½", 16.5 cm
Design: Transfer designs

Description	U.S. $	Can. $	U.K. £
Fruit saucer	10.00	12.00	6.00

Photograph not
available
at press time

Shape 1430 Contemporary TV set

Designer: Albert Hallam in 1956
Issued: 1956 - 1961
Size: Unknown
Design: Transfer designs

Description	U.S. $	Can. $	U.K. £
TV set	25.00	40.00	15.00

Shape 1431 Contemporary teapot,
First version — knob cut-out

Designer:	Albert Hallam in 1956
Issued:	1956 - 1961
Size:	Unknown
Design:	Transfer designs

Description	U.S. $	Can. $	U.K. £
Teapot	40.00	60.00	25.00

Note: Shape 1431 was replaced by shape 1777.

Shape 1432 Contemporary cheese dish,
First version — knobcut-out

Designer:	Albert Hallam in 1956
Issued:	1956 - 1961
Size:	5″ x 4″, 12.7 x 10.1 cm
Design:	Transfer designs

Description	U.S. $	Can. $	U.K. £
Cheese dish	25.00	35.00	15.00

Note: Shape 1432 was replaced by shape 1776.

Shape 1433 Contemporary toast rack

Designer:	Albert Hallam in 1956
Issued:	1956 - 1970
Size:	6 ½″ x 3″ x 3″, 16.5 x 7.6 x 7.6 cm
Design:	1. Gilt edge
	2. Transfer designs
	3. Trend-setters

Description	U.S. $	Can. $	U.K. £
Toast rack	20.00	25.00	12.00

Shape 1434 Contemporary cruet
Salt, pepper and mustard on a base,
First version — knob cut-out

Designer:	Albert Hallam in 1956
Issued:	1956 - 1961
Size:	5 ¼″ x 2 ½″, 13.3 x 6.4 cm
Design:	Transfer designs

Description	U.S. $	Can. $	U.K. £
Cruet	40.00	60.00	25.00

Note: Shape 1434 was replaced by shape 1787.

Shape 1441/1/2/3 Contemporary jug, in three sizes

Designer:	Albert Hallam in 1956
Issued:	1956 - 1966
Height:	1. Unknown
	2. 5 ½", 14.0 cm
	3. Unknown
Design:	Transfer designs

Description	U.S. $	Can. $	U.K. £
Jug	15.00	25.00	10.00

Shape 1442 Contemporary preserve with lid
First version — knob cut-out

Designer:	Albert Hallam in 1956
Issued:	1956 - 1961
Size:	3 ¼" x 3 ¼" x 4", 8.3 x 8.3 x 10.1 cm
Design:	Transfer designs

Description	U.S. $	Can. $	U.K. £
Preserve with lid	30.00	50.00	20.00

Note: Shape 1442 was replaced by shape 1779.

Photograph not
available
at press time

Shape 1443 Contemporary breakfast cup and saucer

Designer:	Albert Hallam in 1956
Issued:	1956 - 1961
Size:	Unknown
Design:	Transfer designs

Description	U.S. $	Can. $	U.K. £
Breakfast cup/saucer	20.00	30.00	12.00

Shape 1444 Contemporary plate, medium size

Designer:	Albert Hallam in 1956
Issued:	1956 - 1961
Diameter:	8 ½", 21.6 cm
Design:	Transfer designs

Description	U.S. $	Can. $	U.K. £
Plate, medium	10.00	15.00	8.00

Shape 1445 Contemporary tray/dish, rectangular, large size

Designer: Albert Hallam in 1956
Issued: 1956 - 1970
Size: 7 ½" x 5 ¼", 19.1 x 13.3 cm
Design: 1. Gilt edge
            2. Transfer designs
            3. Trend-setters

Description	U.S. $	Can. $	U.K. £
Tray/dish, large	15.00	20.00	10.00

Shape 1446 Contemporary tray/dish, triangular, medium size

Designer: Albert Hallam in 1956
Issued: 1956 - 1970
Size: 5" x 5 ½" x 5 ½", 12.7 x 14.0 x 14.0 cm
Design: 1. Gilt edge
            2. Transfer designs

Colour	U.S. $	Can. $	U.K. £
Tray/dish, medium	10.00	15.00	8.00

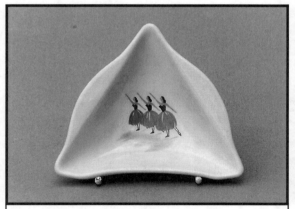

Shape 1447 Contemporary tray/dish, triangular, small size

Designer: Albert Hallam in 1956
Issued: 1956 - 1970
Size: 4 ½" x 4 ½" x 4 ¼", 11.9 x 11.9 x 10.8 cm
Design: 1. Gilt edge
            2. Transfer designs

Description	U.S. $	Can. $	U.K. £
Tray dish, small	8.00	10.00	5.00

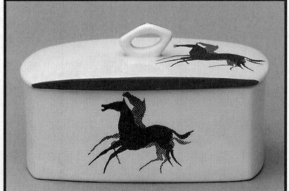

**Shape 1448 Contemporary butter with lid, large
First version — knob cut-out**

Designer: Albert Hallam in 1956
Issued: 1956 - 1959
Size: 6 ¾" x 3 ½" x 3 ¼", 17.2 x 8.9 x 9.5 cm
Design: Transfer designs

Description	U.S. $	Can. $	U.K. £
Butter with lid	25.00	40.00	15.00

Shape 1449 Contemporary double egg cup

Designer: Albert Hallam in 1956
Issued: 1956 - 1961
Size: Unknown
Design: Transfer designs

Description	U.S. $	Can. $	U.K. £
Double egg cup	15.00	20.00	8.00

Shape 1450 Contemporary coffee pot
First version — knob cut-out

Designer: Albert Hallam in 1956
Issued: 1956 - 1961
Size: 7", 17.8 cm
Design: Transfer designs

Description	U.S. $	Can. $	U.K. £
Coffee pot	30.00	50.00	20.00

Note: Shape 1450 was replaced by shape 1778.

Shape 1464 Contemporary TV plate (small)
with location for cup shape 1425A

Designer: Albert Hallam in 1957
Issued: 1957 - 1961
Size: 8 ½" x 8 ½", 21.6" x 21.6 cm
Design: Transfer designs

Description	U.S. $	Can. $	U.K. £
Contemporary TV plate	25.00	35.00	15.00

Shape 1535 Square dish

Designer: Albert Hallam in 1958
Issued: 1958 - 1970
Size: 4 ½" x 4 ½", 11.9 x 11.9 cm
Design: 1. Gilt edge
2. Transfer designs
3. Trend-setters

Description	U.S. $	Can. $	U.K. £
Square dish	8.00	12.00	5.00

Shape 1536 Dish, small

Designer:	Albert Hallam in 1958
Issued:	1958 - 1970
Size:	3 ¼" x 3 ¼", 8.3 x 8.3 cm
Design:	1. Gilt edge
	2. Transfer designs
	3. Trend-setters

Description	U.S. $	Can. $	U.K. £
Dish, small	8.00	12.00	5.00

Shape 1537 Dish

Designer:	Albert Hallam in 1958
Issued:	1958 - by 1965
Size:	5 ¾" x 3 ½", 14.6 x 8.9 cm
Colour:	1. Gilt edge
	2. Transfer designs

Market	Range
U.S.A.	$16.00 - 35.00
Canada	$25.00 - 50.00
U.K.	£10.00 - 20.00

Note: See also Decorative Dishes and Tray, page 194.

Shape 1538 Dish

Designer:	Albert Hallam in 1958
Issued:	1958 - by 1965
Size:	5", 12.7 cm
Colour:	1. Gilt edges
	2. Transfer designs

Market	Range
U.S.A.	$16.00 - 35.00
Canada	$25.00 - 50.00
U.K.	£10.00 - 20.00

Note: See also Decorative Dishes and Trays, page 194.

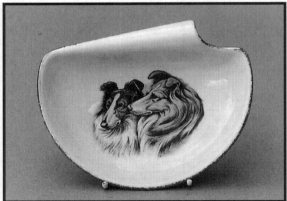

Shape 1539 Dish, large

Designer:	Albert Hallam in 1958
Issued:	1958 - 1965
Size:	5 ¾" x 4 ¼", 14.6 x 10.8 cm
Design:	1. Gilt edge
	2. Transfer designs

Description	U.S. $	Can. $	U.K. £
Dish, large	8.00	12.00	5.00

Shape 1540 Dish, small

Designer:	Albert Hallam in 1958
Issued:	1958 - 1965
Size:	2 ¼" x 3 ½" x 5 ¼", 5.7 x 8.9 x 13.3 cm
Design:	1. Gilt edge
	2. Transfer designs

Description	U.S. $	Can. $	U.K. £
Dish, small	8.00	12.00	5.00

Shape 1594 Contemporary butter dish, ½ lb.
First version — knob cut-out

Designer:	Albert Hallam in 1959
Issued:	1959 - 1961
Size:	5" x 3 ¼" x 2", 12.7 x 8.3 x 5.0 cm
Design:	Transfer designs

Description	U.S. $	Can. $	U.K. £
Butter dish	25.00	40.00	15.00

Note: Shape 1594 was replaced by shape 1775.

Shape 1595 TV set with location for cup
shape 1425B

Designer:	Albert Hallam in 1959
Issued:	1959 - 1961
Size:	8 ¾" x 7", 22.2 x 17.8 cm
Design:	Transfer designs

Description	U.S. $	Can. $	U.K. £
TV set	25.00	35.00	15.00

Note: Shape 1595 was replaced by shape 1782.

Shape 1617 Square dish

Designer:	Albert Hallam in 1959
Issued:	1959 - 1969
Size:	4" x 4", 10.1 x 10.1 cm
Design:	1. Gilt edge
	2. Transfer designs

Description	U.S. $	Can. $	U.K. £
Square dish	8.00	12.00	5.00

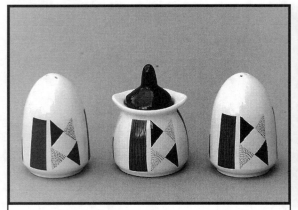

Shape 1618   Cruet, salt, pepper and mustard with lid

Designer: Mr. Wood in 1959
Issued: 1959 - 1970
Height: 3", 7.6 cm
Design: 1. Gilt edge
             2. Transfer designs
             3. Trend-setters

Description	U.S. $	Can. $	U.K. £
Cruet set	25.00	35.00	15.00

Shape 1623   Contemporary meat dish

Designer: Mr. Wood in 1959
Issued: 1959 - 1961
Length: 12 ½", 31.7 cm
Design: Transfer designs

Description	U.S. $	Can. $	U.K. £
Meat dish	25.00	35.00	15.00

Shape 1665/1666 Pepper and salt

Designer: Albert Hallam in 1959
Issued: 1959 - 1967
Height: 4 ½", 11.9 cm
Design: 1. Copper - lustre
             2. Transfer designs
             3. White - satin matt

Description	U.S. $	Can. $	U.K. £
Pepper and salt	8.00	12.00	5.00

Shape 1667   Vinegar with handle and stopper

Designer: Albert Hallam in 1959
Issued: 1959 - 1967
Height: 5 ½", 14 cm incl. stopper
Design: 1. Copper - lustre
             2. Transfer designs
             3. White - satin matt

Description	U.S. $	Can. $	U.K. £
Vinegar	15.00	25.00	10.00

Shape 1674 Tray / Dish

Designer:	Albert Hallam in 1960	
Issued:	1960 - 1963	
Size:	10 ¼" x 9", 26.0 x 22.9 cm	
Design:	Transfer designs	

Description	U.S. $	Can. $	U.K. £
Tray / dish	15.00	25.00	10.00

Shape 1694 Vinegar with stopper

Designer:	Albert Hallam in 1960	
Issued:	1960 - 1965	
Height:	6", 15 cm	
Design:	Transfer designs	

Description	U.S. $	Can. $	U.K. £
Vinegar with stopper	15.00	25.00	10.00

Note: Top and stopper altered in 1961.

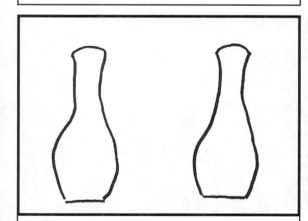

Shape 1695/1696 Salt and pepper

Designer:	Albert Hallam in 1960	
Issued:	1960 - 1965	
Height:	4 ½", 11.9 cm	
Design:	Transfer designs	

Description	U.S. $	Can. $	U.K. £
Salt and pepper	15.00	25.00	10.00

Shape 1703 Sandwich tray

Designer:	Albert Hallam in 1960	
Issued:	1960 - 1965	
Size:	10 ¾" x 5 ¼", 27.8 x 13.3 cm	
Design:	Transfer designs	

Description	U.S. $	Can. $	U.K. £
Sandwich tray	15.00	25.00	10.00

Shape 1719 Mustard Pot

Designer:	Albert Hallam in 1960
Issued:	1960 - 1965
Height:	3", 7.6 cm
Design:	1. Gilt edge
	2. Tranfer designs

Description	U.S. $	Can. $	U.K. £
Mustard pot	10.00	15.00	8.00

Shape 1732 Egg cup

Designer:	Albert Hallam in 1960
Issued:	1961 - 1970
Height:	1 ¾", 4.4 cm
Design:	1. Gilt edge
	2. Nursery ware
	3. Trend-setter
	4. Transfer designs

Description	U.S. $	Can. $	U.K. £
Egg cup	8.00	12.00	5.00

Shape 1755 Eton tea cup and saucer

Designer:	Albert Hallam in 1961
Issued:	1961 - 1965
Cup Dia.:	3 ¼", 8.3 cm
Height:	3", 7.6 cm
Saucer Dia.:	5 ¾", 14.6 cm
Design:	1. Transfer designs
	2. Gilt edge

Description	U.S. $	Can. $	U.K. £
Tea cup and saucer	15.00	20.00	10.00

Shape 1756 Eton sugar

Designer:	Albert Hallam in 1961
Issued:	1961 - 1970
Diameter:	4 ¼", 10.8 cm
Design:	1. Gilt edge
	2. Transfer designs

Description	U.S. $	Can. $	U.K. £
Sugar	10.00	15.00	8.00

Shape 1757 Eton cream

Designer:	Albert Hallam in 1961
Issued:	1961 - 1970
Size:	Unknown
Design:	1. Gilt edge
	2. Transfer designs

Description	U.S. $	Can. $	U.K. £
Cream	10.00	15.00	8.00

Shape 1758 Eton breakfast cup and saucer

Designer:	Albert Hallam in 1961
Issued:	1961 - 1965
Size:	Unknown
Design:	1. Gilt edge
	2. Transfer designs

Description	U.S. $	Can. $	U.K. £
Breakfast cup and saucer	15.00	20.00	10.00

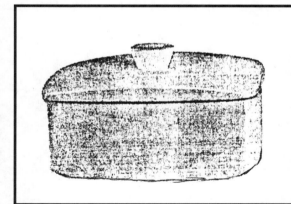

Shape 1775 Contemporary covered butter
Second version — knob solid

Designer:	Albert Hallam in 1961
Issued:	1961 - 1965
Size:	5″ x 3 ¼″ x 2″, 12.7 x 8.3 x 5 cm
Design:	Transfer designs

Description	U.S. $	Can. $	U.K. £
Covered butter	25.00	35.00	15.00

Note: Shape 1775 replaced shape 1594.

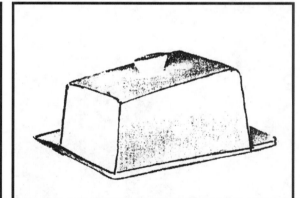

Shape 1776 Cheese dish
Second version — knob solid

Designer:	Albert Hallam in 1961
Issued:	1961 - 1965
Size:	5″ x 4″, 12.7 x 10.1 cm
Design:	Transfer designs

Description	U.S. $	Can. $	U.K. £
Cheese dish	25.00	35.00	15.00

Note: Shape 1776 replaced shape 1432.

Shape 1777 Eton teapot
              Second version — knob solid

Designer:	Albert Hallam in 1961		
Issued:	1961 - 1965		
Size:	6 ½", 16.5 cm		
Design:	Transfer designs		

Description	U.S. $	Can. $	U.K. £
Teapot	40.00	60.00	25.00

Note: Shape 1777 replaced shape 1431.

Shape 1778 Eton coffee pot
              Second version — knob solid

Designer:	Albert Hallam in 1961		
Issued:	1961 - 1965		
Size:	Unknown		
Design:	Transfer designs		

Description	U.S. $	Can. $	U.K. £
Coffee pot	40.00	60.00	25.00

Note: Shape 1778 replaced shape 1450.

Shape 1779 Preserve
              Second version — knob solid

Designer:	Albert Hallam in 1961		
Issued:	1961 - 1965		
Height:	3 ¾", 9.5 cm		
Design:	Transfer designs		

Description	U.S. $	Can. $	U.K. £
Preserve	25.00	35.00	15.00

Note: Shape 1779 replaced shape 1442.

Photograph not
available
at press time

Shape 1780 Oatmeal/Soup

Designer:	Albert Hallam in 1961		
Issued:	1961 - 1965		
Size:	1. 7", 17.8 cm		
	2. 6", 15.0 cm		
Design:	1. Nursery ware		
	2. Transfer designs		

Description	U.S. $	Can. $	U.K. £
Oatmeal/soup	10.00	15.00	8.00

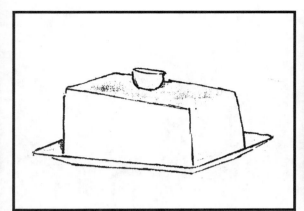

**Shape 1781 Cheese dish, narrow
         Second version — knob solid**

Designer: Albert Hallam in 1961
Issued: 1961 - 1965
Size: 5 ¼" x 3 ¼", 13.3 x 8.3 cm
Design: Transfer designs

Description	U.S.$	Can. $	U.K.£
Cheese dish	25.00	35.00	15.00

Shape 1782 Eton TV set

Designer: Albert Hallam in 1961
Issued: 1961 - 1965
Base size: 9" x 6", 22.9 x 15 cm
Design: Transfer designs

Description	U.S.$	Can. $	U.K.£
TV set	25.00	35.00	15.00

Note: Shape 1782 replaced shape 1595.

Shape 1783 Eton plate, small

Designer   Albert Hallam in 1961
Issued: 1961 - 1970
Diameter: 6 ¾", 17.2 cm
Design: 1. Nursery ware
            2. Plain colours
            3. Transfer designs
            4. Trend-setters

Description	U.S.$	Can.$	U.K.£
Plate	15.00	25.00	10.00

Shape 1784 Eton plate, medium

Designer: Albert Hallam in 1961
Issued: 1961 - 1970
Diameter: 8 ¾", 22.2 cm
Design: 1. Plain colours
            2. Transfer designs
            3. Trend-setters

Description	U.S.$	Can.$	U.K.£
Plate, medium	15.00	25.00	10.00

Shape 1785   Eton plate, large

Designer:	Albert Hallam in 1961
Issued:	1961 - 1970
Diameter:	9 ¾", 24.7 cm
Design:	1. Plain colours
	2. Transfer designs
	3. Trend-setters

Description	U.S.$	Can.$	U.K.£
Plate, large	20.00	30.00	12.00

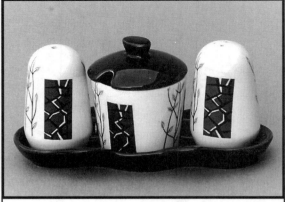

Shape 1787   Cruet - salt, pepper, mustard on base

Designer:	Albert Hallam in 1961
Issued:	1962 - 1970
Size:	5 ¼" x 2 ½", 13.3 cm x 6.4 cm
Design:	1. Gilt edge
	2. Transfer designs
	3. Trend-setters

Description	U.S.$	Can.$	U.K.£
Cruet set	40.00	60.00	25.00

Note: Shape 1787 replaced shape 1434.

Shape 1806   Fruit bowl

Designer:	Unknown
Issued:	1962 - 1967
Diameter:	9", 22.9 cm
Design:	1. Gilt edge
	2. Trend-setters

Description	U.S. $	Can. $	U.K. £
Fruit bowl	25.00	40.00	15.00

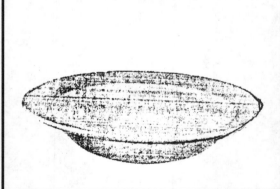

Shape 1807   Fruit saucer

Designer:	Unknown
Issued:	1962 - 1967
Diameter:	6 ½", 16.5 cm
Design:	1. Gilt edge
	2. Trend-setters

Description	U.S. $	Can. $	U.K. £
Fruit saucer	15.00	20.00	8.00

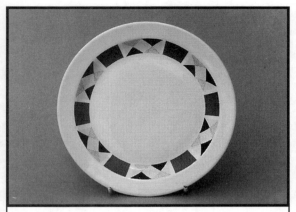

Shape 1822 Eton plate

Designer:	Albert Hallam in 1961
Issued:	1961 - 1970
Diameter:	7 ¾", 19.7 cm
Design:	1. Plain colours
	2. Transfer designs
	3. Trend-setters

Description	U.S. $	Can. $	U.K. £
Plate	12.00	15.00	7.00

Photograph not
available
at press time

Shape 1913 Coupe soup

Designer:	Albert Hallam in 1963
Issued:	1964 - 1970
Diameter:	7 ¾", 19.7 cm
Design:	1. Gilt edge
	2. Plain colours
	3. Trend-setters

Description	U.S. $	Can. $	U.K. £
Coupe soup	12.00	15.00	7.00

Photograph not
available
at press time

Shape 1915 Deep soup

Designer:	Albert Hallam in 1963
Issued:	1964 - 1970
Diameter:	9 ¼", 23.5 cm
Design:	1. Gilt edge
	2. Trend-setters

Description	U.S. $	Can. $	U.K. £
Deep soup	15.00	25.00	10.00

Shape 1919 Tureen

Designer:	Albert Hallam in 1963
Issued:	1964 - 1971
Diameter:	9 ¾", 24.7 cm
Design:	1. Gilt edge
	2. Pewter

Description	U.S. $	Can. $	U.K. £
Tureen	125.00	200.00	75.00

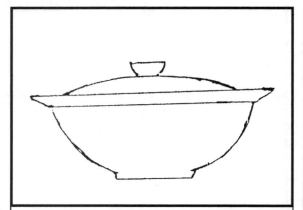

Shape 1922 Covered scallop

Designer:	Albert Hallam in 1964
Issued:	1964 - 1970
Size:	Unknown
Design:	Gilt edge

Description	U.S. $	Can. $	U.K. £
Covered scallop	40.00	60.00	25.00

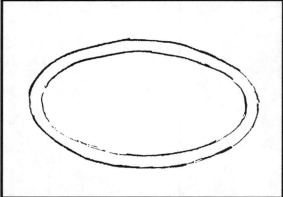

Shape 1923 Meat dish

Designer:	Albert Hallam in 1964
Issued:	1964 - 1969
Size:	12" x 9", 30.5 x 22.9 cm
Design:	Gilt edge

Description	U.S. $	Can. $	U.K. £
Meat dish	30.00	50.00	20.00

Shape 1958 Orbit coffee pot

Designer:	Albert Hallam in 1964
Issued:	1964 - 1971
Height:	9", 22.9 cm
Design:	1. Gilt edge
	2. Plain colours
	3. Transfer designs
	4. Trend-setters

Description	U.S. $	Can. $	U.K. £
Coffee pot	40.00	60.00	25.00

Shape 1959 Orbit teapot

Designer:	Albert Hallam in 1964
Issued:	1964 - 1970
Height:	6 ½", 15.0 cm
Design:	1. Gilt edge
	2. Plain colours
	3. Transfer designs
	4. Trend-setters

Description	U.S. $	Can. $	U.K. £
Teapot	40.00	60.00	25.00

Shape 1960 Orbit tea cup and saucer

Designer:	Albert Hallam in 1964
Issued:	1964 - 1970
Cup Dia.:	3 ¼", 8.3 cm
Height:	2 ¾", 7.0 cm
Saucer Dia.:	5 ½", 14.0 cm
Design:	1. Gilt edge
	2. Trend-setters (not Verona)

Description	U.S. $	Can. $	U.K. £
Tea cup and saucer	15.00	25.00	10.00

Shape 1962 Orbit cream jug

Designer:	Albert Hallam in 1964
Issued:	1964 - 1971
Height:	4", 10.1 cm
Design:	1. Plain colours
	2. Trend-setters

Description	U.S. $	Can. $	U.K. £
Cream jug	20.00	15.00	7.00

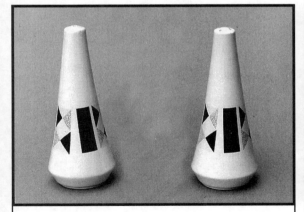

Shape 1963/1964 Pepper and salt

Designer:	Albert Hallam in 1964
Issued:	1964 - 1970
Height:	5 ½", 14.0 cm
Design:	1. Gilt edge
	2. Plain colours
	3. Trend-setters

Description	U.S. $	Can. $	U.K. £
Pepper and salt	10.00	15.00	8.00

Shape 1965 Vinegar with stopper

Designer:	Albert Hallam in 1964
Issued:	1964 - 1970
Height:	5 ½", 14.0 cm
Design:	1. Gilt edge
	2. Plain colours
	3. Trend-setters

Description	U.S. $	Can. $	U.K. £
Vinegar	10.00	15.00	6.00

Shape 1966 Orbit vegetable dish

Designer:	Albert Hallam in 1964
Issued:	1964 - 1970
Width:	10 ¼″, 26.0 cm
Design:	1. Gilt edge
	2. Trend-setters

Description	U.S. $	Can. $	U.K. £
Vegetable dish	30.00	50.00	20.00

Shape 1967 Orbit gravy boat and stand

Designer:	Albert Hallam in 1964
Issued:	1964 - 1970
Boat size:	9 ¼″ x 3″ x 3 ¾″, 23.5 x 7.6 x 9.5 cm
Design:	1. Gilt edge
	2. Trend-setters

Description	U.S. $	Can. $	U.K. £
Gravy boat and stand	25.00	35.00	15.00

Shape 1968 Orbit preserve

Designer:	Albert Hallam in 1964
Issued:	1964 - 1970
Height:	3 ¾″, 9.5 cm
Design:	1. Gilt edge
	2. Plain colours
	3. Trend-setters

Description	U.S. $	Can. $	U.K. £
Preserve	25.00	35.00	15.00

Shape 1969 Orbit butter

Designer:	Albert Hallam in 1964
Issued:	1964 - 1970
Size:	5 ¼″ x 3 ½″, 13.3 x 8.9 cm
Design:	1. Gilt edge
	2. Plain colours
	3. Trend-setters

Description	U.S. $	Can. $	U.K. £
Butter dish	25.00	35.00	15.00

Shape 1970 Orbit cheese dish

Designer:	Albert Hallam in 1964
Issued:	1964 - 1970
Size:	6 ¾" x 5 ¾", 17.2 x 14.6 cm (base)
Height :	5", 12.7 cm
Design:	1. Gilt edge
	2. Plain colours
	3. Trend-setters

Description	U.S. $	Can. $	U.K. £
Cheese dish	25.00	35.00	15.00

Shape 1972 Orbit coffee cup and saucer

Designer:	Albert Hallam in 1964
Issued:	1964 - 1971
Size:	Cup - 3 ¼" x 2 ¾", 8.3 x 7.0 cm;
	saucer (diameter) - 5 ¾", 14.6 cm
Design:	1. Gilt edge
	2. Plain colours
	3. Trend-setters

Description	U.S. $	Can. $	U.K. £
Cup and saucer	10.00	12.00	5.00

Shape 1973 Orbit hot milk jug

Designer:	Albert Hallam in 1964
Issued:	1964 - 1971
Height:	7 ¾", 19.7 cm
Design:	1. Gilt edge
	2. Plain colours
	3. Trend-setters

Description	U.S. $	Can. $	U.K. £
Hot milk jug	25.00	35.00	15.00

Photograph not
available
at press time

Shape 1974 Orbit fruit bowl

Designer:	Albert Hallam in 1964
Issued:	1964 - 1970
Diameter:	7 ¾", 19.7 cm
Design:	1. Gilt edge
	2. Trend-setters

Description	U.S. $	Can. $	U.K. £
Fruit bowl	25.00	35.00	15.00

Shape 1975 Orbit fruit saucer

Designer: Albert Hallam in 1964
Issued: 1964 - 1970
Size: 6 ½", 16.5 cm
Design: 1. Gilt edge
           2. Transfer designs
           3. Trend-setters

Description	U.S. $	Can. $	U.K. £
Fruit saucer	10.00	15.00	5.00

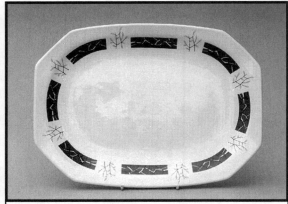

Shape 1976 Orbit meat dish

Designer: Albert Hallam in 1964
Issued: 1964 - 1969
Size: 12 ¼" x 9 ¼", 31.1 x 23.5 cm
Design: 1. Plain colours
           2. Trend-setters

Description	U.S. $	Can. $	U.K. £
Meat dish	25.00	35.00	15.00

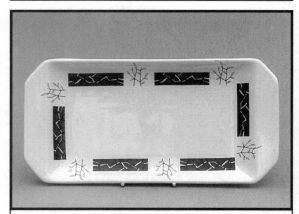

Shape 1977 Orbit sandwich tray

Designer: Albert Hallam in 1964
Issued: 1964 - 1970
Size: 11" x 5 ¼", 27.0 x 13.3 cm
Design: 1. Gilt edge
           2. Trend-setters

Description	U.S. $	Can. $	U.K. £
Sandwich tray	15.00	25.00	10.00

Shape 1978 Orbit open sugar

Designer: Albert Hallam in 1964
Issued: 1964 - 1969
Height: 2 ½", 6.4 cm
Diameter: 3 ½" 8.9 cm
Design: 1. Plain colours
           2. Trend-setters

Description	U.S. $	Can. $	U.K. £
Open sugar	8.00	12.00	5.00

Photograph not
available
at press time

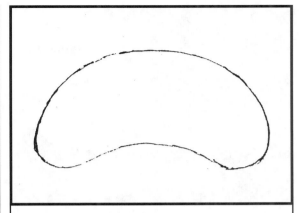

Shape 2002 Orbit oatmeal dish

Designer:	Albert Hallam in 1964
Issued:	1965 - 1970
Diameter:	6 ½", 16.5 cm
Design:	1. Gilt edge
	2. Nursery ware
	3. Trend-setters

Description	U.S. $	Can. $	U.K. £
Oatmeal dish	8.00	12.00	5.00

Shape 2004 Kidney dish

Designer:	Albert Hallam in 1965
Issued:	1965 - 1969
Length:	9 ½", 24.0 cm
Deep:	3 ¼, 1.9 cm
Design:	1. Gilt edge
	2. Trend setters

Description	U.S. $	Can. $	U.K. £
Kidney dish	8.00	12.00	5.00

Shape 2027 Orbit soup jug

Designer:	Albert Hallam in 1964
Issued:	1964 - 1969
Height:	7 ¼", 18.4 cm
Design:	Trend-setters

Description	U.S. $	Can. $	U.K. £
Soup jug	30.00	45.00	20.00

Shape 2028 Soup cup and saucer

Designer:	Albert Hallam in 1965
Issued:	1965 - 1970
Height:	2 ¼", 5.7 cm
Design:	1. Gilt edge
	2. Plain colours
	3. Trend-setters

Description	U.S. $	Can. $	U.K. £
Soup cup/saucer	15.00	25.00	10.00

Note: Saucer not shown.

Shape 2039 TV tray with cup shape 1972

Designer: Albert Hallam in 1965
Issued: 1965 - 1970
Length: 9", 22.9 cm
Design: 1. Gilt edge
              2. Plain colours
              3. Trend-setters

Description	U.S. $	Can. $	U.K. £
TV tray	15.00	25.00	10.00

Shape 2113-2116 Dish

Designer: Albert Hallam in 1967
Issued: 1967 - 1969
Size: Shape 2113 — 5 ½", 14.0 cm
              Shape 2116 — 6 ½", 16.5 cm
Design: Gilt edge

Description	U.S. $	Can. $	U.K. £
Dish	8.00	12.00	5.00

Note: Set of four with shapes 2117 and 2120.

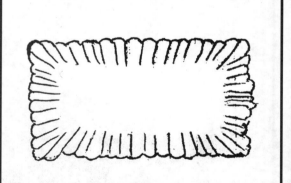

Shape 2117 Dish

Designer: Albert Hallam in 1967
Issued: 1967 - 1969
Size: 7 ½" x 5", 19.1 x 12.7 cm
Design: Gilt edge

Description	U.S. $	Can. $	U.K. £
Dish	15.00	25.00	10.00

Note: Set of four with shapes 2113, 2116 and 2120.

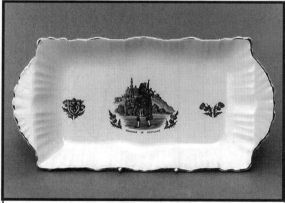

Shape 2120 Sandwich tray

Designer: Albert Hallam in 1967
Issued: 1967 - 1969
Size: 11" x 5 ½", 27.9 x 14.0 cm
Design: Gilt edge

Description	U.S. $	Can. $	U.K. £
Sandwich tray	15.00	25.00	10.00

Note: Set of four with shapes 2113, 2116 and 2117.

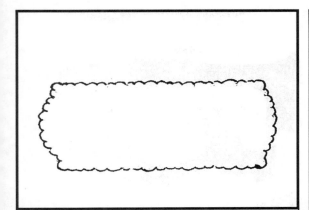

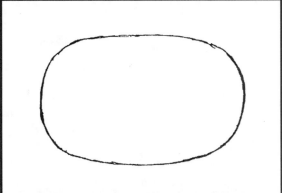

Shape 2164 Sandwich tray, large

Designer:	Albert Hallam in 1967
Issued:	1967 - 1969
Size:	12 ½" x 5 ½", 31.7 x 14.0 cm
Design:	Gilt edge

Description	U.S. $	Can. $	U.K. £
Sandwich tray	15.00	25.00	10.00

Shape 2244 Steak dish, no rim

Designer:	Graham Tongue in 1968
Issued:	1968 - 1969
Size:	10" x 8", 25.4 x 20.3 cm
Design:	Trend-setters (Verona only)

Description	U.S. $	Can. $	U.K. £
Steak dish	15.00	25.00	10.00

Note: Price ranges are retail market indicators of prices for models under the following conditions:
- Lower end of range = price of monochrome models
- Higher end of range = price of multicoloured models

Cruet Set, Shape 1787

TROUGHS

This section lists fourteen pieces for holding flowers which because of their shape can not be included with the vases and bowls. Some of these were posy troughs, designed in a variety of shapes to hold short stemmed flowers, moss or heather in a well or trough of water. A special small-sized candle-holder (Shape 295) was modelled to slide into these (e.g. Shape 294), thus making it possible to combine flowers and candles in the one display. Other shapes of troughs are more in the nature of window boxes.

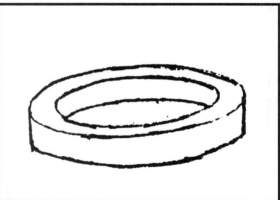

Shape 268   **Round posy trough**

Designer: Unknown
Issued: 1934 - by 1954
Diameter: 6", 15 cm
Colour: 1. Assorted decorations - satin matt
            2. White - matt

Market	Range
U.S.A.	$15.00 - 25.00
Canada	$25.00 - 35.00
U.K.	£10.00 - 15.00

Shape 294   **Round posy trough**

Designer: Mr. Symcox in 1935
Issued: 1935 - by 1963
Diameter: 10", 25.4 cm
Colour: 1. Assorted decorations - satin matt
            2. White - matt

Market	Range
U.S.A.	$15.00 - 25.00
Canada	$25.00 - 35.00
U.K.	£10.00 - 15.00

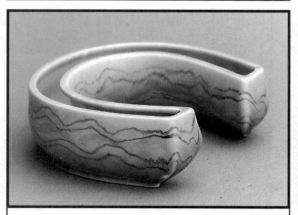

Shape 296   **Horseshoe posy trough**

Designer: Mr. Symcox in 1935
Issued: 1935 - by 1963
Width: 5 ½, 14 cm
Colour: 1. Assorted decorations - satin matt
            2. White - matt

Market	Range
U.S.A.	$15.00 - 25.00
Canada	$25.00 -35.00
U.K.	£10.00 - 15.00

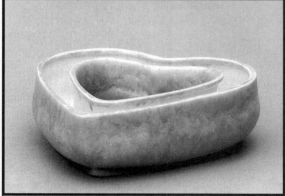

Shape 297   **Heart shaped posy trough**

Designer: Mr. Symcox in 1935
Issued: 1935 - by 1963
Width: 6, 15 cm
Colour: 1. Assorted decorations - satin matt
            2. White - matt

Market	Range
U.S.A.	$15.00 - 25.00
Canada	$25.00 - 35.00
U.K.	£10.00 - 15.00

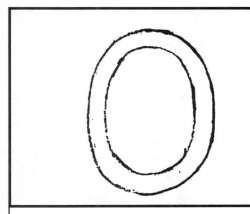

Shape 298   **Oval shaped posy trough**

Designer: Mr. Symcox in 1935
Issued: 1935 - by 1954
Size: 10 x 8, 25.4 x 20.3 cm
Colour: 1. Assorted decorations - satin matt
            2. White - matt

Market	Range
U.S.A.	$15.00 - 25.00
Canada	$25.00 - 35.00
U.K.	£10.00 - 15.00

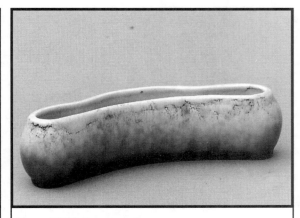

Shape 452/1/2 Posy trough

Designer: Mr. Symcox in 1936
Issued: 1936 - by 1963
Size: 1. Shape 452/1 — 9 ½ x 2, 24 x 5 cm
            2. Shape 452/2 — 7 ½ x 2, 19.1 x 5 cm
Colour: 1. Assorted decorations - satin matt
            2. White - matt

Market	Range
U.S.A.	$15.00 - 25.00
Canada	$25.00 - 35.00
U.K.	£10.00 - 15.00

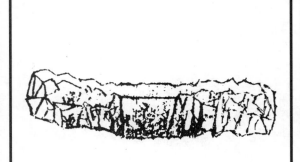

Shape 459   **Posy trough**

Designer: James Hayward in 1936
Issued: 1937 - by 1954
Length: 10, 25.4 cm
Colour: 1. Assorted decorations - satin matt
            2. White - matt

Market	Range
U.S.A.	$15.00 - 25.00
Canada	$25.00 - 35.00
U.K.	£10.00 - 15.00

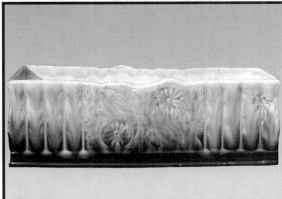

Shape 491   **Window box, trough**

Designer: Mr. Symcox in 1937
Issued: 1937 - by 1969
Size: 12 x 3 ½, 30.5 x 8.9 cm
Colour: 1. Assorted decorations - satin matt
            2. White or black - matt

Market	Range
U.S.A.	$25.00 - 40.00
Canada	$40.00 - 60.00
U.K.	£15.00 - 25.00

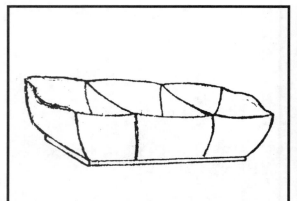

Shape 608   **Trough with three sections**

Designer: Mr. Symcox in 1938
Issued: 1938 - by 1954
Size: Unknown
Colour: 1. Assorted decorations - satin matt
             2. White - matt

Market	Range
U.S.A.	$15.00 - 25.00
Canada	$25.00 - 35.00
U.K.	£15.00 - 25.00

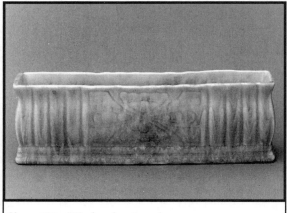

Shape 732   **Window box trough**

Designer: James Hayward in 1939
Issued: 1939 - by 1968
Size: 12 x 3 ½, 30.5 x 8.9 cm
Colour: 1. Assorted decorations - satin matt
             2. White - matt

Market	Range
U.S.A.	$15.00 - 25.00
Canada	$25.00 - 35.00
U.K.	£15.00 - 25.00

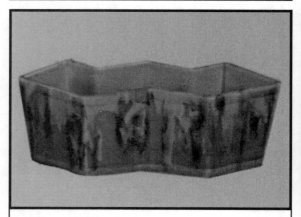

Shape 746   **Trough**

Designer: Mr. Watkin in 1939
Issued: 1939 - by 1954
Size: 10 x 3 ½, 25.4 x 8.9 cm
Colour: 1. Assorted decorations - satin matt
             2. White - matt

Market	Range
U.S.A.	$25.00 - 40.00
Canada	$40.00 - 60.00
U.K.	£15.00 - 25.00

Shape 747   **Trough**

Designer: Mr. Symcox in 1939
Issued: 1939 - by 1954
Size: 11 x 7 ¼ x 3 ½, 27.9 x 18.4 x 8.9 cm
Colour: 1. Assorted decorations - satin matt
             2. White - matt

Market	Range
U.S.A.	$25.00 - 40.00
Canada	$40.00 - 60.00
U.K.	£15.00 - 25.00

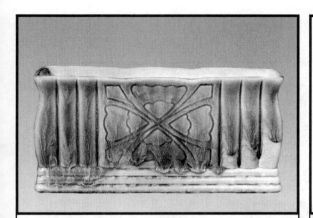

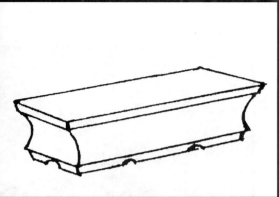

Shape 1356 Window box trough

Designer:	Albert Hallam in 1954
Issued:	1955 - 1967
Length:	8, 20.3 cm
Colour:	1. Assorted decorations - satin matt
	2. White or black - matt

Market	Range
U.S.A.	$15.00 - 25.00
Canada	$25.00 - 35.00
U.K.	£15.00 - 25.00

Shape 2279 Trough

Designer:	Albert Hallam in 1969
Issued:	1969 - 1970
Size:	10 x 5 x 2 ½, 25.4 x 12.7 x 6.4 cm
Colour:	1. Assorted decorations - satin matt
	2. White or black - matt
	3. Copper - lustre

Market	Range
U.S.A.	$25.00 - 40.00
Canada	$40.00 - 60.00
U.K.	£15.00 - 25.00

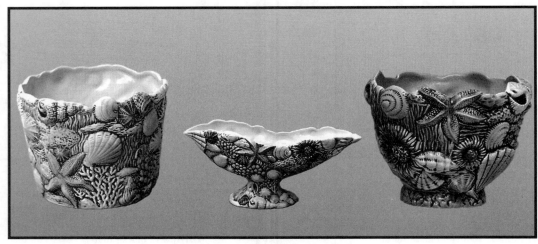

Shape 2016, Shape 2014, Shape 2012

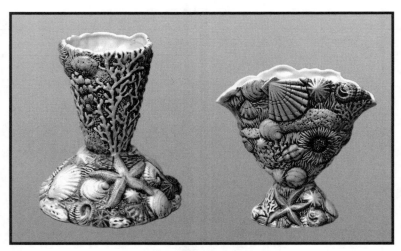

Shape 2020, Shape 2015

VASES AND PLANT POT HOLDERS

This section lists three hundred and thirteen shapes and is the largest single group.

Following the development of the matt glazes in 1933 there was an explosion in the number of vases modelled and by 1934 a hundred new shapes, which included jugs, in a multitude of different decorations, had been produced. Many of these were exhibited at The British Industries Fair in February of the same year.

Beswick continued to produce many vases over the years until 1972, when production of ornamental ware ceased.

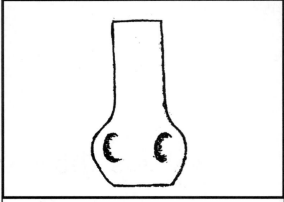

Shape 21	**Vase, two-handled**
Designer:	Mr. Symcox c.1933
Issued:	c.1933 - by 1940
Height:	12″, 30.5 cm
Colour:	1. Assorted decorations - satin matt
	2. White - matt

Market	Range
U.S.A.	$100.00 - 135.00
Canada	$150.00 - 225.00
U.K.	£60.00 - 85.00

Shape 24	**Vase**
Designer:	Mr. Symcox c.1933
Issued:	c.1933 - by 1940
Size:	Unknown
Colour:	1. Assorted decorations - satin matt
	2. White - matt

Market	Range
U.S.A.	$100.00 - 135.00
Canada	$150.00 - 225.00
U.K.	£60.00 - 85.00

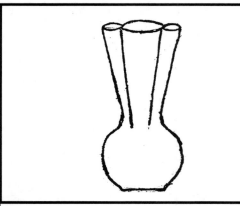

Shape 25	**Vase**
Designer:	Mr. Symcox c.1933
Issued:	c.1933 - by 1940
Height:	11″, 27.9 cm
Colour:	1. Assorted decorations - satin matt
	2. White - matt

Market	Range
U.S.A.	$100.00 - 135.00
Canada	$150.00 - 225.00
U.K.	£60.00 - 85.00

Shape 27	**Fluted Vase**
Designer:	Mr. Symcox c.1933
Issued:	c.1933 - by 1940
Size:	Unknown
Colour:	1. Assorted decorations - satin matt
	2. White - matt

Market	Range
U.S.A.	$100.00 - 135.00
Canada	$150.00 - 225.00
U.K.	£60.00 - 85.00

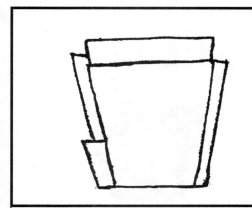

Shape 29   Vase

Designer:	Mr. Symcox c.1933
Issued:	c.1933 - by 1940
Size:	Unknown
Colour:	1. Assorted decorations - satin matt
	2. White - matt

Market	Range
U.S.A.	$75.00 - 125.00
Canada	$125.00 - 175.00
U.K.	£45.00 - 75.00

Shape 30   Vase

Designer:	Mr. Symcox c.1933
Issued:	c.1933 - by 1940
Height:	9", 22.9 cm
Colour:	1. Assorted decorations - satin matt
	2. White - matt

Market	Range
U.S.A.	$75.00 - 125.00
Canada	$125.00 - 175.00
U.K.	£45.00 - 75.00

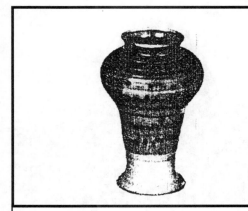

Shape 31   Vase

Designer:	Mr. Symcox c.1933
Issued:	c.1933 - by 1940
Size:	10", 25.4 cm
Colour:	1. Assorted decorations - satin matt
	2. White - matt

Market	Range
U.S.A.	$75.00 - 125.00
Canada	$125.00 - 175.00
U.K.	£60.00 - 85.00

Shape 32   Vase

Designer:	Mr. Symcox c.1933
Issued:	c.1933 - by 1940
Size:	Unknown
Colour:	1. Assorted decorations - satin matt
	2. White - matt

Market	Range
U.S.A.	$100.00 - 135.00
Canada	$150.00 - 225.00
U.K.	£60.00 - 85.00

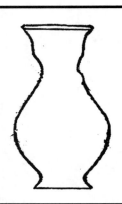

Shape 33   **Vase**

Designer:	Mr. Symcox c.1933
Issued:	c.1933 - by 1940
Size:	Unknown
Colour:	1. Assorted decorations - satin matt
	2. White - matt

Market	Range
U.S.A.	$75.00 - 125.00
Canada	$125.00 - 175.00
U.K.	£45.00 - 75.00

Shape 34   **Vase**

Designer:	Mr. Symcox c.1933
Issued:	c.1933 - by 1940
Size:	8 ½", 21.6 cm
Colour:	1. Assorted decorations - satin matt
	2. White- matt

Market	Range
U.S.A.	$75.00 - 125.00
Canada	$125.00 - 175.00
U.K.	£45.00 - 75.00

Shape 35   **Ribbed vase**

Designer:	Mr. Symcox c.1933
Issued:	c.1933 - by 1940
Size:	8", 20.3 cm
Colour:	1. Assorted decorations - satin matt
	2. White- matt

Market	Range
U.S.A.	$75.00 - 125.00
Canada	$125.00 - 175.00
U.K.	£45.00 - 75.00

Shape 36   **Vase, two-handled**

Designer:	Mr. Symcox c.1933
Issued:	c.1933 - by 1940
Size:	7 ½", 19.1 cm
Colour:	1. Assorted decorations - satin matt
	2. White- matt

Market	Range
U.S.A.	$75.00 - 125.00
Canada	$125.00 - 175.00
U.K.	£45.00 - 75.00

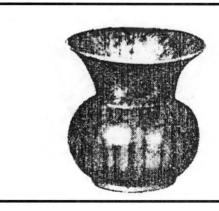

Shape 37   Vase, two-handled

Designer: Mr. Symcox c.1933
Issued: c.1933 - by 1954
Size: 6 ½", 16.5 cm
Colour: 1. Assorted decorations - satin matt
            2. White - matt

Market	Range
U.S.A.	$65.00 - 100.00
Canada	$100.00 - 150.00
U.K.	£40.00 - 60.00

Shape 38   Vase

Designer: Mr. Symcox c.1933
Issued: c.1933 - by 1954
Size: 6 ½", 16.5 cm
Colour: 1. Assorted decorations - satin matt
            2. White - matt

Market	Range
U.S.A.	$650.00 - 100.00
Canada	$100.00 - 150.00
U.K.	£40.00 - 60.00

Shape 39   Vase

Designer: Mr. Symcox c.1933
Issued: c.1933 - by 1940
Size: 7", 17.8 cm
Colour: 1. Assorted decorations - satin matt
            2. White - matt

Market	Range
U.S.A.	$65.00 - 100.00
Canada	$100.00 - 150.00
U.K.	£40.00 - 60.00

Shape 40   Vase, two-handled

Designer: Mr. Symcox c.1933
Issued: c.1933 - by 1940
Size: 6", 15 cm
Colour: 1. Assorted decorations - satin matt
            2. White - matt

Market	Range
U.S.A.	$65.00 - 100.00
Canada	$100.00 - 150.00
U.K.	£40.00 - 60.00

Shape 41   Vase, two-handled

Designer: Mr. Symcox c.1933
Issued: c.1933 - by 1940
Size: 5 ¾", 14.6 cm
Colour: 1. Assorted decorations - satin matt
              2. White - matt

Market	Range
U.S.A.	$45.00 - 65.00
Canada	$65.00 - 100.00
U.K.	£25.00 - 45.00

Shape 42   Vase

Designer: Mr. Symcox c.1933
Issued: c.1933 - by 1940
Size: 7", 17.8 cm
Colour: 1. Assorted decorations - satin matt
              2. White - matt

Market	Range
U.S.A.	$65.00 - 100.00
Canada	$100.00 - 150.00
U.K.	£40.00 - 60.00

Shape 43   Vase, two-handled

Designer: Mr. Symcox c.1933
Issued: c.1933 - by 1940
Size: 4", 10.1 cm
Colour: 1. Assorted decorations - satin matt
              2. White - matt

Market	Range
U.S.A.	$45.00 - 65.00
Canada	$65.00 - 100.00
U.K.	£25.00 - 45.00

Shape 44   Vase

Designer: Mr. Symcox c.1933
Issued: c.1933 - by 1940
Size: 6", 15 cm
Colour: 1. Assorted decorations - satin matt
              2. White - matt

Market	Range
U.S.A.	$65.00 - 100.00
Canada	$100.00 - 150.00
U.K.	£40.00 - 60.00

Shape 45   **Ribbed vase**

Designer: Mr. Symcox c.1933
Issued: c.1933 - by 1940
Size: 3 ½", 8.9 cm
Colour: 1. Assorted decorations - satin matt
    2. White - matt

Market	Range
U.S.A.	$45.00 - 65.00
Canada	$65.00 - 100.00
U.K.	£25.00 - 45.00

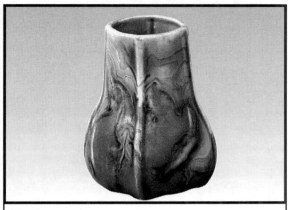

Shape 46   **Vase**

Designer: Mr. Symcox c.1933
Issued: c.1933 - by 1940
Size: 4", 10.1 cm
Colour: 1. Assorted decorations - satin matt
    2. White - matt

Market	Range
U.S.A.	$45.00 - 65.00
Canada	$65.00 - 100.00
U.K.	£25.00 - 45.00

Shape 47   **Vase/Lamp**

Designer: Mr. Symcox c.1933
Issued: c.1933 - by 1940
Size: 4", 10.1 cm
Colour: 1. Assorted decorations - satin matt
    2. White - matt

Market	Range
U.S.A.	$45.00 - 65.00
Canada	$65.00 - 100.00
U.K.	£25.00 - 45.00

Shape 50   **Leyden, vase**

Designer: Unknown
Issued: By 1930 - by 1937
Size: 11 ½", 29.2 cm
Colour: Assorted decorations - gloss

Market	Range
U.S.A.	$100.00 - 135.00
Canada	$150.00 - 225.00
U.K.	£60.00 - 85.00

Photograph not
available
at press time

Shape 51   **Opal, two-handled footed vase, with or without handles**

Designer:	Unknown
Issued:	By 1930 - by 1937
Size:	12", 30.5 cm
Colour:	Assorted decorations - gloss

Market	Range
U.S.A.	$100.00 - 135.00
Canada	$150.00 - 225.00
U.K.	£60.00 - 85.00

Shape 52   **Bude, vase**

Designer:	Unknown
Issued:	By 1931 - by 1937
Size:	10", 25.4 cm
Colour:	Assorted decorations - gloss

Market	Range
U.S.A.	$100.00 - 135.00
Canada	$150.00 - 225.00
U.K.	£60.00 - 85.00

Shape 54   **Roslin, vase**

Designer:	Unknown
Issued:	By 1926 - by 1937
Size:	10 ½", 26.7 cm
Colour:	Assorted decorations - gloss

Market	Range
U.S.A.	$100.00 - 135.00
Canada	$150.00 - 225.00
U.K.	£60.00 - 85.00

Shape 55   **Ryde, footed vase**

Designer:	Unknown
Issued:	By 1930 - by 1937
Size:	10 ½", 26.7 cm
Colour:	Assorted decorations - gloss

Market	Range
U.S.A.	$100.00 - 135.00
Canada	$150.00 - 225.00
U.K.	£60.00 - 85.00

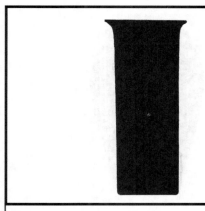

Shape 56   **Rose, vase in three sizes**

Designer:	Unknown
Issued:	By 1930 - by 1937
Sizes:	1. Large — 8 ½", 21.6 cm
	2. Medium — 7 ½", 19.1 cm
	3. Small — 6 ½", 16.5 cm
Colour:	Assorted decorations - gloss

Market	Large	Medium	Small
U.S.A.	$75.00-125.00	$75.00-125.00	$65.00-100.00
Canada	$125.00-175.00	$125.00-175.00	$100.00-150.00
U.K.	£45.00-75.00	£45.00-75.00	£40.00-60.00

Shape 57   **Rhos, vase**

Designer:	Unknown
Issued:	By 1929 - by 1937
Size:	9", 22.9 cm
Colour:	Assorted decorations - gloss

Market	Range
U.S.A.	$75.00 - 125.00
Canada	$125.00 - 175.00
U.K.	£45.00 - 75.00

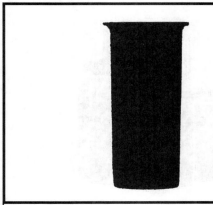

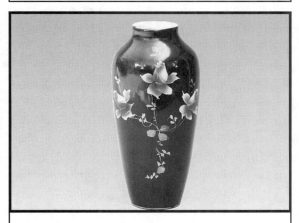

Shape 58   **Flora, vase in three sizes**

Designer:	Unknown
Issued:	By 1926 - by 1937
Sizes:	1. Large — 8 ½", 21.6 cm
	2. Medium — 7 ½", 19.1 cm
	3. Small — 6 ½", 16.5 cm
Colour:	Assorted decorations - gloss

Market	Large	Medium	Small
U.S.A .	$75.00-125.00	$75.00-125.00	$65.00-100.00
Canada	$125.00-175.00	$125.00-175.00	$100.00-150.00
U.K.	£45.00 - 75.00	£45.00-75.00	£40.00-60.00

Shape 59   **Len, vase in three sizes**

Designer:	Unknown
Issued:	By 1923 - by 1937
Sizes:	1. Large — 8 ½", 21.6 cm
	2. Medium — 7 ½", 19.1 cm
	3. Small — 5 ½", 14 cm
Colour:	Assorted decorations - gloss

Market	Large	Medium	Small
U.S.A.	$75.00-125.00	$75.00-125.00	$45.00-65.00
Canada	$125.00-175.00	$125.00-175.00	$65.00-100.00
U.K.	£45.00 - 75.00	£45.00-75.00	£25.00-45.00

Shape 60   **Windsor, vase**

Designer: Unknown
Issued: By 1930 - by 1937
Size: 9", 22.9 cm
Colour: Assorted decorations - gloss

Market	Range
U.S.A.	$75.00 - 125.00
Canada	$125.00 - 175.00
U.K.	£45.00 - 75.00

Shape 61   **Regal, vase**

Designer: Unknown
Issued: By 1926 - by 1937
Size: 6 ½", 16.5 cm
Colour: Assorted decorations - gloss

Market	Range
U.S.A.	$65.00 - 100.00
Canada	$100.00 - 150.00
U.K.	£40.00 - 60.00

Shape 64   **Alfa, vase**

Designer: Unknown
Issued: c.1933 - by 1940
Size: 8 ½", 21.6 cm
Colour: 1. Assorted decorations - satin matt
         2. White - matt

Market	Range
U.S.A.	$75.00 - 125.00
Canada	$125.00 - 175.00
U.K.	£45.00 - 75.00

Shape 65   **Cleo, vase**

Designer: Unknown
Issued: c.1933 - by 1940
Size: 8", 20.3 cm
Colour: 1. Assorted decorations - satin matt
         2. White - matt

Market	Range
U.S.A.	$75.00 - 125.00
Canada	$125.00 - 175.00
U.K.	£45.00 - 75.00

Shape 66   Crete, vase

Designer:	Unknown
Issued:	c.1933 - by 1940
Size:	8", 20.3 cm
Colour:	1. Assorted decorations - satin matt
	2. White - matt

Market	Range
U.S.A.	$75.00 - 125.00
Canada	$125.00 - 175.00
U.K.	£45.00 - 75.00

Shape 68   Arran, vase

Designer:	Unknown
Issued:	c.1933 - by 1940
Size:	4 ½", 11.9 cm
Colour:	1. Assorted decorations - satin matt
	2. White - matt

Market	Range
U.S.A.	$45.00 - 65.00
Canada	$65.00 - 100.00
U.K.	£25.00 - 45.00

Shape 69   Eler , vase

Designer:	Unknown
Issued:	c.1933 - by 1963
Size:	4 ¼", 10.8 cm
Colour:	1. Assorted decorations - satin matt
	2. White - matt

Market	Range
U.S.A.	$45.00 - 65.00
Canada	$65.00 - 100.00
U.K.	£25.00 - 45.00

Shape 70   Ciro, vase

Designer:	Unknown
Issued:	c.1933 - by 1940
Size:	7", 17.8 cm
Colour:	1. Assorted decorations - satin matt
	2. White - matt

Market	Range
U.S.A.	$75.00 - 125.00
Canada	$125.00 - 175.00
U.K.	£45.00 - 75.00

Shape 71　　**Delta, vase**

Designer:	Unknown
Issued:	c.1933 - by 1940
Size:	9", 22.9 cm
Colour:	1. Assorted decorations
	2. White - matt

Market	Range
U.S.A.	$75.00 - 125.00
Canada	$125.00 - 175.00
U.K.	£45.00 - 75.00

Shape 73　　**Elite, vase**

Designer:	Unknown
Issued:	c.1934 - by 1940
Size:	8", 20.3 cm
Colour:	1. Assorted decorations - satin matt
	2. White - matt

Market	Range
U.S.A.	$75.00 - 125.00
Canada	$125.00 - 175.00
U.K.	£45.00 - 75.00

Shape 75　　**Vase/Lamp base**

Designer:	Mr. Symcox c.1933
Issued:	c.1933 - by 1940
Size:	6", 15.0 cm
Colour:	1. Assorted decorations - satin matt
	2. White - matt

Market	Range
U.S.A.	$65.00 - 100.00
Canada	$100.00 - 150.00
U.K.	£40.00 - 60.00

Shape 76　　**Vase**

Designer:	Mr. Symcox c.1933
Issued:	c.1934 - by 1940
Size:	Unknown
Colour:	1. Assorted decorations - satin matt
	2. White - matt

Market	Range
U.S.A.	$75.00 - 125.00
Canada	$125.00 - 175.00
U.K.	£45.00 - 75.00

Shape 77   **Vase**

Designer: Mr. Symcox c.1933
Issued: c.1934 - by 1940
Size: 9", 22.9 cm
Colour: 1. Assorted decorations - satin matt
          2. White - matt

Market	Range
U.S.A.	$75.00 - 125.00
Canada	$125.00 - 175.00
U.K.	£45.00 - 75.00

Shape 79   **Vase**

Designer: Mr. Symcox c.1933
Issued: c.1934 - by 1940
Size: 8", 20.3 cm
Colour: 1. Assorted decorations - satin matt
          2. White - matt

Market	Range
U.S.A.	$75.00 - 125.00
Canada	$125.00 - 175.00
U.K.	£45.00 - 75.00

Shape 80/1/2   **Vase, in two sizes**

Designer: Mr. Symcox c.1933
Issued: c.1934 - by 1954
Size: 1. Shape 80/1 — 10 ½", 26.7 cm
          2. Shape 80/2 — unknown
Colour: 1. Assorted decorations - satin matt
          2. White - matt

Market	Range 80/1	Range 80/2
U.S.A.	$100.00 - 135.00	$75.00 - 125.00
Canada	$150.00 - 225.00	$125.00 - 175.00
U.K.	£60.00 - 85.00	£45.00 - 75.00

Shape 90   **Vase**

Designer: Mr. Symcox c.1933
Issued: c.1934 - by 1940
Size: 9", 22.9 cm
Colour: 1. Assorted decorations - satin matt
          2. White - matt

Market	Range
U.S.A.	$75.00 - 125.00
Canada	$125.00 - 175.00
U.K.	£45.00 - 75.00

Shape 93   **Vase**

Designer: Mr. Symcox c.1933
Issued: c.1934 - by 1954
Size: 7 ½", 19.0 cm
Colour: 1. Assorted decorations - satin matt
            2. White - matt

Market	Range
U.S.A.	$75.00 - 125.00
Canada	$125.00 - 175.00
U.K.	£45.00 - 75.00

Shape 95   **Vase, three-handled**

Designer: Mr. Symcox c.1933
Issued: c.1934 - by 1940
Size: 10", 25.4 cm
Colour: 1. Assorted decorations - satin matt
            2. White - matt

Market	Range
U.S.A.	$100.00 - 135.00
Canada	$150.00 - 225.00
U.K.	£60.00 - 85.00

Shape 96   **Vase**

Designer: Mr. Symcox c.1933
Issued: c.1934 - by 1940
Size: 8", 20.3 cm
Colour: 1. Assorted decorations - satin matt
            2. White - matt

Market	Range
U.S.A.	$75.00 - 125.00
Canada	$125.00 - 175.00
U.K.	£45.00 - 75.00

Shape 97   **Vase**

Designer: Mr. Symcox c.1933
Issued: c.1934 - by 1940
Size: 5 ½", 14 cm
Colour: 1. Assorted decorations - satin matt
            2. White - matt

Market	Range
U.S.A.	$45.00 - 65.00
Canada	$65.00 - 100.00
U.K.	£25.00 - 45.00

Shape 100   Vase

Designer: Mr. Symcox c.1933
Issued: c.1934 - by 1940
Size: 8", 20.3 cm
Colour: 1. Assorted decorations - satin matt
          2. White - matt

Market	Range
U.S.A.	$75.00 - 125.00
Canada	$125.00 - 175.00
U.K.	£45.00 - 75.00

Shape 101   Vase

Designer: Mr. Symcox c.1933
Issued: c.1934 - by 1966
Size: 6 ¼", 15.9 cm
Colours: 1. Various decorations - satin matt
           2. White or black - matt

Market	Range
U.S.A.	$65.00 - 100.00
Canada	$100.00 - 150.00
U.K.	£40.00 - 60.00

Shape 102   Vase

Designer: Mr. Symcox c.1933
Issued: c.1934 - by 1940
Size: 9", 22.9 cm
Colour: 1. Assorted decorations - satin matt
          2. White - matt

Market	Range
U.S.A.	$75.00 - 125.00
Canada	$125.00 - 175.00
U.K.	£45.00 - 75.00

Shape 105/1/2/3 Lille, vase with cover in three sizes

Designer: Unknown
Issued: By 1929 - by 1937
Size: 1. Shape 105/1 — 10 ½", 26.7 cm
        2. Shape 105/2 — Unknown
        3. Shape 105/3 — Unknown
Colour: Assorted decorations - gloss

Market	105/1	105/2	105/3
U.S.A.	$100.00-135.00	$75.00-125.00	$75.00-125.00
Canada	$150.00-225.00	$125.00-175.00	$125.00-175.00
U.K.	£60.00-85.00	£45.00-75.00	£45.00-75.00

Shape 106   Blythe, vase

Designer:	Unknown
Issued:	By 1923 - by 1937
Size:	9", 22.9 cm
Colour:	Assorted decorations - gloss

Market	Range
U.S.A.	$75.00 - 125.00
Canada	$125.00 - 175.00
U.K.	£45.00 - 75.00

Shape 107   Sparta, vase

Designer:	Unknown
Issued:	By 1930 - by 1937
Size:	9 ½", 24 cm
Colour:	Assorted decorations - gloss

Market	Range
U.S.A.	$75.00 - 125.00
Canada	$125.00 - 175.00
U.K.	£45.00 - 75.00

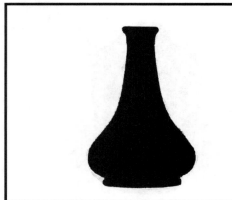

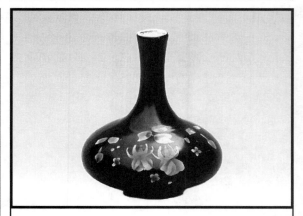

Shape 108   York, vase

Designer:	Unknown
Issued:	By 1930 - by 1937
Size:	9", 22.9 cm
Colour:	Assorted decorations - gloss

Market	Range
U.S.A.	$75.00 - 125.00
Canada	$125.00 - 175.00
U.K.	£45.00 - 75.00

Shape 109   Lily, vase

Designer:	Unknown
Issued:	By 1923 - by 1937
Size:	5 ½", 14 cm
Colour:	Assorted decorations - gloss

Market	Range
U.S.A.	$45.00 - 65.00
Canada	$65.00 - 100.00
U.K.	£25.00 - 45.00

Shape 110/1/2 Bell, vase

Designer:	Unknown
Issued:	By 1930 - by 1937
Size:	1. Shape 110/1 — 6 ¼", 15.9 cm
	2. Shape 110/2 — 7 ¼", 18.4 cm
Colour:	Assorted decorations - gloss

Market	Range110/1	Range110/2
U.S.A.	$65.00 - 100.00	$75.00 - 125.00
Canada	$100.00 - 150.00	$125.00 - 175.00
U.K.	£40.00 - 60.00	£45.00 - 75.00

Shape 111   Lynton, vase

Designer:	Unknown
Issued:	By 1930 - by 1937
Size:	7 ½", 19.1 cm
Colour:	Assorted decorations - gloss

Market	Range
U.S.A.	$75.00 - 125.00
Canada	$125.00 - 175.00
U.K.	£45.00 - 75.00

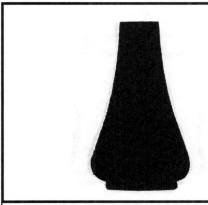

Shape 113   Kew, vase

Designer:	Unknown
Issued:	By 1923 - by 1937
Size:	12", 30.5 cm
Colour:	Assorted decorations - gloss

Market	Range
U.S.A.	$100.00 - 135.00
Canada	$150.00 - 225.00
U.K.	£60.00 - 85.00

Shape 115   Ruby, vase

Designer:	Unknown
Issued:	By 1930 - by 1937
Size:	9", 22.9 cm
Colour:	Assorted decorations - gloss

Market	Range
U.S.A.	$75.00 - 125.00
Canada	$125.00 -175.00
U.K.	£45.00 - 75.00

Shape 116   Vase/Lamp base

Designer:	Mr. Symcox c.1933
IssuedL:	c.1934 - 1940
Size:	Unknown
Colour:	1. Assorted decorations - satin matt
	2. White - matt

Market	Range
U.S.A.	$75.00 - 125.00
Canada	$125.00 - 175.00
U.K.	£45.00 - 75.00

Shape 117   Vase

Designer:	Mr. Symcox c.1933
Issued:	c.1934 - by 1940
Size:	5", 12.7 cm
Colour:	1. Assorted decorations - satin matt
	2. White - matt

Market	Range
U.S.A.	$65.00 - 100.00
Canada	$100.00 - 150.00
U.K.	£40.00 - 60.00

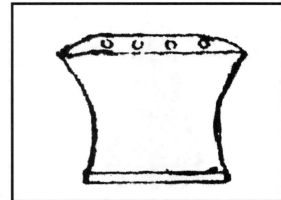

Shape 118   Vase with flower holder

Designer:	Mr. Symcox c.1933
Issued:	c.1934 - 1940
Size:	Unknown
Colour:	1. Assorted decorations - satin matt
	2. White - matt

Market	Range
U.S.A.	$75.00 - 125.00
Canada	$125.00 - 175.00
U.K.	£45.00 - 75.00

Shape 120   Vase

Designer:	Mr. Symcox c.1934
Issued:	c.1934 - by 1966
Size:	8 ½", 21.6 cm
Colour:	1. Assorted decorations - satin matt
	2. White or black - matt

Market	Range
U.S.A.	$75.00 - 125.00
Canada	$125.00 - 175.00
U.K.	£45.00 - 75.00

Shape 121   Vase

Designer:	Albert Hallam c.1934
Issued:	c.1934 - by 1940
Size:	7", 17.8 cm
Colour:	1. Assorted decorations - satin matt
	2. White - matt

Market	Range
U.S.A.	$65.00 - 100.00
Canada	$100.00 - 150.00
U.K.	£40.00 - 60.00

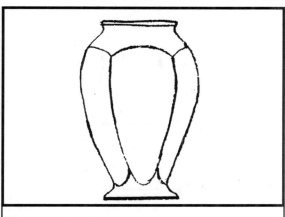

Shape 122   Dresden, vase

Designer:	Albert Hallam c.1934
Issued:	c.1934 - by 1940
Size:	Unknown
Colour:	1. Assorted decorations - satin matt
	2. White - matt

Market	Range
U.S.A.	$75.00 - 125.00
Canada	$125.00 - 175.00
U.K.	£45.00 - 75.00

Shape 124   Vase

Designer:	Albert Hallam c.1934
Issued:	c.1934 - by 1940
Size:	5 ½", 14 cm
Colour:	1. Assorted decorations - satin matt
	2. White - matt

Market	Range
U.S.A.	$45.00 - 65.00
Canada	$65.00 - 100.00
U.K.	£25.00 - 45.00

Shape 126   Vase

Designer:	Mr. Owen c.1934
Issued:	c.1934 - by 1940
Size:	9", 22.9 cm
Colour:	1. Assorted decorations - satin matt
	2. White - matt

Market	Range
U.S.A.	$75.00 - 125.00
Canada	$125.00 - 175.00
U.K.	£45.00 - 75.00

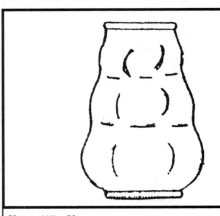

Shape 127   Vase

Designer: Mr. Symcox c.1934
Issued: c.1934 - by 1940
Size: Unknown
Colour: 1. Assorted decorations - satin matt
             2. White - matt

Market	Range
U.S.A.	$75.00 - 125.00
Canada	$125.00 - 175.00
U.K.	£45.00 - 75.00

Shape 128   Vase

Designer: Mr. Symcox c.1934
Issued: 1935 - by 1954
Reissued: 1962 - 1967; and 1968 - by 1972 as the (Caprice
             Series) Colours: Orange, turquoise, yellow
Size: 11 ½", 29.2 cm
Colour: 1. Various decorations - satin matt
             2. White or black - matt

Market	Range
U.S.A.	$100.00 - 135.00
Canada	$150.00 - 225.00
U.K.	£60.00 - 85.00

Shape 130   Vase

Designer: Mr. Symcox c.1934
Issued: c.1934 - by 1940
Size: 5 ½", 14 cm
Colour: 1. Assorted decorations - satin matt
             2. White - matt

Market	Range
U.S.A.	$40.00 - 65.00
Canada	$65.00 - 100.00
U.K.	£25.00 - 45.00

Shape 132   Vase

Designer: Mr. Symcox c.1934
Issued: c.1934 - by 1940
Size: 7 ½", 19.1 cm
Colour: 1. Assorted decorations - satin matt
             2. White - matt

Market	Range
U.S.A.	$45.00 -65.00
Canada	$65.00 - 100.00
U.K.	£45.00 - 75.00

Shape 133   **Vase**

Designer: Albert Hallam and Mr. Owen c.1934
Issued: c.1934 - by 1940
Height: 8 ½", 21.6 cm
Colour: 1. Assorted decorations - satin matt
          2. White - matt

Market	Range
U.S.A.	$75.00 - 125.00
Canada	$125.00 - 175.00
U.K.	£45.00 - 75.00

Shape 134   **Vase**

Designer: Mr. Owen c.1934
Issued: c.1934 - by 1940
Height: 10", 25.4 cm
Colour: 1. Assorted decorations - satin matt
          2. White - matt

Market	Range
U.S.A.	$100.00 - 135.00
Canada	$150.00 - 225.00
U.K.	£60.00 - 85.00

Shape 135   **Vase/Lamp base**

Designer: Unknown c.1934
Issued: c.1934 - by 1940
Height :   5 ½", 14 cm
Colour: 1. Assorted decorations - satin matt
          2. White - matt

Market	Range
U.S.A.	$45.00 - 65.00
Canada	$65.00 - 100.00
U.K.	£25.00 - 45.00

Shape 138   **Vase, two-handled**

Designer: Mr. Symcox c.1934
Issued: c.1934 - by 1940
Height: 3 ½", 8.9 cm
Colour: 1. Assorted decorations - satin matt
          2. White - matt

Market	Range
U.S.A.	$45.00 - 65.00
Canada	$65.00 - 100.00
U.K.	£25.00 - 45.00

Shape 142   Vase

Designer: Mr. Symcox c.1934
Issued: c.1934 - by 1940
Height :   6", 15 cm
Colour: 1. Assorted decorations - satin matt
              2. White - matt

Market	Range
U.S.A.	$65.00 - 100.00
Canada	$100.00 - 150.00
U.K.	£40.00 - 60.00

Shape 143   Vase/Lamp

Designer: Albert Hallam c.1934
Issued: c.1934 - by 1940
Height: 9", 22.9 cm
Colour: 1. Assorted decorations - satin matt
              2. White - matt

Market	Range
U.S.A.	$7500 - 125.00
Canada	$125.00 - 175.00
U.K.	£45.00 - 75.00

Shape 144   Vase/Lamp

Designer: Albert Hallam c.1934
Issued: c.1934 - by 1940
Height :   10 ¾", 27.8 cm
Colour: 1. Assorted decorations - satin matt
              2. White - matt

Market	Range
U.S.A.	$100.00 - 135.00
Canada	$150.00 - 200.00
U.K.	£60.00 - 80.00

Shape 145   Vase

Designer: Albert Hallam c.1934
Issued: c.1934 - by 1940
Height: 6", 15 cm
Colour: 1. Assorted decorations - satin matt
              2. White - matt

Market	Range
U.S.A.	$65.00 - 100.00
Canada	$100.00 - 150.00
U.K.	£40.00 - 60.00

Shape 147   Vase

Designer: Mr. Symcox c.1934
Issued: c.1934 - by 1940
Height :   Unknown
Colour: 1. Assorted decorations - satin matt
            2. White - matt

Market	Range
U.S.A.	$75.00 - 125.00
Canada	$125.00 - 175.00
U.K.	£45.00 - 75.00

Shape 149   Vase, two-handled

Designer: Mr. Symcox c.1934
Issued: c.1934 - by 1940
Height: 6 ½", 16.5 cm
Colour: 1. Assorted decorations - satin matt
            2. White - matt

Market	Range
U.S.A.	$65.00 - 100.00
Canada	$100.00 - 150.00
U.K.	£40.00 - 60.00

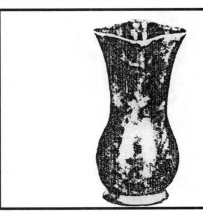

Shape 152   Vase

Designer: Mr. Symcox c.1934
Issued: c.1934 - by 1940
Height :   11 ½", 29.2 cm
Colour: 1. Assorted decorations - satin matt
            2. White - matt

Market	Range
U.S.A.	$100.00 - 135.00
Canada	$150.00 - 225.00
U.K.	£60.00 - 85.00

Shape 153   Vase

Designer: Mr. Symcox c.1934
Issued: c.1934 - by 1963
Height: 5 ¼", 13.3 cm
Colour: 1. Assorted decorations - satin matt
            2. White - matt

Market	Range
U.S.A.	$45.00 - 65.00
Canada	$65.00 - 100.00
U.K.	£25.00 - 45.00

Shape 154   Vase

Designer: Mr. Symcox c.1934
Issued: c.1934 - by 1940
Height: 5", 12.7 cm
Colour: 1. Assorted decorations - satin matt
             2. White - matt

Market	Range
U.S.A.	$45.00 - 65.00
Canada	$65.00 - 100.00
U.K.	£25.00 - 45.00

Shape 158   Vase, two-handled

Designer: Mr. Symcox c.1933
Issued: c.1934 - by 1940
Height: 5 ¼", 13.3 cm
Colour: 1. Assorted decorations - satin matt
             2. White - matt

Market	Range
U.S.A.	$45.00 - 65.00
Canada	$65.00 - 100.00
U.K.	£25.00 - 45.00

Shape 159   Vase, two-handled

Designer: Mr. Symcox c.1934
Issued: c.1934 - by 1940
Height: 5 ½", 14 cm
Colour: 1. Assorted decorations - satin matt
             2. White - matt

Market	Range
U.S.A.	$45.00 - 65.00
Canada	$65.00 - 100.00
U.K.	£25.00 - 45.00

Shape 161   Vase, two sizes

Designer: Mr. Symcox c.1934
Issued: c.1934 - by 1940
Heights: 1. 11 ¾", 29.8 cm
             2. Unknown
Colour: 1. Assorted decorations - satin matt
             2. White - matt

Market	Range161/1	Range161/2
U.S.A.	$100.00 - 135.00	$75.00 - 125.00
Canada	$150.00 - 225.00	$125.00 - 175.00
U.K.	£60.00 - 85.00	£45.00 - 75.00

Shape 164   Vase

Designer:	Mr. Symcox c.1934
Issued:	c.1934 - by 1940
Height :	6 ¾", 17.2 cm
Colour:	1. Assorted decorations - satin matt
	2. White - matt

Market	Range
U.S.A.	$65.00 - 100.00
Canada	$100.00 - 150.00
U.K.	£40.00 - 60.00

Shape 166   Vase, two-handled

Designer:	Mr. Symcox c.1934
Issued:	c.1934 - by 1940
Height:	6 ½", 16.5 cm
Colour:	1. Assorted decorations - satin matt
	2. White - matt

Market	Range
U.S.A.	$65.00 - 100.00
Canada	$100.00 - 150.00
U.K.	£40.00 - 60.00

Shape 167   Vase, two-handled

Designer:	Mr. Symcox c.1934
Issued:	c.1934 - by 1940
Height :	8 ½", 21.6 cm
Colour:	1. Assorted decorations - satin matt
	2. White - matt

Market	Range
U.S.A.	$75.00 - 125.00
Canada	$125.00 - 175.00
U.K.	£45.00 - 75.00

Shape 168   Vase, two-handled

Designer:	Mr. Symcox c.1934
Issued:	c.1934 - by 1940
Height:	7 ½", 19.1 cm
Colour:	1. Assorted decorations - satin matt
	2. White - matt

Market	Range
U.S.A.	$75.00 - 125.00
Canada	$125.00 - 175.00
U.K.	£45.00 - 75.00

Shape 169   Vase

Designer: Mr. Owen c.1934
Issued: c.1934 - by 1940
Height :   9", 22.9 cm
Colour: 1. Assorted decorations - satin matt
              2. White - matt

Market	Range
U.S.A.	$75.00 - 125.00
Canada	$125.00 - 175.00
U.K.	£45.00 - 75.00

Shape 180   Vase

Designer: Mr. Symcox c.1934
Issued: c.1934 - by 1954
Height: 8", 20.3 cm
Colour: 1 Assorted decorations - satin matt
              2. White - matt

Market	Range
U.S.A.	$75.00 - 125.00
Canada	$125.00 - 175.00
U.K.	£45.00 - 75.00

Shape 181   Vase

Designer: Mr. Symcox c.1934
Issued: c.1934 - by 1940
Height :   7", 17.8 cm
Colour: 1. Assorted decorations - satin matt
              2. White - matt

Market	Range
U.S.A.	$65.00 - 100.00
Canada	$100.00 - 150.00
U.K.	£40.00 - 60.00

Shape 182   Vase, two- handled

Designer: Mr. Symcox c.1934
Issued: c.1934 - by 1940
Height: 11 ¼", 28.5 cm
Colour: 1. Assorted decorations - satin matt
              2. White - matt

Market	Range
U.S.A.	$100.00 - 135.00
Canada	$150.00 - 225.00
U.K.	£60.00 - 85.00

Shape 183   Vase, two-handled

Designer:	Mr. Symcox c.1934
Issued:	c.1934 - by 1940
Height :	7 ¾", 19.7 cm
Colour:	1. Assorted decorations - satin matt
	2. White - matt

Market	Range
U.S.A.	$75.00 - 125.00
Canada	$125.00 - 175.00
U.K.	£45.00 - 75.00

Shape 184   Vase

Designer:	Mr. Symcox c.1934
Issued:	c.1934 - by 1940
Height:	6 ½", 16.5 cm
Colour:	1. Assorted decorations - satin matt
	2. White - matt

Market	Range
U.S.A.	$65.00 - 100.00
Canada	$100.00 - 150.00
U.K.	£40.00 - 60.00

Shape 185   Vase, two-handled

Designer:	Mr. Symcox c.1934
Issued:	c.1934 - by 1940
Height :	8 ¼", 21 cm
Colour:	1. Assorted decorations - satin matt
	2. White - matt

Market	Range
U.S.A.	$75.00 - 125.00
Canada	$125.00 - 175.00
U.K.	£45.00 - 75.00

Shape 186   Vase, two-handled

Designer:	Mr. Symcox c.1934
Issued:	c.1934 - by 1940
Height:	7 ½", 19.1 cm
Colour:	1. Assorted decorations - satin matt
	2. White - matt

Market	Range
U.S.A.	$75.00 - 125.00
Canada	$125.00 - 175.00
U.K.	£45.00 - 75.00

Shape 187   Vase

Designer: Mr. Symcox c.1934
Issued: c.1934 - by 1940
Height :   8", 20.3 cm
Colour: 1. Assorted decorations - satin matt
              2. White - matt

Market	Range
U.S.A.	$75.00 - 125.00
Canada	$125.00 - 175.00
U.K.	£45.00 - 75.00

Shape 188   Vase

Designer: Mr. Symcox c.1934
Issued: c.1934 - by 1940
Height: 5", 12.7 cm
Colour: 1. Assorted decorations - satin matt
              2. White - matt

Market	Range
U.S.A.	$45.00 - 65.00
Canada	$65.00 - 100.00
U.K.	£25.00 - 45.00

Shape 189   Vase

Designer: Mr. Symcox c.1934
Issued: c.1934 - by 1940
Height :   8 ¾", 22.2 cm
Colour: 1. Assorted decorations - satin matt
              2. White - matt

Market	Range
U.S.A.	$75.00 - 125.00
Canada	$125.00 - 175.00
U.K.	£45.00 - 75.00

Shape 190   Vase, two-handled

Designer: Mr. Symcox c.1934
Issued: c.1934 - by 1940
Height: 7 ¾", 19.7 cm
Colour: 1. Assorted decorations - satin matt
              2. White - matt

Market	Range
U.S.A.	$75.00 - 125.00
Canada	$125.00 - 175.00
U.K.	£45.00 - 75.00

Shape 191   Vase

Designer: Mr. Symcox c.1934
Issued: c.1934 - by 1940
Height :   Unknown
Colour: 1. Assorted decorations - satin matt
            2. White - matt

Market	Range
U.S.A.	$65.00 - 100.00
Canada	$100.00 - 150.00
U.K.	£40.00 - 60.00

Shape 192   Vase

Designer: Mr. Symcox c.1934
Issued: c.1934 - by 1940
Height: 7", 17.8 cm
Colour: 1. Assorted decorations - satin matt
            2. White - matt

Market	Range
U.S.A.	$65.00 - 100.00
Canada	$100.00 - 150.00
U.K.	£40.00 - 60.00

Shape 193   Vase

Designer: Mr. Symcox c.1934
Issued: c.1934 - by 1940
Height :   6", 15.0 cm
Colour: 1. Assorted decorations - satin matt
            2. White - matt

Market	Range
U.S.A.	$65.00 - 100.00
Canada	$100.00 - 150.00
U.K.	£40.00 - 60.00

Shape 194   Vase

Designer: Albert Hallam c.1934
Issued: c.1934 - by 1940
Height: Unknown
Colour: 1. Assorted decorations - satin matt
            2. White - matt

Market	Range
U.S.A.	$65.00 - 100.00
Canada	$100.00 - 150.00
U.K.	£40.00 - 60.00

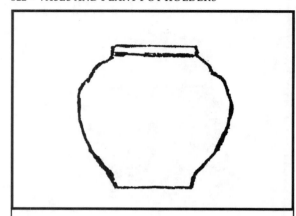

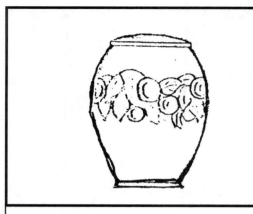

Shape 195   Vase

Designer:	Albert Hallam c.1934
Issued:	c.1934 - by 1940
Height :	Unknown
Colour:	1. Assorted decorations - satin matt
	2. White - matt

Market	Range
U.S.A.	$65.00 - 100.00
Canada	$100.00 - 150.00
U.K.	£40.00 - 60.00

Shape 196   Vase

Designer:	Albert Hallam and Mr. Hayward c.1934
Issued:	c.1934 - by 1940
Height:	Unknown
Colour:	1. Assorted decorations - satin matt
	2. White - matt

Market	Range
U.S.A.	$65.00 - 100.00
Canada	$100.00 - 150.00
U.K.	£40.00 - 60.00

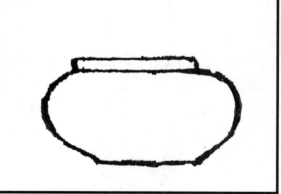

Shape 198   Vase, two-handled

Designer:	Mr. Symcox and Mr. Hayward c.1934
Issued:	c.1934 - by 1940
Height :	7 ¼", 18.4 cm
Colour:	1. Assorted decorations - satin matt
	2. White - matt

Market	Range
U.S.A.	$65.00 - 100.00
Canada	$100.00 - 150.00
U.K.	£40.00 - 60.00

Shape 204   Vase

Designer:	Albert Hallam c.1934
Issued:	c.1934 - by 1940
Height:	Unknown
Colour:	1. Assorted decorations - satin matt
	2. White - matt

Market	Range
U.S.A.	$65.00 - 100.00
Canada	$100.00 - 150.00
U.K.	£40.00 - 60.00

Shape 208   Vase

Designer: Unknown
Issued: c.1934 - by 1940
Height: 6 ½", 16.5 cm
Colour: 1. Assorted decorations - satin matt
             2. White - matt

Market	Range
U.S.A.	$45.00 - 65.00
Canada	$65.00 - 100.00
U.K.	£25.00 - 45.00

Shape 267   Posy holder for vase

Designer   Unknown c.1934
Issued: c.1934 - by 1940
Height: 3 ¼", 8.3 cm
Colour: 1. Assorted decorations - satin matt
            2. White - matt

Market	Range
U.S.A.	$45.00 - 65.00
Canada	$65.00 - 100.00
U.K.	£25.00 - 45.00

Shape 289   Vase

Designer: Mr. Symcox in 1934
Issued: 1934 - by 1963
Height :   4 ¼", 10.8 cm
Colour: 1. Assorted decorations - satin matt
             2. White - matt

Market	Range
U.S.A.	$45.00 - 65.00
Canada	$65.00 - 100.00
U.K.	£25.00 - 45.00

Shape 290   Vase

Designer: Mr. Symcox in 1934
Issued: 1934 - by 1940
Height: 4", 10.1 cm
Colour: 1. Assorted decorations - satin matt
             2. White - matt

Market	Range
U.S.A.	$45.00 - 65.00
Canada	$65.00 - 100.00
U.K.	£25.00 - 45.00

Shape 341 **Vase**

Designer:	Mr. Symcox in 1935
Issued:	1935 - by 1940
Height :	Unknown
Colour:	1. Assorted decorations -satin matt
	2. White - matt

Market	Range
U.S.A.	$45.00 - 65.00
Canada	$65.00 - 100.00
U.K.	£25.00 - 45.00

Shape 345 **Vase**

Designer:	Mr. Symcox in 1935
Issued:	1935 - by 1940
Height:	Unknown
Colour:	1. Assorted decorations - satin matt
	2. White - matt

Market	Range
U.S.A.	$75.00 - 125.00
Canada	$125.00 - 175.00
U.K.	£45.00 - 75.00

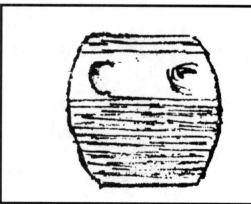

Shape 347 **Vase**

Designer:	Mr. Symcox in 1935
Issued:	1935 - by 1940
Height :	4 ½", 11.9 cm
Colour:	1. Assorted decorations -satin matt
	2. White - matt

Market	Range
U.S.A.	$45.00 - 65.00
Canada	$65.00 - 100.00
U.K.	£25.00 - 45.00

Shape 351 **Vase**

Designer:	Mr. Symcox in 1935
Issued:	1935 - by 1940
Height:	8 ½", 21.6 cm
Colour:	1. Assorted decorations - satin matt
	2. White - matt

Market	Range
U.S.A.	$75.00 - 125.00
Canada	$125.00 - 175.00
U.K.	£45.00 - 75.00

Shape 352   **Vase, two-handled**

Designer: Mr. Watkin in 1935
Issued: 1935 - by 1963
Height :   9 ¾", 24.7 cm
Colour: 1. Assorted decorations - satin matt
    2. White - matt

Market	Range
U.S.A.	$75.00 - 125.00
Canada	$125.00 - 175.00
U.K.	£45.00 - 75.00

Shape 353   **Vase, two-handled**

Designer: Mr. Symcox in 1935
Issued: 1935 - by 1940
Height: 6 ¼", 15.9 cm
Colour: 1. Assorted decorations - satin matt
    2. White - matt

Market	Range
U.S.A.	$65.00 - 100.00
Canada	$100.00 - 150.00
U.K.	£40.00 - 60.00

Shape 357   **Vase**

Designer: Mr. Symcox in 1935
Issued: 1935 - by 1940
Height :   4 ¾", 12.1 cm
Colour: 1. Assorted decorations - satin matt
    2. White - matt

Market	Range
U.S.A.	$45.00 - 65.00
Canada	$65.00 - 100.00
U.K.	£25.00 - 45.00

Shape 358   **Vase, two-handled**

Designer: Albert Hallam in 1935
Issued: 1935 - by 1954
Height: 7", 17.8 cm
Colour: 1. Assorted decorations - satin matt
    2. White - matt

Market	Range
U.S.A.	$65.00 - 100.00
Canada	$100.00 - 150.00
U.K.	£40.00 - 60.00

Shape 378/1/2 Plant pot holder, in two sizes

Designer: Mr. Symcox in 1936
Issued: 1936 - by 1940
Height: 1. 8 ¼", 21 cm
2. 7 ¼", 18.4 cm
Colour: 1. Assorted decorations - satin matt
2. White - matt

Market	Range 378/1	Range 378/2
U.S.A.	$75.00 - 100.00	$75.00 - 100.00
Canada	$125.00 - 150.00	$125.00 - 150.00
U.K.	£45.00 - 60.00	£45.00 - 60.00

Photograph not
available
at press time

Shape 385 Vase

Designer: Mr. Symcox in 1936
Issued: 1936 - by 1940
Height: 6", 15 cm
Colour: 1. Assorted decorations - satin matt
2. White - matt

Market	Range
U.S.A.	$65.00 - 100.00
Canada	$100.00 - 150.00
U.K.	£40.00 - 60.00

Shape 386 Vase

Designer: Mr. Symcox in 1936
Issued: 1936 - by 1954
Height : 10", 25.4 cm
Colour: 1. Assorted decorations - satin matt
2. White - matt

Market	Range
U.S.A.	$100.00 - 135.00
Canada	$150.00 - 225.00
U.K.	£60.00 - 85.00

Shape 395 Vase, two-handled

Designer: Mr. Symcox in 1936
Issued: 1936 - by 1963
Height: 6", 15 cm
Colour: 1. Assorted decorations - satin matt
2. White - matt

Market	Range
U.S.A.	$65.00 - 100.00
Canada	$100.00 - 150.00
U.K.	£40.00 - 60.00

Shape 396 Vase

Designer: Mr. Symcox in 1936
Issued: 1936 - by 1940
Height : 4", 10.1 cm
Colour: 1. Assorted decorations - satin matt
　　　　2. White - matt

Market	Range
U.S.A.	$65.00 - 100.00
Canada	$100.00 - 150.00
U.K.	£40.00 - 60.00

Shape 418 Vase

Designer: Mr. Symcox in 1936
Issued: 1936 - by 1940
Height: 6", 15 cm
Colour: 1. Assorted decorations - satin matt
　　　　2. White - matt

Market	Range
U.S.A.	$65.00 - 100.00
Canada	$100.00 - 150.00
U.K.	£40.00 - 60.00

Shape 428 Vase, two-handled

Designer: Mr. Symcox in 1936
Issued: 1936 - by 1940
Height : 8", 20.3 cm
Colour: 1. Assorted decorations -satin matt
　　　　2. White - matt

Market	Range
U.S.A.	$75.00 - 125.00
Canada	$125.00 - 175.00
U.K.	£45.00 - 75.00

Shape 429/1/2 Vase, two-handled

Designer: Mr. Owen in 1936
Issued: 1936 - by 1940
Heights : Unknown
Colour: 1. Assorted decorations - satin matt
　　　　2. White - matt

Market	Range
U.S.A.	$75.00 - 125.00
Canada	$125.00 - 175.00
U.K.	£45.00 - 75.00

Shape 431   Vase

Designer:	Mr. Symcox in 1936
Issued:	1936 - by 1940
Height :	7 ½", 19.1 cm
Colour:	1. Assorted decorations - satin matt
	2. White - matt

Market	Range
U.S.A.	$75.00 - 125.00
Canada	$125.00 - 175.00
U.K.	£45.00 - 75.00

Shape 432   Vase, two-handled

Designer:	Mr. Owen in 1936
Issued:	1936 - by 1940
Height:	11 ¼", 28.5 cm
Colour:	1. Assorted decorations - satin matt
	2. White - matt

Market	Range
U.S.A.	$75.00 - 125.00
Canada	$125.00 - 175.00
U.K.	£45.00 - 75.00

Shape 439   Vase, two-handled

Designer:	Mr. Symcox in 1936
Issued:	1936 - by 1940
Height :	5 ¼", 13.3 cm
Colour:	1. Assorted decorations - satin matt
	2. White - matt

Market	Range
U.S.A.	$45.00 - 65.00
Canada	$65.00 - 100.00
U.K.	£25.00 - 45.00

Shape 466   Vase

Designer:	Mr. Symcox in1937
Issued:	1937 - by 1940
Height:	Unknown
Colour:	1. Assorted decorations - satin matt
	2. White - matt

Market	Range
U.S.A.	$65.00 - 100.00
Canada	$100.00 - 150.00
U.K.	£40.00 - 60.00

Shape 473   Vase, two-handled

Designer: Mr. Symcox in 1937
Issued: 1937 - by 1940
Height :   Unknown
Colour: 1. Assorted decorations - satin matt
            2. White - matt

Market	Range
U.S.A.	$75.00 - 125.00
Canada	$125.00 - 175.00
U.K.	£45.00 - 75.00

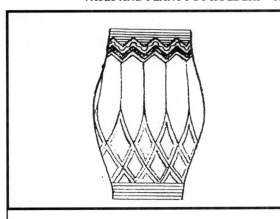

Shape 479   Vase

Designer: Mr. Symcox in 1937
Issued: 1937 - by 1940
Height: Unknown
Colour: 1. Assorted decorations - satin matt
            2. White - matt

Market	Range
U.S.A.	$75.00 - 125.00
Canada	$125.00 - 175.00
U.K.	£45.00 - 75.00

Photograph not
available
at press time

Shape 481   Vase

Designer: Mr. Symcox in 1937
Issued: 1937 - by 1940
Height :   5 ¼", 13.3 cm
Colour: 1. Assorted decorations - satin matt
            2. White - matt

Market	Range
U.S.A.	$45.00 - 6500
Canada	$65.00 - 100.00
U.K.	£25.00 - 45.00

Shape 482   Vase

Designer: Mr. Symcox in 1937
Issued: 1937 - by 1954
Height: 6", 15 cm
Colour: 1. Assorted decorations - satin matt
            2. White - matt

Market	Range
U.S.A.	$65.00 - 100.00
Canada	$100.00 - 150.00
U.K.	£40.00 - 60.00

Shape 484   Vase

Designer:	Mr. Symcox in 1937
Issued:	1937 - by 1940
Height :	7", 17.8 cm
Colour:	1. Assorted decorations - satin matt
	2. White - matt

Market	Range
U.S.A.	$65.00 - 100.00
Canada	$100.00 - 150.00
U.K.	£40.00 - 60.00

Shape 485   Vase

Designer:	Mr. Symcox in 1937
Issued:	1937 - by 1940
Height:	6 ¾", 17.2 cm
Colour:	1. Assorted decorations - satin matt
	2. White - matt

Market	Range
U.S.A.	$65.00 - 100.00
Canada	$100.00 - 150.00
U.K.	£40.00 - 60.00

Photograph not
available
at press time

Shape 486   Vase

Designer:	Mr. Symcox in 1937
Issued:	1937 - by 1940
Height :	Unknown
Colour:	1. Assorted decorations - satin matt
	2. White - matt

Market	Range
U.S.A.	$75.00 - 125.00
Canada	$125.00 - 175.00
U.K.	£45.00 - 75.00

Shape 487   Vase

Designer:	Mr. Symcox in 1937
Issued:	1937 - by 1940
Height:	7 ¾", 19.7 cm
Colour:	1. Assorted decorations - satin matt
	2. White - matt

Market	Range
U.S.A.	$75.00 - 125.00
Canada	$125.00 - 175.00
U.K.	£45.00 - 75.00

Shape number 350

Shape number 578

Shape number 448

Shape number 150

Shape number 183

Shape number 489

Shape number 353

Shape number 395

Shape number 184

Shape number 484

Shape number 135

"Ciro" Shape number 70

Shape number 192

"Eler" Shape number 69

"Louvain" shape; deco Garland

Shape number 357

"Wolstan"; Shape number 266

Shape number 28

Shape number 260

Shape number 137

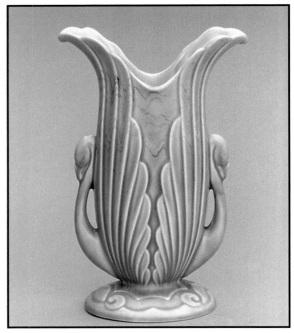

Shape number 1185

Shape number 25

Shape number 482

"Alfa" Shape number 64

Shape number 1749

Shape number 101

"Roslin" Shape number 54

Shape number 509

"Strawberry Fair" Shape numbers 1566, 1567, 1568

"Salad Ware" Shape numbers 210, 228, 238

"Tit-Willow" Shape numbers 1832, 1838, 1841, 1843

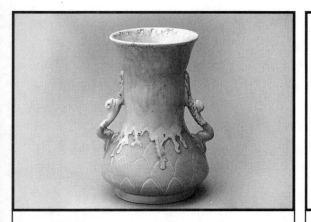

Shape 489   **Vase - two-handled (monkeys)**

Designer: Mr. Symcox in 1937
Issued: 1937 - by 1940
Height :   9 ½", 24 cm
Colour: 1. Assorted decorations - satin matt
            2. White - matt

Market	Range
U.S.A.	$75.00 - 125.00
Canada	$125.00 - 175.00
U.K.	£45.00 - 75.00

Shape 494   **Vase**

Designer: Mr. Watkin in 1937
Issued: 1937 - by 1940
Height: 11", 27.9 cm
Colour: 1. Assorted decorations -satin matt
            2. White - matt

Market	Range
U.S.A.	$100.00 - 135.00
Canada	$150.00 - 225.00
U.K.	£60.00 - 85.00

Shape 495   **Vase, two-handled**

Designer: Mr. Symcox in 1937
Issued: 1937 - by 1940
Height :   5 ½", 14 cm
Colour: 1. Assorted decorations -satin matt
            2. White - matt

Market	Range
U.S.A.	$45.00 - 65.00
Canada	$65.00 - 100.00
U.K.	£25.00 - 45.00

Shape 496   **Vase**

Designer: Mr. Watkin in 1937
Issued: 1937 - by 1940
Height: 8 ½", 21.6 cm
Colour: 1. Assorted decorations - satin matt
            2. White - matt

Market	Range
U.S.A.	$75.00 - 125.00
Canada	$125.00 - 175.00
U.K.	£45.00 - 75.00

Shape 499   Vase

Designer: Mr. Symcox in 1937
Issued: 1937 - by 1940
Height :   6 ½", 16.5 cm
Colour: 1. Assorted decorations - satin matt
             2. White - matt

Market	Range
U.S.A.	$65.00 -100.00
Canada	$100.00 - 150.00
U.K.	£40.00 - 60.00

Shape 500   Vase

Designer: Mr. Watkin in 1937
Issued: 1937 - by 1940
Height: 8", 20.3 cm
Colour: 1. Assorted decorations - satin matt
             2. White - matt

Market	Range
U.S.A.	$75.00 - 125.00
Canada	$125.00 - 175.00
U.K.	£45.00 - 75.00

Shape 504   Vase

Designer: Mr. Watkin in 1937
Issued: 1937 - 1954
Height :   6 ¾", 17.2 cm
Colour: 1. Assorted decorations - satin matt
             2. White - matt

Market	Range
U.S.A.	$65.00 - 100.00
Canada	$100.00 - 150.00
U.K.	£40.00 - 60.00

Shape 509   Vase

Designer: Mr. Symcox in 1937
Issued: 1938 - by 1940
Height: 9", 22.9 cm
Colour: 1. Assorted decorations - satin matt
             2. White - matt

Market	Range
U.S.A.	$75.00 - 125.00
Canada	$125.00 - 175.00
U.K.	£45.00 - 75.00

Photograph not
available
at press time

Shape 529   Vase

Designer: Mr. Watkin in 1937
Issued: 1938 - by 1940
Height: Unknown
Colour: 1. Assorted decorations - satin matt
             2. White - matt

Market	Range
U.S.A.	$75.00 - 125.00
Canada	$125.00 -175.00
U.K.	£45.00 - 75.00

Shape 543   Vase

Designer: Mr. Symcox in 1937
Issued: 1938 - by 1954
Height: 10", 25.4 cm
Colour: 1. Assorted decorations - satin matt
             2. White - matt

Market	Range
U.S.A.	$100.00 - 135.00
Canada	$150.00 - 225.00
U.K.	£60.00 - 85.00

Shape 545   Vase

Designer: Mr. Symcox in 1937
Issued: 1938 - by 1954
Height :   8", 20.3 cm
Colour: 1. Assorted decorations - satin matt
             2. White - matt

Market	Range
U.S.A.	$75.00 - 125.00
Canada	$125.00 - 175.00
U.K.	£45.00 - 75.00

Shape 546   Handled vase

Designer: Mr. Symcox in 1937
Issued: 1938 - by 1963
Height: 8", 20.3 cm
Colour: 1. Assorted decorations - satin matt
             2. White - matt

Market	Range
U.S.A.	$75.00 - 125.00
Canada	$125.00 - 175.00
U.K.	£45.00 - 75.00

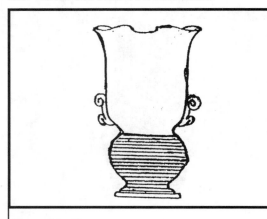

Shape 548   Vase

Designer:	Mr. Symcox in 1937
Issued:	1938 - by 1940
Height :	Unknown
Colour:	1. Assorted decorations - satin matt
	2. White - matt

Market	Range
U.S.A.	$75.00 - 125.00
Canada	$125.00 - 175.00
U.K.	£45.00 - 75.00

Shape 552   Vase

Designer:	Mr. Symcox in 1937
Issued:	1938 - by 1940
Height:	7 ½", 19.1 cm
Colour:	1. Assorted decorations - satin matt
	2. White - matt

Market	Range
U.S.A.	$75.00 - 125.00
Canada	$125.00 - 175.00
U.K.	£45.00 - 75.00

Photograph not
available
at press time

Shape 553   Vase

Designer:	Mr. Symcox in 1937
Issued:	1938 - by 1954
Height :	11", 27.9 cm
Colour:	1. Assorted decorations - satin matt
	2. White - matt

Market	Range
U.S.A.	$100.00 - 135.00
Canada	$150.00 - 225.00
U.K.	£60.00 - 85.00

Shape 558   Vase

Designer:	Mr. Symcox in 1937
Issued:	1938 - by 1940
Height:	Unknown
Colour:	1. Assorted decorations - satin matt
	2. White - matt

Market	Range
U.S.A.	$75.00 - 125.00
Canada	$125.00 - 175.00
U.K.	£45.00 - 75.00

Shape 560   Vase, two-handled

Designer: Mr. Symcox in 1937
Issued: 1938 - by 1940
Height :   10", 25.4 cm
Colour: 1. Assorted decorations - satin matt
             2. White - matt

Market	Range
U.S.A.	$75.00 - 125.00
Canada	$125.00 - 175.00
U.K.	£45.00 - 75.00

Shape 562   Vase, two-handled

Designer: Mr. Symcox in 1937
Issued: 1938 - by 1940
Height: 5", 12.7 cm
Colour: 1. Assorted decorations - satin matt
             2. White - matt

Market	Range
U.S.A.	$45.00 - 65.00
Canada	$65.00 - 100.00
U.K.	£25.00 - 45.00

Shape 563   Vase, two-handled

Designer: Mr. Symcox in 1937
Issued: 1938 - by 1940
Height :   8", 20.3 cm
Colour: 1. Assorted decorations - satin matt
             2. White - matt

Market	Range
U.S.A.	$75.00 - 125.00
Canada	$125.00 - 175.00
U.K.	£45.00 - 75.00

Shape 566   Vase, two-handled

Designer: Mr. Symcox in 1937
Issued: 1938 - by 1940
Height: 6 ¾", 17.2 cm
Colour: 1. Assorted decorations - satin matt
             2. White - matt

Market	Range
U.S.A.	$65.00 - 100.00
Canada	$100.00 - 150.00
U.K.	£40.00 - 60.00

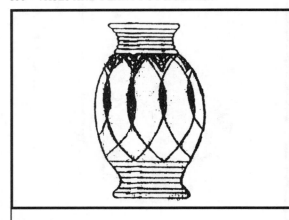

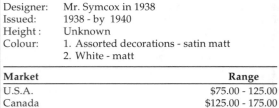

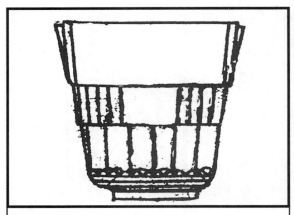

Shape 573   Vase

Designer:	Mr. Symcox in 1938
Issued:	1938 - by 1940
Height :	Unknown
Colour:	1. Assorted decorations - satin matt
	2. White - matt

Market	Range
U.S.A.	$75.00 - 125.00
Canada	$125.00 - 175.00
U.K.	£45.00 - 75.00

Shape 588   Plant pot holder

Designer:	Mr. Symcox in 1938
Issued:	1938 - by 1940
Height:	Unknown
Colour:	1. Assorted decorations - satin matt
	2. White - matt

Market	Range
U.S.A.	$65.00 - 100.00
Canada	$100.00 - 150.00
U.K.	£40.00 - 60.00

Photograph not
available
at press time

Shape 589   Vase, two-handled

Designer:	Mr. Symcox in 1938
Issued:	1938 - by 1940
Height :	Unknown
Colour:	1. Assorted decorations - satin matt
	2. White - matt

Market	Range
U.S.A.	$75.00 - 125.00
Canada	$125.00 - 175.00
U.K.	£45.00 - 75.00

Shape 597   Plant pot holder

Designer:	Albert Hallam in 1938
Issued:	1938 - by 1940
Height:	Unknown
Colour:	1. Assorted decorations - satin matt
	2. White - matt

Market	Range
U.S.A.	$65.00 - 100.00
Canada	$100.00 - 150.00
U.K.	£40.00 - 60.00

Shape 615   **Vase**

Designer: Mr. Symcox in 1938
Issued: 1938 - by 1940
Height :   7", 17.8 cm
Colour: 1. Assorted decorations - satin matt
            2. White - matt

Market	Range
U.S.A.	$65.00 - 100.00
Canada	$100.00 - 150.00
U.K.	£40.00 - 60.00

Shape 620   **Vase**

Designer: Mr. Symcox in 1938
Issued: 1939 - by 1940
Height: Unknown
Colour: 1. Assorted decorations - satin matt
            2. White - matt

Market	Range
U.S.A.	$75.00 - 125.00
Canada	$125.00 - 175.00
U.K.	£45.00 - 75.00

Shape 621   **Vase**

Designer: Mr. Symcox in 1938
Issued: 1939 - by 1940
Height :   6 ¾", 17.2 cm
Colour: 1. Assorted decorations - satin matt
            2. White - matt

Market	Range
U.S.A.	$75.00 - 125.00
Canada	$125.00 - 175.00
U.K.	£45.00 - 75.00

Shape 626   **Vase**

Designer: Mr. Symcox in 1938
Issued: 1939 - by 1940
Height: Unknown
Colour: 1. Assorted decorations - satin matt
            2. White - matt

Market	Range
U.S.A.	$75.00 - 125.00
Canada	$125.00 - 175.00
U.K.	£45.00 - 75.00

MODELLE SERIES

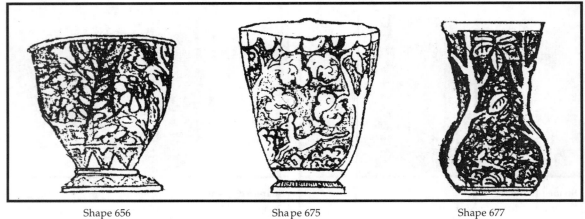

| Shape 656 | Shape 675 | Shape 677 |

| Shape 678 | Shape 680 | Shape 699 | Shape 700 |

Designers: Shapes 655 - 677; 680 - 700 Mr. Watkin in 1938
Shape 678 James Hayward in 1938
Issued: 1939 - by 1963
Height: See below
Colour: 1. Assorted decorations - satin matt
2. White - matt

Shape	Height	U.S. $	Market Range Can. $	U.K. £
Shape 655	11", 27.9 cm	100.00 - 135.00	150.00 - 225.00	60.00 - 85.00
Shape 656	10 ½", 26.7 cm	100.00 - 135.00	150.00 - 225.00	60.00 - 85.00
Shape 675	9 ¼", 23.5 cm	75.00 - 125.00	125.00 - 175.00	45.00 - 75.00
Shape 677	7 ½", 19.1 cm	75.00 - 125.00	125.00 - 175.00	45.00 - 75.00
Shape 678	10", 25.4 cm	100.00 - 135.00	150.00 - 225.00	60.00 - 85.00
Shape 680	8 ¼", 21 cm	75.00 - 125.00	125.00 - 175.00	45.00 - 75.00
Shape 699	8", 20.3 cm	75.00 - 125.00	125.00 - 175.00	45.00 - 75.00
Shape 700	9 ¼", 23.5 cm	75.00 - 125.00	125.00 - 175.00	45.00 - 75.00

Shape 702/1/2/3/4 Vase

Designer:	Mr. Symcox in 1939
Issued:	1939 - 1971
Height :	1. Shape 702/1 — 13", 33 cm
	2. Shape 702/2 — 11", 27.9 cm
	3. Shape 702/3 — 9", 22.9 cm
	4. Shape 702/4 — 7", 17.8 cm
Colour:	1. Various decorations - satin matt
	2. White or black - matt
	3. Copper - lustre

Market	Range
Shape 702/1	
U.S.A.	$125.00 - 175.00
Canada	$200.00 - 250.00
U.K.	£75.00 - 100.00
Shape 702/2	
U.S.A.	$100.00 - 135.00
Canada	$150.00 - 225.00
U.K.	£60.00 - 85.00
Shape 702/3	
U.S.A.	$75.00 - 125.00
Canada	$125.00 - 175.00
U.K.	£45.00 - 75.00
Shape 702/4	
U.S.A.	$65.00 - 100.00
Canada	$100.00 - 150.00
U.K.	£40.00 - 60.00

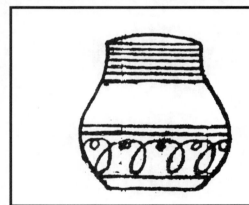

Shape 703   Vase/Lamp

Designer:	Albert Hallam in 1939
Issued:	1939 - by 1940
Height:	Unknown
Colour:	1. Assorted decorations - satin matt
	2. White - matt

Market	Range
U.S.A.	$65.00 - 100.00
Canada	$100.00 - 150.00
U.K.	£40.00 - 60.00

Shape 725   Vase, two-handled

Designer:	Mr. Symcox in 1939
Issued:	1939 - by 1954
Height :	8 ¾", 22.2 cm
Colour:	1. Assorted decorations - satin matt
	2. White - matt

Market	Range
U.S.A.	$75.00 - 125.00
Canada	$125.00 - 175.00
U.K.	£45.00 - 75.00

Shape 726 **Vase**

Designer:	Mr. Symcox in 1939
Issued:	1939 - by 1954
Height:	8 ½", 21.6 cm
Colour:	1. Assorted decorations - satin matt
	2. White - matt

Market	Range
U.S.A.	$75.00 - 125.00
Canada	$125.00 - 175.00
U.K.	£45.00 - 75.00

Shape 809/1/2/3 Vase

Designer:	Mr. Symcox in 1940
Issued:	1940 - by 1954
Height :	12 ¼", 10 ¼", 9", 31.1, 26, 22.9 cm
Colour:	1 Assorted decorations - satin matt
	2. White - matt

Market	809/1	809/2	809/3
U.S.A.	$100.00-135.00	$100.00-135.00	$75.00-125.00
Canada	$150.00 -225.00	$150.00-225.00	$125.00-175.00
U.K.	£60.00-85.00	£60.00-85.00	£45.00-75.00

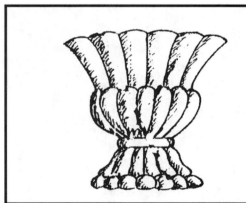

Shape 829 **Vase**

Designer:	Mr. Watkin in 1940
Issued:	1940 - by 1954
Height:	Unknown
Colour:	1. Assorted decorations - satin matt
	2. White - matt

Market	Range
U.S.A.	$75.00 - 125.00
Canada	$125.00 - 175.00
U.K.	£45.00 - 75.00

Shape 840/1/2/3 Vase

Designer:	Unknown
Issued:	1940 - by 1954
Height :	1. Shape 840/1/3 — Unknown
	2. Shape 840/2 — 9", 23.0 cm
Colour:	1. Assorted decorations - satin matt
	2. White - matt

Market	840/1	840/2	840/3
U.S.A.	$100.00-135.00	$75.00-125.00	$75.00-125.00
Canada	$150.00-225.00	$125.00-175.00	$125.00-175.00
U.K.	60.00-85.00	£45.00-75.00	£45.00-75.00

TULIP VASES

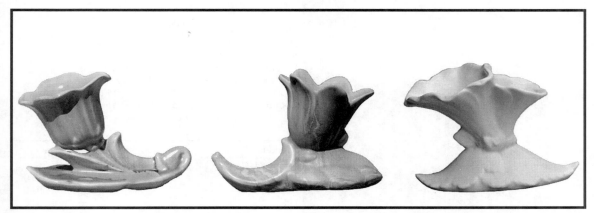

Shape 846   Shape 848   Shape 852

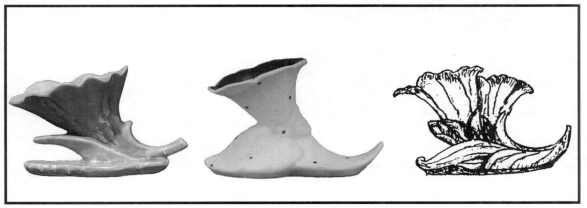

Shape 843   Shape 847   Shape 851

Designer:	Mr. Watkin in 1940
Issued:	1940 - by 1954
Size:	See below
Colour:	1. Assorted decorations - satin matt
	2. White - matt

Shape	Height	Market Range		
		U.S. $	Can. $	U.K. £
Shape 843	3 ¾", 9.5 cm	25.00 - 40.00	40.00 - 60.00	15.00 - 25.00
Shape 846	4 ¼", 10.8 cm	25.00 - 40.00	40.00 - 60.00	15.00 - 25.00
Shape 847	3 ¼", 8.3 cm	25.00 - 40.00	40.00 - 60.00	15.00 - 25.00
Shape 848	4", 10.1 cm	25.00 - 40.00	40.00 - 60.00	15.00 - 25.00
Shape 851	4", 10.1 cm	25.00 - 40.00	40.00 - 60.00	15.00 - 25.00
Shape 852	4", 10.1 cm	25.00 - 40.00	40.00 - 60.00	15.00 - 25.00

Shape 844/1/2/3 Vase

Designer:	Mr. Symcox in 1940
Issued:	1940 - 1972
Height :	1. Shape 844/1 — 11", 27.9 cm
	2. Shape 844/2 — 9", 22.9 cm
	3. Shape 844/3 — 7 ½", 19.1 cm
Colours:	1. Assorted decorations - satin matt
	2. White or black - matt
	3. Copper - lustre

Market	Range
Shape 844/1	
U.S.A.	$100.00 - 135.00
Canada	$150.00 - 225.00
U.K.	£60.00 - 85.00
Shape 844/2	
U.S.A.	$75.00 - 125.00
Canada	$125.00 - 175.00
U.K.	£45.00 - 75.00
Shape 844/3	
U.S.A.	$75.00 - 125.00
Canada	$125.00 - 175.00
U.K.	£45.00 - 75.00

Photograph not
available
at press time

Shape 923   Oval vase

Designer:	Unknown
Issued:	1941 - by 1954
Height :	Unknown
Colour:	1. Assorted decorations - satin matt
	2. White - matt

Market	Range
U.S.A.	$75.00 - 125.00
Canada	$125.00 - 175.00
U.K.	£45.00 - 75.00

Shape 1051 Deer vase

Designer:	Albert Hallam, James Hayward in 1943
Issued:	1943 - by 1963
Height:	10", 25.4 cm
Colour:	1. Assorted decorations - satin matt
	2. White - matt
Series:	Festival

Market	Range
U.S.A.	$100.00 - 135.00
Canada	$150.00 - 225.00
U.K.	£60.00 - 85.00

Shape 1075 Primrose vase

Designer:	Albert Hallam in 1946
Issued:	1947 - by 1954
Height	2 ½", 6.4 cm
Colour:	Assorted decorations - satin matt

Market	Range
U.S.A.	$45.00 - 65.00
Canada	$65.00 - 100.00
U.K.	£25.00 - 45.00

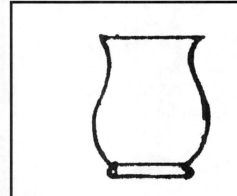

Shape 1076 Primrose vase

Designer:	Albert Hallam in 1946
Issued:	1947 - by 1954
Height:	Unknown
Colour:	Assorted decorations - satin matt

Market	Range
U.S.A.	$45.00 - 65.00
Canada	$65.00 - 100.00
U.K.	£25.00 - 45.00

Shape 1077 Primrose vase

Designer:	Albert Hallam in 1946
Issued:	1947 - by 1954
Height:	Unknown
Colour:	1. Assorted decorations - satin matt
	2. White - matt

Market	Range
U.S.A.	$45.00 - 65.00
Canada	$65.00 - 100.00
U.K.	£25.00 - 45.00

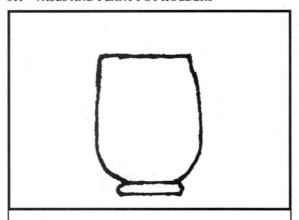

Shape 1078 Primrose vase

Designer: Albert Hallam in 1946
Issued: 1947 - by 1954
Height: Unknown
Colour: 1. Assorted decorations - satin matt
              2. White - matt

Market	Range
U.S.A.	$45.00 - 65.00
Canada	$65.00 - 100.00
U.K.	£25.00 - 45.00

Shape 1083 Galleon vase

Designer: Albert Hallam, James Hayward in 1946
Issued: 1947 - by 1963
Height: 6 ½", 16.5 cm
Colour: Assorted colours - satin matt
Series: Festival

Market	Range
U.S.A.	$65.00 - 100.00
Canada	$100.00 - 150.00
U.K.	£40.00 - 60.00

Shape 1095 Nymph vase

Designer: Albert Hallam, James Hayward in 1943
Issued: 1943 - by 1963
Height: 10 ½", 26.7 cm
Colour: Assorted colours - satin matt
Series: Festival

Market	Range
U.S.A.	$100.00 - 135.00
Canada	$150.00 - 225.00
U.K.	£60.00 - 85.00

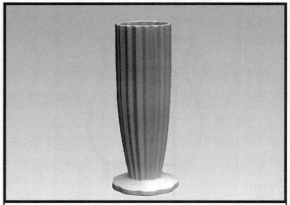

Shape 1184 Column vase

Designer: Albert Hallam in 1949
Issued: 1949 - 1971
Height: 11 ½", 29.2 cm
Colour: 1. Assorted decorations - satin matt
              2. White or black - matt
              3. Copper - lustre
Series: Festival

Market	Range
U.S.A.	$100.00 - 135.00
Canada	$150.00 - 225.00
U.K.	£60.00 - 85.00

Shape 1185 Flamingo vase

Designer:	James Hayward in 1950
Issued:	1950 - 1967
Height:	10 ½", 26.7 cm
Colour:	1. Assorted decorations - satin matt
	2. White or black - matt
	3. Copper - lustre
Series:	Festival

Market	Range
U.S.A.	$100.00 - 135.00
Canada	$150.00 - 225.00
U.K.	£60.00 - 85.00

Shape 1186 Shell vase

Designer:	Albert Hallam, James Hayward in 1950
Issued:	1950 - 1967
Height:	7 ½", 19.1 cm
Colour:	1. Assorted decorations - satin matt
	2. White or black - matt
	3. Copper - lustre
Series:	Festival

Market	Range
U.S.A.	$75.00 - 125.00
Canada	$125.00 - 175.00
U.K.	£45.00 - 75.00

Shape 1189 Square chequered vase

Designer:	Albert Hallam, James Hayward in 1950
Issued:	1950 - by 1959
Height:	6 ½", 16.5 cm
Colour:	Assorted decorations - satin matt
Series:	Festival

Market	Range
U.S.A.	$65.00 - 100.00
Canada	$100.00 - 150.00
U.K.	£40.00 - 60.00

Shape 1190 Urn vase

Designer:	Albert Hallam, James Hayward in 1950
Issued:	1950 - 1971
Height:	10", 25.4 cm
Colour:	1. Assorted decorations - satin matt
	2. White or black - matt
	3. Copper - lustre
Series:	Festival

Market	Range
U.S.A.	$100.00 - 135.00
Canada	$150.00 - 225.00
U.K.	£60.00 - 85.00

Shape 1191A   Fern vase (Festival)

Designer:	James Hayward in 1950
Issued:	1950 - 1964
Height:	12″, 30.5 cm
Colour:	1. Assorted decorations - satin matt
	2. White or black - matt
	3. Copper - lustre
Series:	Festival

Market	Range
U.S.A.	$100.00 - 135.00
Canada	$150.00 - 225.00
U.K.	£60.00 - 85.00

Shape 1191B   Fern vase (Elizabethan)

Designer:	James Hayward in 1950
Issued:	1950 - 1964
Height:	12″, 30.5 cm
Colour:	1. Chartreuse
	2. Holly green
	3. Maroon
Series:	Elizabethan

Market	Range
U.S.A.	$100.00 - 135.00
Canada	$150.00 - 225.00
U.K.	£60.00 - 85.00

Shape 1193   Bell flower vase

Designer:	Albert Hallam, James Hayward in 1950
Issued:	1950 - 1968
Height:	9″, 22.9 cm
Colour:	1. Assorted decorations - satin matt
	2. White or black - matt
	3. Copper - lustre
Series:	Festival

Market	Range
U.S.A.	$75.00 - 125.00
Canada	$125.00 - 175.00
U.K.	£45.00 - 75.00

Shape 1194   Magnolia Vase

Designer:	Albert Hallam, James Hayward in 1950
Issued:	1950 - 1964
Height:	7″, 17.8 cm
Colour:	1. Assorted decorations - satin matt
	2. White or black - matt
	3. Copper - lustre
Series:	Festival

Market	Range
U.S.A.	$65.00 - 100.00
Canada	$100.00 - 150.00
U.K.	£40.00 - 60.00

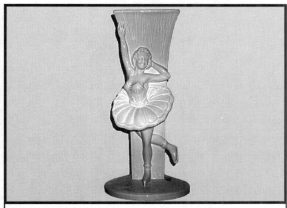

Shape 1284 Trout vase

Designer:	Albert Hallam, James Hayward in 1953
Isssued:	1953 - by 1959
Height:	8", 20.3 cm
Colour:	Chartreuse, holly green or maroon - gloss
Series:	Elizabethan

Market	Range
U.S.A.	$100.00 - 135.00
Canada	$150.00 - 225.00
U.K.	£60.00 - 85.00

Shape 1287 Skater vase

Designer:	Albert Hallam, James Hayward in 1953
Issued:	1953 - by 1959
Height:	11", 27.9 cm
Colour:	Chartreuse, holly green or maroon - gloss
Series:	Elizabethan

Market	Range
U.S.A.	$125.00 - 175.00
Canada	$200.00 - 250.00
U.K.	£75.00 - 100.00

Shape 1293 Dove vase

Designer:	Albert Hallam, James Hayward in 1953
Issued:	1953 - by 1959
Height:	6 ½", 16.5 cm
Colour:	Chartreuse, holly green or maroon - gloss
Series:	Elizabethan

Market	Range
U.S.A.	$65.00 - 100.00
Canada	$100.00 - 150.00
U.K.	£40.00 - 60.00

Shape 1295 Maple bud vase

Designer:	Albert Hallam, James Hayward in 1953
Issued	1953 - by 1966
Height:	12", 30.5 cm
Colour:	1. Assorted decorations - satin matt
	2. White or black - matt
	3. Chartreuse, holly green or maroon - gloss
Series:	Elizabethan

Market	Range
U.S.A.	$100.00 - 135.00
Canada	$150.00 - 225.00
U.K.	£60.00 - 85.00

Shape 1298 Apple vase

Designer:	Albert Hallam, James Hayward in 1953
Issued:	1953 - by 1962
Height:	9″, 22.9 cm
Colour:	Chartreuse, holly green or maroon - gloss
Series:	Elizabethan

Market	Range
U.S.A.	$75.00 - 125.00
Canada	$125.00 - 175.00
U.K.	£45.00 - 75.00

Shape 1300 Stardust vase

Designer:	Albert Hallam, James Hayward in 1953
Issued:	1953 - by 1959
Height:	Unknown
Colour:	Chartreuse, holly green or maroon - gloss
Series:	Elizabethan

Market	Range
U.S.A.	$75.00 - 125.00
Canada	$125.00 - 175.00
U.K.	£45.00 - 75.00

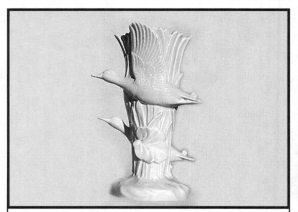

Shape 1305 Mallard vase

Designer:	Albert Hallam, James Hayward in 1953
Issued	1953 - by 1959
Height:	11″, 27.9 cm
Colour:	Chartreuse, holly green or maroon - gloss
Series:	Elizabethan

Market	Range
U.S.A.	$125.00 - 175.00
Canada	$200.00 - 250.00
U.K.	£75.00 - 100.00

Shape 1306 Pinewood vase

Designer:	Albert Hallam, James Hayward in 1953
Issued:	1953 - by 1959
Height:	8 ½″, 21.6 cm
Colour:	Chartreuse, holly green or maroon - gloss
Series:	Elizabethan

Market	Range
U.S.A.	$75.00 - 125.00
Canada	$125.00 - 175.00
U.K.	£45.00 - 75.00

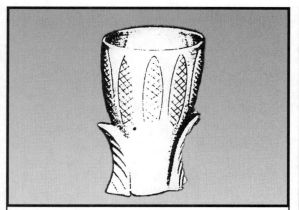

Shape 1342 Vase

Designer: Albert Hallam in 1954
Issued: 1954 - 1962
Height: 8 ½" , 21.6 cm
Colour: 1. Assorted decorations - satin matt
                2. White - matt

Market	Range
U.S.A.	$75.00 - 125.00
Canada	$125.00 - 175.00
U.K.	£45.00 - 75.00

Shape 1343/1/2 Vase

Designer: Albert Hallam in 1954
Issued: 1954 - by 1962
Height :   1. Shape 1343/1 — 10", 25.4 cm
                2. Shape 1343/2 — 6", 15 cm
Colour: 1. Assorted decorations - satin matt
                2. White - matt

Market	Range1343/1	Range1343/2
U.S.A.	$100.00 - 135.00	$65.00 - 100.00
Canada	$150.00 - 225.00	$100.00 - 150.00
U.K.	£60.00 - 85.00	£40.00 - 60.00

Shape 1349 Vase

Designer: Albert Hallam in 1954
Issued: 1954 - 1962
Height: 5", 12.7 cm
Colour: 1. Assorted decorations - satin matt
                2. White - matt

Market	Range
U.S.A.	$45.00 - 65.00
Canada	$65.00 - 100.00
U.K.	£25.00 - 45.00

Shape 1351 Vase

Designer: Albert Hallam in 1954
Issued: 1954 - by 1962
Height :   9 ½", 24 cm
Colour: 1. Assorted decorations - satin matt
                2. White - matt

Market	Range
U.S.A.	$75.00 - 125.00
Canada	$125.00 - 175.00
U.K.	£45.00 - 75.00

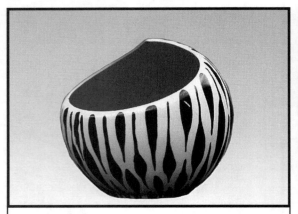

Shape 1352 Vase

Designer: Albert Hallam in 1954
Issued: 1954 - by 1962
Height: 4 ½", 11.9 cm
Colour: 1. Assorted decorations - satin matt
               2. White - matt

Market	Range
U.S.A.	$40.00 - 65.00
Canada	$65.00 - 100.00
U.K.	£25.00 - 45.00

Shape 1357 Vase

Designer: Albert Hallam in 1954
Issued: 1954 - by 1962
Height :   8", 20.3 cm
Colour: 1. Assorted decorations - satin matt
               2. White - matt

Market	Range
U.S.A.	$75.00 - 125.00
Canada	$125.00 - 175.00
U.K.	£45.00 - 75.00

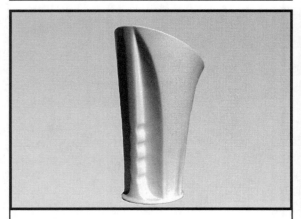

Shape 1370 Vase

Designer: Albert Hallam in 1955
Issued: 1955 - by 1962
Height :   12", 30.5 cm
Colour: 1. Assorted decorations - satin matt
               2. White - matt

Market	Range
U.S.A.	$100.00 - 135.00
Canada	$150.00 - 225.00
U.K.	£60.00 - 85.00

Shape 1371 Vase

Designer: Albert Hallam in 1955
Issued: 1955 - 1962
Height: 6", 15 cm
Colour: 1. Assorted decorations - satin matt
               2. White - matt

Market	Range
U.S.A.	$45.00 - 65.00
Canada	$65.00 - 100.00
U.K.	£25.00 - 45.00

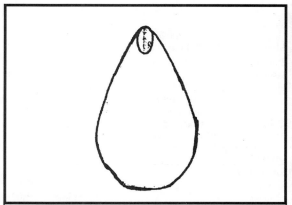

Shape 1389 Vase

Designer:	Albert Hallam in 1955
Issued:	1955 - 1962
Height :	8 ¼", 21 cm
Colour:	1. Assorted decorations - satin matt
	2. White - matt

Market	Range
U.S.A.	$75.00 - 125.00
Canada	$125.00 - 175.00
U.K.	£45.00 - 75.00

Shape 1455 Vase

Designer:	Albert Hallam in 1956
Issued:	1956 - 1962
Height:	10 ½", 26.7 cm
Colour:	1. Assorted decorations - satin matt
	2. White - matt

Market	Range
U.S.A.	$100.00 - 135.00
Canada	$150.00 - 225.00
U.K.	£60.00 - 85.00

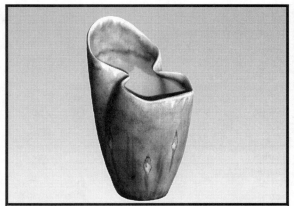

Shape 1456 Vase

Designer:	Albert Hallam in 1956
Issued:	1957 - 1965
Height :	9 ½", 24 cm
Colour:	1. Assorted decorations - satin matt
	2. White or black - matt

Market	Range
U.S.A.	$75.00 - 125.00
Canada	$125.00 - 175.00
U.K.	£45.00 - 75.00

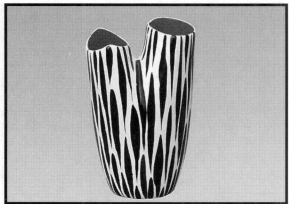

Shape 1457 Vase

Designer:	Albert Hallam in 1956
Issued:	1957 - by 1962
Height:	7", 17.8 cm
Colour:	1. Assorted decorations - satin matt
	2. White - matt

Market	Range
U.S.A.	$75.00 - 125.00
Canada	$125.00 - 175.00
U.K.	£45.00 - 75.00

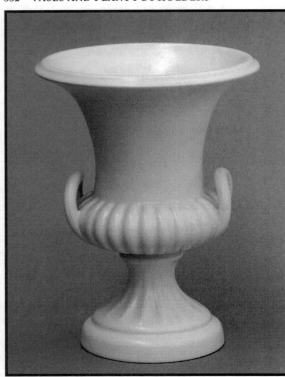

Shape No 1496 /1/2/3 Urn Vase

Designer:	Albert Hallam in 1957
Issued:	1957 - 1972
Height:	1. Shape 1496/1 — 10", 25.4 cm
	2. Shape 1496/2 — 8", 20.3 cm
	3. Shape 1496/3 — 6", 15 cm
Colour:	1. Assorted decorations - satin matt
	2. White or black - matt

Market	Range
Shape 1496/1	
U.S.A.	$100.00 - 135.00
Canada	$150.00 - 225.00
U.K.	£60.00 - 85.00
Shape 1496/2	
U.S.A.	$75.00 - 125.00
Canada	$125.00 - 175.00
U.K.	£45.00 - 75.00
Shape 1496/3	
U.S.A.	$65.00 - 100.00
Canada	$100.00 - 150.00
U.K.	£40.00 - 60.00

Shape 1502A/1/2/3 Vase

Designer:	Albert Hallam in 1957
Issued:	1957 - 1967
Height:	1. Shape 1502A/1 — 13", 33 cm
	2. Shape 1502A/2 — 10 ¼", 26 cm
	3. Shape 1502A/3 — 8 ¼", 21 cm
Colour:	1. Various decorations - satin matt
	2. White or black - matt
	3. Copper - lustre

Market	Range
Shape 1502A/1	
U.S.A.	$125.00 - 175.00
Canada	$200.00 - 250.00
U.K.	£75.00 - 100.00
Shape 1502A/2	
U.S.A.	$100.00 - 135.00
Canada	$150.00 - 225.00
U.K.	£60.00 - 85.00
Shape 1502A/3	
U.S.A.	$70.00 - 125.00
Canada	$125.00 - 175.00
U.K.	£45.00 - 75.00

Note: Continued as Caprice Series, see shape 1502B/2/3.

Shape 1502B/2/3 Vase, Caprice series

Designer:	Albert Hallam in 1957
Issued:	1968 - by 1972
Height:	2. Shape 1502B/2 — 10 ¼",26 cm
	3. Shape 1502B/3 — 8 ¼", 21 cm
Colour:	Orange, turquoise or yellow

Market	Range1502B/2	Range1502B/3
U.S.A.	$100.00 - 135.00	$75.00 - 125.00
Canada	$150.00 - 225.00	$125.00 - 175.00
U.K.	£60.00 - 85.00	£45.00 - 75.00

Shape 1552 Vase

Designer:	Albert Hallam in 1958
Issued:	1958 - by 1966
Height:	8", 20.3 cm
Colour:	1. Various decorations - satin matt
	2. White or black - matt

Market	Range
U.S.A.	$75.00 - 125.00
Canada	$125.00 - 175.00
U.K.	£45.00 - 75.00

Shape 1554/1/2 Plant pot holder

Designer:	Albert Hallam in 1958
Issued:	1958 - 1966
Size:	1. Shape 1554/1 — 6 ¼", 15.9 cm
	2. Shape 1554/2 — 5", 12.7 cm
Colour:	1. Various decorations - satin matt
	2. White or black - matt

Market	Range1554/1	Range1554/2
U.S.A.	$65.00 - 100.00	$45.00 - 65.00
Canada	$100.00 - 150.00	$65.00 - 100.00
U.K.	£40.00 - 60.00	£25.00 - 45.00

Shape 1555 Vase in shape of swan

Designer:	Kathi Urbach
Modeller:	Albert Hallam in 1958
Issued:	1959 - by 1965
Size:	9 ¾" x 6 ¾", 24.7 x 17.2 cm
Colour:	Various colours - gloss

Market	Range
U.S.A.	$75.00 - 125.00
Canada	$125.00 - 175.00
U.K.	£45.00 - 75.00

Note: Pair with vase, shape no. 1556.

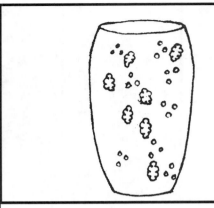

Shape 1556 Vase in shape of swan

Designer:	Kathi Urbach
Modeller:	Albert Hallam in 1958
Issued:	1959 - by 1965
Size:	9 ¾" x 6 ¾", 24.7 x 17.2 cm
Colour:	Various colours - gloss

Market	Range
U.S.A.	$75.00 - 125.00
Canada	$125.00 - 175.00
U.K.	£45.00 - 75.00

Note: Pair with vase, shape no. 1555.

Shape 1590 Vase, oval

Designer:	Kathi Urbach
Modeller:	Albert Hallam in 1959
Issued:	1959 - by 1965
Height :	9", 22.9 cm
Colour:	Various colours - gloss

Market	Range
U.S.A.	$75.00 - 125.00
Canada	$125.00 - 175.00
U.K.	£45.00 - 75.00

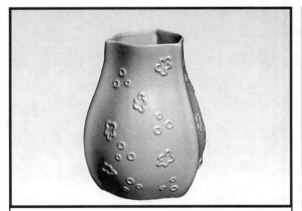

Shape 1591 Vase, triangular

Designer:	Kathi Urbach
Modeller:	Albert Hallam in 1959
Issued:	1959 - by 1965
Height:	7", 17.8 cm
Colour:	Various colours - gloss

Market	Range
U.S.A.	$65.00 - 100.00
Canada	$100.00 - 150.00
U.K.	£40.00 - 60.00

Shape 1592 Vase, square

Designer:	Kathi Urbach
Modeller:	Albert Hallam in 1959
Issued:	1959 - by 1965
Height :	11", 27.9 cm
Colour:	Various colours - gloss

Market	Range
U.S.A.	$100.00 - 135.00
Canada	$150.00 - 225.00
U.K.	£60.00 - 85.00

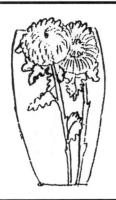

Shape 1602 Chrysanthemum vase

Designer:	Albert Hallam in 1959
Issued:	1959 - by 1963
Height:	11", 27.9 cm
Colour:	Coloured flowers on a white background
Series:	Chrysanthemum

Market	Range
U.S.A.	$100.00 - 135.00
Canada	$150.00 - 225.00
U.K.	£60.00 - 85.00

Shape 1604 Chrysanthemum vase

Designer:	Albert Hallam in 1959
Issued:	1959 - by 1963
Height:	12", 30.5 cm
Colour:	Coloured flowers on a white background
Series:	Chrysanthemum

Market	Range
U.S.A.	$100.00 - 135.00
Canada	$150.00 - 225.00
U.K.	£60.00 - 85.00

Shape 1605 Chrysanthemum vase

Designer:	Albert Hallam in 1959
Issued:	1959 - by 1963
Height:	Unknown
Colour:	Bronze and pink flowers on a white background
Series:	Chrysanthemum

Market	Range
U.S.A.	$75.00 - 125.00
Canada	$125.00 - 175.00
U.K.	£45.00 - 75.00

Shape 1606 Chrysanthemum vase

Designer:	Albert Hallam in 1959
Issued:	1959 - by 1963
Height:	8", 20.3 cm
Colour:	Coloured flowers on a white background
Series:	Chrysanthemum

Market	Range
U.S.A.	$75.00 - 125.00
Canada	$125.00 - 175.00
U.K.	£45.00 - 75.00

Shape 1607   Chrysanthemum vase

Designer:	Albert Hallam in 1959
Issued:	1959 - by 1963
Height:	Unknown
Colour:	Coloured flowers on a white background
Series:	Chrysanthemum

Market	Range
U.S.A.	$100.00 - 135.00
Canada	$150.00 - 225.00
U.K.	£60.00 - 85.00

Shape 1608   Chrysanthemum vase

Designer:	Albert Hallam in 1959
Issued:	1959 - by 1963
Height:	Unknown
Colour:	Coloured flowers on a white background
Series:	Chrysanthemum

Market	Range
U.S.A.	$100.00 - 135.00
Canada	$150.00 - 225.00
U.K.	£60.00 - 85.00

Shape 1611   Vase

Designer:	Albert Hallam in 1959
Issued:	1960 - 1968
Height:	10", 25.4 cm
Colour:	1. Various decorations - satin matt
	2. White or black - matt

Market	Range
U.S.A.	$100.00 - 135.00
Canada	$150.00 - 225.00
U.K.	£60.00 - 85.00

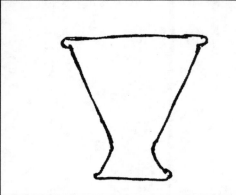

Shape 1612   Vase

Designer:	Albert Hallam in 1959
Issued:	1959 - by 1962
Height :	6", 15.0 cm
Colour:	1. Various decorations - satin matt
	2. White - matt

Market	Range
U.S.A.	$45.00 - 65.00
Canada	$65.00 - 100.00
U.K.	£25.00 - 45.00

Shape 1613A   Vase, Cornflower

Designer: Albert Hallam in 1959
Issued: 1960 - 1967
Height: 9", 22.9 cm
Colour: 1. Various decorations - satin matt
             2. White or black - matt
             3. Copper- lustre

Market	Range
U.S.A.	$75.00 - 125.00
Canada	$125.00 - 175.00
U.K.	£45.00 - 75.00

Shape 1613B   Vase, Caprice Series

Designer: Albert Hallam in 1959
Issued: 1968 - by 1972
Height: 9", 22.9 cm
Colour: Orange, turquoise or yellow

Market	Range
U.S.A.	$75.00 - 125.00
Canada	$125.00 - 175.00
U.K.	£45.00 - 75.00

Shape 1649 Vase

Designer: Albert Hallam in 1960
Issued: 1960 - by 1965
Height :   8", 20.3 cm
Colour: 1. Various decorations - satin matt
             2. White or black - matt

Market	Range
U.S.A.	$75.00 - 125.00
Canada	$125.00 - 175.00
U.K.	£45.00 - 75.00

Shape 1651A   Vase

Designer: Albert Hallam in 1959
Issued: 1959 - 1967
Height: 6", 15.0 cm
Colour: 1. Various decorations - satin matt
             2. White or black - matt
             3. Copper- lustre

Market	Range
U.S.A.	$45.00 - 65.00
Canada	$65.00 - 100.00
U.K.	£25.00 - 45.00

Shape 1651B   Vase, Caprice series

Designer: Albert Hallam in 1959
Issued: 1968 - by 1972
Height: 6", 15.0 cm
Colour: Orange, turquoise or yellow

Market	Range
U.S.A.	$45.00 - 65.00
Canada	$65.00 - 100.00
U.K.	£25.00 - 45.00

Shape 1652   Vase

Designer: Albert Hallam in 1959
Issued: 1959 - by 1962
Height :   7", 17.8 cm
Colour: 1. Various decorations - satin matt
             2. White - matt

Market	Range
U.S.A.	$65.00 - 100.00
Canada	$100.00 - 150.00
U.K.	£40.00 - 60.00

Shape 1653   Vase

Designer: Albert Hallam in 1959
Issued: 1959 - by 1966
Height: 10 ½", 26.7 cm
Colour: 1. Various decorations - satin matt
             2. White or black - matt

Market	Range
U.S.A.	$100.00 - 135.00
Canada	$150.00 - 225.00
U.K.	£60.00 - 85.00

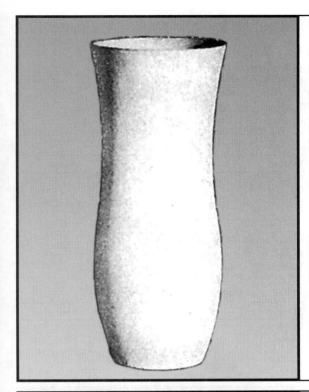

Shape 1654A   Vase

Designer: Albert Hallam in 1959
Issued: 1959 - 1967
Height :   10", 25.4 cm
Colour: 1. Various decorations - satin matt
            2. White or black - matt
            3. Copper - lustre

Market	Range
U.S.A.	$100.00 - 135.00
Canada	$150.00 - 225.00
U.K.	£60.00 - 85.00

Shape 1654B   Vase, Caprice series

Designer: Albert Hallam in 1959
Issued: 1968 - by 1972
Height :   10", 25.4 cm
Colour: Orange, turquoise or yellow

Market	Range
U.S.A.	$100.00 - 135.00
Canada	$150.00 - 225.00
U.K.	£60.00 - 85.00

Shape 1655 Vase

Designer: Albert Hallam in 1959
Issued: 1959 - by 1965
Height: 7", 17.8 cm
Colour: 1. Various decorations - satin matt
            2. White or black - matt

Market	Range
U.S.A.	$65.00 - 100.00
Canada	$100.00 - 150.00
U.K.	£40.00 - 60.00

Shape 1656A   Goblet vase

Designer: Albert Hallam in 1959
Issued: 1959 - 1967
Height :   8", 20.3 cm
Colour: 1. Various decorations - satin matt
            2. White or black - matt
            3. Copper - lustre

Market	Range
U.S.A.	$75.00 - 125.00
Canada	$125.00 - 175.00
U.K.	£45.00 - 75.00

Shape 1656B   Goblet Vase, Caprice series

Designer: Albert Hallam in 1959
Issued: 1968 - by 1972
Height :   8", 20.3 cm
Colour: Orange, turquoise or yellow

Market	Range
U.S.A.	$75.00 - 125.00
Canada	$125.00 - 175.00
U.K.	£45.00 - 75.00

Shape 1657   Vase

Designer: Albert Hallam in 1959
Issued: 1959 - by 1966
Height: 11", 27.9 cm
Colour: 1. Various decorations - satin matt
            2. White or black - matt

Market	Range
U.S.A.	$100.00 - 135.00
Canada	$150.00 - 225.00
U.K.	£60.00 - 85.00

Shape 1658   Rose vase, "Queen Elizabeth"

Designer: Albert Hallam in 1959
Issued: 1960 - 1965
Height: 10", 25.4 cm
Colour: Deep pink rose, green leaves on cream
            background - satin matt

Description	U.S. $	Can. $	U.K. £
"Queen Elizabeth"	150.00	200.00	85.00

Note: Set of six with no. 1659 (basket), 1660, 1661, 1662 and 1663.

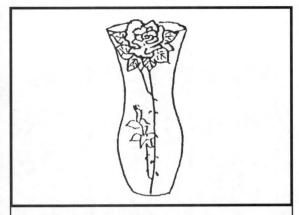

Shape 1660 Rose vase, "Peace"

Designer:	Albert Hallam in 1959
Issued:	1960 - 1965
Height:	11", 27.9 cm
Colour:	Yellow rose, green leaves on cream background - satin matt

Description	U.S. $	Can. $	U.K. £
"Peace"	150.00	200.00	85.00

Note: Set of six with no. 1658, 1659 (basket), 1661, 1662 and 1663.

Shape 1661 Rose vase, "Bayadere"

Designer:	Albert Hallam in 1959
Issued:	1960 - 1965
Height :	8", 20.3 cm
Colour:	Coloured rose, green leaves on cream background - satin matt

Description	U.S. $	Can. $	U.K. £
"Bayadere"	150.00	200.00	85.00

Note: Set of six with no. 1658, 1659 (basket), 1660, 1662 and 1663.

Shape 1662 Rose vase, "Cirius"

Designer:	Albert Hallam in 1959
Issued:	1960 - 1965
Height:	8", 20.3 cm
Colour:	Coloured rose, green leaves on cream background - satin matt

Description	U.S. $	Can. $	U.K. £
"Cirius"	150.00	200.00	85.00

Note: Set of six with no. 1658, 1659 (basket), 1660, 1661 and 1663.

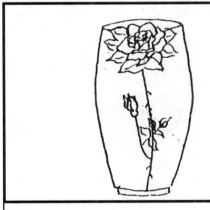

Shape 1663 Rose vase, "Soraya"

Designer:	Albert Hallam in 1959
Issued:	1960 - 1965
Height :	10", 25.4 cm
Colour:	Coloured rose, green leaves on cream background - satin matt

Colour	U.S. $	Can. $	U.K. £
"Soraya"	150.00	200.00	85.00

Note: Set of six with no. 1658, 1659 (basket), 1660, 1661 and 1662.

Shape 1664/0/1/2 Vase

Designer:	Albert Hallam in 1959
Issued:	Shape 1664/0 — 1963 - 1969
	Shape 1664/1/2 — 1960 - 1969
Height:	1. Shape 1664/0 — 12 ½", 31.7 cm
	2. Shape 1664/1 — 9", 22.9 cm
	3. Shape 1664/2 — 7", 17.8 cm
Colour:	1. Various decorations - satin matt
	2. White or black - matt
	3. Copper - lustre

Market	Range
Shape 1664/0	
U.S.A.	$100.00 - 135.00
Canada	$150.00 - 225.00
U.K.	£60.00 - 85.00
Shape 1664/1	
U.S.A.	$75.00 - 125.00
Canada	$125.00 - 175.00
U.K.	£45.00 - 75.00
Shape 1664/2	
U.S.A.	$65.00 - 100.00
Canada	$100.00 - 150.00
U.K.	£40.00 - 60.00

Shape 1682 Goblet vase

Designer:	Albert Hallam in 1960
Issued:	1960 - 1969
Height :	8", 20.3 cm
Colour:	1. Various decorations - satin matt
	2. White or black - matt
	3. Copper - lustre

Market	Range
U.S.A.	$75.00 - 125.00
Canada	$125.00 - 175.00
U.K.	£45.00 - 75.00

Shape 1719 Vase (mustard pot without the lid)

Designer:	Albert Hallam in 1960
Issued:	1960 - 1970
Height:	2 ¾", 7.0 cm
Colour:	1. Various decorations - satin matt
	2. White or black - matt
	3. Copper - lustre

Market	Range
U.S.A.	$45.00 - 65.00
Canada	$65.00 - 100.00
U.K.	£25.00 - 45.00

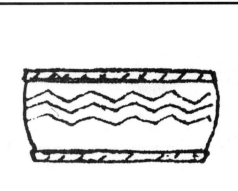

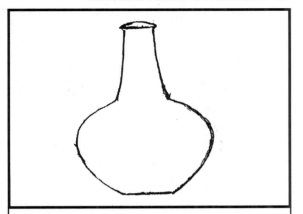

Shape 1723 Bongo flower holder

Designer:	Albert Hallam in 1960
Issued:	c.1960
Height :	Unknown
Colour:	1. Various decorations - satin matt
	2. White or black - matt
	3. Copper - lustre

Market	Range
U.S.A.	$45.00 - 65.00
Canada	$65.00 - 100.00
U.K.	£25.00 - 45.00

Shape 1724 Vase in shape of a bottle

Designer:	Mr. Garbet in 1960
Issued:	c.1960
Height:	13 ¾", 34.9 cm
Colour:	1. Various decorations - satin matt
	2. White or black - matt
	3. Copper - lustre

Market	Range
U.S.A.	$125.00 - 175.00
Canada	$200.00 - 250.00
U.K.	£75.00 - 100.00

Shape 1749A   Vase

Designer:	Albert Hallam in 1961
Issued:	1961 - 1967
Height :	9", 22.9 cm
Colour:	1. Various decorations - satin matt
	2. White or black - matt

Market	Range
U.S.A.	$75.00 - 125.00
Canada	$125.00 - 175.00
U.K.	£45.00 - 75.00

Shape 1749B   Vase, Caprice series

Designer:	Albert Hallam in 1961
Issued:	1968 - by 1972
Height:	9", 22.9 cm
Colour:	Orange, turquoise or yellow

Market	Range
U.S.A.	$75.00 - 125.00
Canada	$125.00 - 175.00
U.K.	£45.00 - 75.00

Shape 1750A   Vase

Designer: Albert Hallam in 1961
Issued: 1961 - 1967
Height: 9", 22.9 cm
Colour: 1. Various decorations - satin matt
             2. White or black - matt

Market	Range
U.S.A.	$75.00 - 125.00
Canada	$125.00 - 175.00
U.K.	£45.00 - 75.00

Shape 1750B   Vase, Caprice Series

Designer: Albert Hallam in 1961
Issued   1968 - by 1972
Height: 9", 22.9 cm
Colour: Orange, turquoise or yellow

Market	Range
U.S.A.	$75.00 - 125.00
Canada	$125.00 - 175.00
U.K.	£45.00 - 75.00

Shape 1751A   Vase

Designer: Albert Hallam in 1961
Issued: 1961 - 1967
Height :   7", 17.8 cm
Colour: 1. Various decorations - satin matt
             2. White or black - matt

Market	Range
U.S.A.	$65.00 - 100.00
Canada	$100.00 - 150.00
U.K.	£40.00 - 60.00

Shape 1751B   Vase, Caprice series

Designer: Albert Hallam in 1961
Issued: 1968 - by 1972
Height :   7", 17.8 cm
Colour: Orange, turquoise or yellow

Market	Range
U.S.A.	$65.00 - 100.00
Canada	$100.00 - 150.00
U.K.	£40.00 - 60.00

Shape 1752A   Vase

Designer: Albert Hallam in 1961
Issued: 1961 - 1967
Height: 6", 15.0 cm
Colour: 1. Various decorations - satin matt
            2. White or black - matt
            3. Copper - lustre

Market	Range
U.S.A.	$65.00 - 100.00
Canada	$100.00 - 150.00
U.K.	£40.00 - 60.00

Shape 1752B   Vase, Caprice Series

Designer: Albert Hallam in 1961
Issued: 1968 - by 1972
Height: 6", 15.0 cm
Colour: Orange, turquoise or yellow

Market	Range
U.S.A.	$65.00 - 100.00
Canada	$100.00 - 150.00
U.K.	£40.00 - 60.00

Shape 1773   Vase

Designer: Albert Hallam in 1961
Issued: 1961 - by 1965
Height :   8", 20.3 cm
Colour: 1. Various decorations - satin matt
            2. White or black - matt

Market	Range
U.S.A.	$75.00 - 125.00
Canada	$125.00 - 175.00
U.K.	£45.00 - 75.00

Shape 1799 Chalice vase

Designer: Albert Hallam in 1962
Issued: 1962 - 1969
Height: 12", 30.5 cm
Colour: 1. Various decorations - satin matt
            2. White or black - matt
            3. Copper - lustre

Market	Range
U.S.A.	$65.00 - 100.00
Canada	$100.00 - 150.00
U.K.	£40.00 - 60.00

Shape 1858 Vase

Designer:	Albert Hallam in 1962
Issued:	1963 - 1968
Height :	8", 20.3 cm
Colour:	1. Various decorations - satin matt
	2. White or black - matt
	3. Copper - lustre

Market	Range
U.S.A.	$65.00 - 100.00
Canada	$100.00 - 150.00
U.K.	£40.00 - 60.00

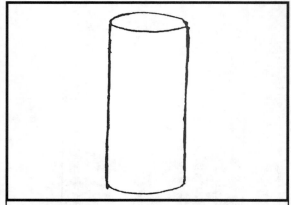

Shape 1873 Vase

Designer:	Albert Hallam in 1963
Issued:	1963 - by 1965
Height:	8 ¾", 22.2 cm
Colour:	1. Various decorations - satin matt
	2. White or black - matt

Market	Range
U.S.A.	$75.00 - 125.00
Canada	$125.00 - 175.00
U.K.	£45.00 - 75.00

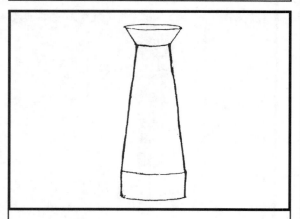

Shape 1879 Vase

Designer:	Albert Hallam in 1963
Issued:	1963 - by 1965
Height :	10 ½", 26.7 cm
Colour:	1. Various decorations - satin matt
	2. White or black - matt

Market	Range
U.S.A.	$100.00 - 135.00
Canada	$150.00 - 225.00
U.K.	£60.00 - 85.00

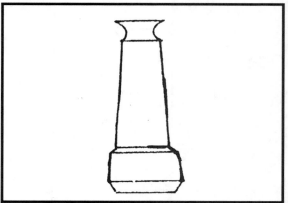

Shape 1881 Vase

Designer:	Albert Hallam in 1963
Issued:	1963 - by 1965
Height:	8", 20.3 cm
Colour:	1. Various decorations - satin matt
	2. White or black - matt

Market	Range
U.S.A.	$75.00 - 125.00
Canada	$125.00 - 175.00
U.K.	£45.00 - 75.00

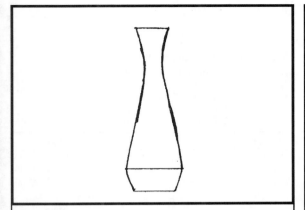

Shape 1884 Vase

Designer:	Albert Hallam in 1963
Issued:	1963 - by 1965
Height :	9″, 22.9 cm
Colour:	1. Various decorations - satin matt
	2. White or black - matt

Market	Range
U.S.A.	$75.00 - 125.00
Canada	$125.00 - 175.00
U.K.	£45.00 - 75.00

Shape 1888 Vase

Designer:	Albert Hallam in 1963
Issued:	1963 - by 1965
Height:	5 ¾″, 14.6 cm
Colour:	1. Various decorations - satin matt
	2. White or black - matt

Market	Range
U.S.A.	$45.00 - 65.00
Canada	$65.00 - 100.00
U.K.	£25.00 - 45.00

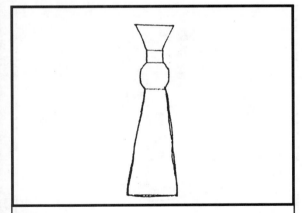

Shape 1890 Vase

Designer:	Albert Hallam in 1963
Issued:	1963 - by 1967
Height :	11 ½″, 29.2 cm
Colour:	1. Various decorations - satin matt
	2. White or black - matt

Market	Range
U.S.A.	$100.00 - 135.00
Canada	$150.00 - 225.00
U.K.	£60.00 - 85.00

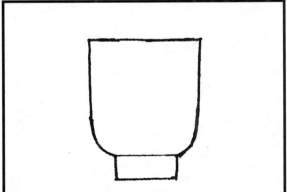

Shape 1891 Vase

Designer:	Albert Hallam in 1963
Issued:	1963 - by 1967
Height:	5 ½″, 14.0 cm
Colour:	1. Various decorations - satin matt
	2. White or black - matt

Market	Range
U.S.A.	$45.00 - 65.00
Canada	$65.00 - 100.00
U.K.	£25.00 - 45.00

Shape 1896A   Plant pot holder

Designer:	Albert Hallam in 1963
Issued:	1963 - 1967
Size :	5 ½" x 6 ½", 14 x 16.5 cm
Colour:	1. Various decorations - satin matt
	2. White or black - matt

Market	Range
U.S.A.	$45.00 - 65.00
Canada	$65.00 - 100.00
U.K.	£25.00 - 45.00

Shape 1896B   Vase, Caprice series

Designer:	Albert Hallam in 1963
Issued:	1968 - by 1972
Height:	5 ½" x 6 ½", 14 x 16.5 cm
Colour:	Orange, turquoise or yellow

Market	Range
U.S.A.	$45.00 - 65.00
Canada	$65.00 - 100.00
U.K.	£25.00 - 45.00

Shape 1935   Vase two-handled

Designer:	Albert Hallam in 1964
Issued:	1964 - 1967
Height:	5 ½", 14.0 cm
Colour:	1. Various decorations - satin matt
	2. White or black - matt
	3. Copper - lustre

Market	Range
U.S.A.	$45.00 - 65.00
Canada	$65.00 - 100.00
U.K.	£25.00 - 45.00

Shape 1936   Goblet vase

Designer:	Albert Hallam in 1964
Issued:	1964 - 1971
Height :	7 ¾",19.7 cm
Colour:	1. Various decorations - satin matt
	2. White or black - matt
	3. Copper - lustre

Market	Range
U.S.A.	$45.00 - 65.00
Canada	$65.00 - 100.00
U.K.	£25.00 - 45.00

Shape 2003 Plant pot holder

Designer: Albert Hallam in 1965
Issued: 1965 - by 1972
Height: 6 ¼″, 15.9 cm
Colour: Soft variegated pastel colours - gloss
Series: Sea Shell

Market	Range
U.S.A.	$65.00 - 100.00
Canada	$100.00 - 150.00
U.K.	£40.00 - 60.00

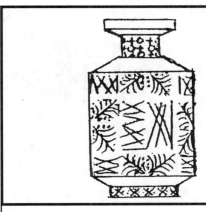

Shape 2006 Vase

Designer: Albert Hallam in 1965
Issued: 1965 - by 1972
Height :   7 ½″, 19.1 cm
Colour: 1. Various decorations - satin matt
            2. White or black - matt

Market	Range
U.S.A.	$75.00 - 125.00
Canada	$125.00 - 175.00
U.K.	£45.00 - 75.00

Shape 2012 Shell vase

Designer: Albert Hallam in 1965
Issued: 1965 - by 1972
Height: 4 ½″, 11.9 cm
Colour: Soft variegated pastel colours - gloss
Series: Sea Shell

Market	Range
U.S.A.	$45.00 - 65.00
Canada	$65.00 - 100.00
U.K.	£25.00 - 45.00

Shape 2014 Shell vase

Designer: Albert Hallam in 1965
Issued: 1965 - by 1972
Size: 6″ x 12 ½″, 15 x 32.7 cm
Colour: Soft variegated pastel colours - gloss
Series: Sea Shell

Market	Range
U.S.A.	$65.00 - 100.00
Canada	$100.00 - 150.00
U.K.	£40.00 - 60.00

Shape 2015 Shell vase

Designer:	Albert Hallam in 1965
Issued:	1965 - by 1972
Height:	8", 20.3 cm
Colour:	Soft variegated pastel colours - gloss
Series:	Sea Shell

Market	Range
U.S.A.	$75.00 - 125.00
Canada	$125.00 - 175.00
U.K.	£45.00 - 75.00

Shape 2016 Shell plant pot holder

Designer:	Albert Hallam in 1965
Issued:	1965 - by 1972
Height:	4 ¾", 12.1 cm
Colour:	Soft variegated pastel colours - gloss
Series:	Sea Shell

Market	Range
U.S.A.	$45.00 - 65.00
Canada	$65.00 - 100.00
U.K.	£25.00 - 45.00

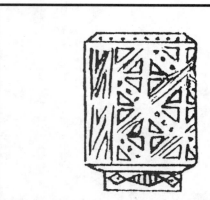

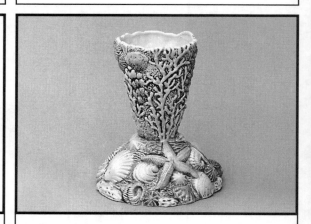

Shape 2017 Vase

Designer:	Albert Hallam in 1965
Issued:	1965 - by 1972
Height:	5 ¼", 13.3 cm
Colour:	1. Various decorations - satin matt
	2. White or black - matt

Market	Range
U.S.A.	$45.00 - 65.00
Canada	$65.00 - 100.00
U.K.	£25.00 - 45.00

Shape 2020 Shell vase

Designer:	Albert Hallam in 1965
Issued:	1965 - by 1972
Height:	6 ½", 16.5 cm
Colour:	Soft variegated pastel colours - gloss
Series:	Sea Shell

Market	Range
U.S.A.	$65.00 - 100.00
Canada	$100.00 - 150.00
U.K.	£40.00 - 60.00

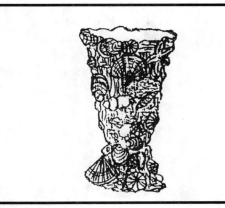

Shape 2021 Shell vase

Designer:	Albert Hallam in 1965
Issued:	1965 - by 1972
Height:	9 ¾", 24.7 cm
Colour:	Soft variegated pastel colours - gloss
Series:	Sea Shell

Market	Range
U.S.A.	$75.00 - 125.00
Canada	$125.00 - 175.00
U.K.	£45.00 - 75.00

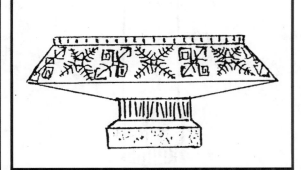

Shape 2022 Vase on pedestal

Designer:	Albert Hallam in 1965
Issued:	1965 - by 1972
Size:	5 ½" x 11 ¾", 14 x 29.8 cm
Colour:	1. Various decorations - satin matt
	2. White or black - matt

Market	Range
U.S.A.	$75.00 - 125.00
Canada	$125.00 - 175.00
U.K.	£45.00 - 75.00

Shape 2025 Goblet vase

Designer:	Albert Hallam in 1965
Issued:	1965 - by 1972
Height:	8 ¾", 22.2 cm
Colour:	1. Various decorations - satin matt
	2. White or black - matt

Market	Range
U.S.A.	$75.00 - 125.00
Canada	$125.00 - 175.00
U.K.	£45.00 - 75.00

Shape 2046 Vase

Designer:	Albert Hallam in 1965
Issued:	1965 - by 1972
Height :	8", 20.3 cm
Colour:	1. Various decorations - satin matt
	2. White or black - matt

Market	Range
U.S.A.	$75.00 - 125.00
Canada	$125.00 - 175.00
U.K.	£45.00 - 75.00

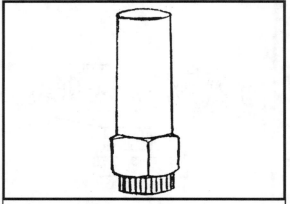

Shape 2049 Vase

Designer: Albert Hallam in 1965
Issued: 1965 - by 1972
Height: 10", 25.4 cm
Colour: 1. Various decorations - satin matt
             2. White or black - matt

Market	Range
U.S.A.	$100.00 - 135.00
Canada	$150.00 - 225.00
U.K.	£60.00 - 85.00

Shape 2070 Chalice vase

Designer: Albert Hallam in 1962
Issued: 1962 - 1969
Height :   9 ½", 24 cm
Colour: 1. Various decorations - satin matt
             2. White or black - matt
             3. Copper - lustre

Market	Range
U.S.A.	$45.00 - 65.00
Canada	$65.00 - 100.00
U.K.	£25.00 - 45.00

Shape 2081 Vase, round

Designer: Graham Tongue in 1966
Issued: 1967 - 1972
Height: Unknown
Colour: 1. Various decorations - satin matt
             2. White or black - matt

Market	Range
U.S.A.	$65.00 - 100.00
Canada	$100.00 - 150.00
U.K.	£40.00 - 60.00

Shape 2111 Vase

Designer: Albert Hallam in 1967
Issued: 1967 - by 1972
Height :   7", 17.8 cm
Colour: 1. Various decorations - satin matt
             2. White or black - matt
             3. Copper - lustre

Market	Range
U.S.A.	$65.00 - 100.00
Canada	$100.00 - 150.00
U.K.	£40.00 - 60.00

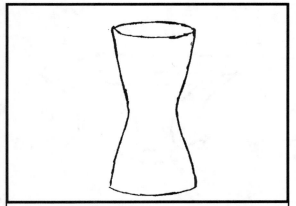

Shape 2121 Vase

Designer:	Graham Tongue in 1967
Issued:	1967 - by 1972
Height:	8 ½", 21.6 cm
Colour:	1. Various decorations - satin matt
	2. White or black - matt
	3. Copper - lustre

Range	Market
U.S.A.	$75.00 - 125.00
Canada	$125.00 - 175.00
U.K.	£45.00 - 75.00

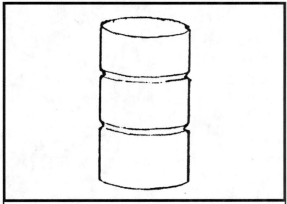

Shape 2122 Vase

Designer:	Graham Tongue in 1967
Issued:	1967 - by 1972
Height :	8", 20.3 cm
Colour:	1. Various decorations - satin matt
	2. White or black - matt
	3. Copper - lustre

Range	Market
U.S.A.	$75.00 - 125.00
Canada	$125.00 - 175.00
U.K.	£45.00 - 75.00

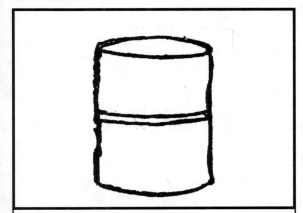

Shape 2123 Vase

Designer:	Graham Tongue in 1967
Issued:	1967 - by 1972
Height:	5 ½", 14.0 cm
Colour:	1. Various decorations - satin matt
	2. White or black - matt
	3. Copper - lustre

Market	Range
U.S.A.	$45.00 - 65.00
Canada	$65.00 - 100.00
U.K.	£25.00 - 45.00

Shape 2124 Vase

Designer:	Graham Tongue in 1967
Issued:	1967 - by 1972
Height :	6 ½", 16.5 cm
Colour:	1. Various decorations - satin matt
	2. White or black - matt
	3. Copper - lustre

Market	Range
U.S.A.	$65.00 - 100.00
Canada	$100.00 - 150.00
U.K.	£40.00 - 60.00

Shape 2134 Vase, oval top

Designer: Graham Tongue in 1967
Issued: 1967 - by 1972
Height: 11", 27.9 cm
Colour: 1. Various decorations - satin matt
2. White or black - matt
3. Copper - lustre

Market	Range
U.S.A.	$100.00 - 135.00
Canada	$150.00 - 225.00
U.K.	£60.00 - 85.00

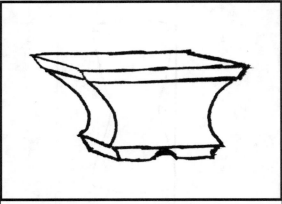

Shape 2140 Vase

Designer: Albert Hallam in 1967
Issued: 1968 - 1970
Height: 2 ½", 6.4 cm
Colour: 1. Various decorations - satin matt
2. White or black - matt
3. Copper - lustre

Market	Range
U.S.A.	$45.00 - 65.00
Canada	$65.00 - 100.00
U.K.	£25.00 - 45.00

Shape 2288 Cherub vase

Designer: Graham Tongue in 1969
Issued: 1969 - 1972
Height: 10", 25.4 cm
Colour: 1. Various decorations - satin matt
2. White or black - matt
3. Copper - lustre

Market	Range
U.S.A.	$125.00 - 175.00
Canada	$200.00 - 250.00
U.K.	£75.00 - 100.00

Photograph not
available
at press time

Shape 2297 Goblet vase

Designer: Unknown
Issued: 1969 - by 1972
Height : 9", 22.9 cm
Colour: 1. Various decorations - satin matt
2. White or black - matt
3. Copper - lustre

Market	Range
U.S.A.	$75.00 - 125.00
Canada	$125.00 - 175.00
U.K.	£45.00 - 75.00

Shape 2356 Chalice vase, two-handled

Designer:	Graham Tongue in 1971
Issued:	1972 only
Height:	10 ½", 26.7 cm
Colour:	1. Pewteramic
	2. White - matt

Market	Range
U.S.A.	$100.00 - 135.00
Canada	$150.00 - 225.00
U.K.	£60.00 - 85.00

Shape 2378 Goblet vase

Designer:	Graham Tongue in 1971
Issued:	1972 only
Height :	8 ½", 21.6 cm
Colour:	1. Pewteramic
	2. White - matt

Market	Range
U.S.A.	$75.00 - 125.00
Canada	$125.00 - 175.00
U.K.	£45.00 - 75.00

Shape 2379 Goblet vase

Designer:	Graham Tongue in 1971
Issued:	1972 only
Height:	6", 15 cm
Colour:	1. Pewteramic
	2. White - matt

Market	Range
U.S.A.	$65.00 - 100.00
Canada	$100.00 - 150.00
U.K.	£40.00 - 60.00

Note: Price ranges are retail market indicators of prices for models under the following conditions:
- Lower end of range = price of monochrome models
- Higher end of range = price of multicoloured models

Vase, Shape 169

WALL ORNAMENTS/MASKS/PLAQUES/VASES

There are eighty-eight wall ornaments listed here. These do not include character ware or the animal, bird, butterfly and horse plaques. Details for this latter group can be found in *The Charlton Standard Catalogue of Beswick Animals.*

Here we have eighteen face masks, mostly of thirties style girls, also two plaques in the Shakespearian Series, three Beatrix Potter, seven of Christmas Around The World and various wall vases, advertising wares and four plaques featuring animals.

In 1940, a freelance modeller, Miss Joachim, modelled eleven plaques for Beswick. Four featured scenes from the book *Alice In Wonderland,* they were No. 857 - Alice with the White Rabbit, No. 858 - After the Caucus Race, No. 859 - The Duchess with the Baby and No. 860 - A Game of Croquet. Five featured scenes from *Cinderella,* these were No. 861 - Cinderella with the Birds, No. 863 - The Ugly Sisters getting ready for the Ball, No. 865 Cinderella with the Prince, No. 866 - The Herald with the Slipper and No. 867 - The Slipper Fits Cinderella. In addition to these there were two floral plaques (No. 856 a single rose and No. 864 a floral spray). No further information is available and although samples must have been made up at the time and possibly even some were marketed, it is quite likely that these plaques were never put into full commercial production.

Shape 139 **Plaque**

Designer: Albert Hallam c.1933
Issued: c.1933 - by 1940
Diameter: 12", 30.5 cm
Colour: 1. Assorted decos - satin matt
  2. White - matt

Market	Range
U.S.A.	$75.00 - 125.00
Canada	$125.00 - 175.00
U.K.	£45.00 - 75.00

Shape 197 **Girl with hat, wall mask**

Designer: Unknown
Issued: c.1933 - by 1954
Height: 6 ½", 16.5 cm
Colour: 1. Hat in various colours, hair blonde - gloss
  2. White - matt

Colour	U.S. $	Can. $	U.K. £
1. Coloured hat - gloss	325.00	500.00	200.00
2. White - matt		Rare	

Shape 263 **Galleon, plaque**

Designer: Mr. Fletcher
Issued: c.1934 - by 1954
Height: 9 ½", 24.0 cm
Colour: 1. Blue sea, galleon in grey and brown, on
  a cream background - gloss
  2. Stone - satin matt

Market	Range
U.S.A.	$100.00 - 135.00
Canada	$150.00 - 225.00
U.K.	£60.00 - 85.00

Shape 277 **Girl with hat, wall mask**

Designer: Unknown
Issued: c.1934 - by 1940
Height: 4 ½" 11.9 cm
Colour: Blonde hair, hat black and green - gloss

Description	U.S. $	Can. $	U.K. £
Girl with hat	325.00	500.00	200.00

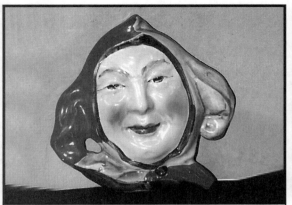

Shape 279   Jester, wall mask

Designer: Mr. Dean c.1933
Issued: c.1934 - by 1954
Height: 6", 15 cm
Colour: Orange and green motley with
           brown trim - gloss

Description	U.S. $	Can. $	U.K. £
Jester	200.00	300.00	100.00

Shape 282   Red Indian, wall mask

Designer: Mr. Dean c.1933
Issued: c.1934 - by 1954
Height: 7 ½", 19.1 cm
Colour: 1. Blue, green, cream, and dark brown - gloss
           2. White - matt

Colour	U.S. $	Can. $	U.K. £
1. Blue, green, cream, brown	200.00	300.00	125.00
2. White		Rare	

Shape 314   Girl with black beret, wall mask

Designer: Miss Greaves c.1934
Issued: c.1935 - by 1940
Height: 9 ¼", 23.5 cm
Colour: Blonde hair, black beret - gloss

Description	U.S. $	Can. $	U.K. £
Girl with black beret	325.00	500.00	200.00

Shape 362   Girl with orange beret, wall mask

Designer: Unknown
Issued: c.1935 - by 1940
Height: 3 ¾", 9.5 cm
Colour: Orange beret, black hair and
           orange bow - gloss

Description	U.S. $	Can. $	U.K. £
Girl with orange beret	325.00	500.00	200.00

Shape 363   Girl with hat (facing right), wall mask

Designer: Unknown
Issued: c.1935 - by 1940
Size: Unknown
Colour: Unknown - gloss

Description	U.S. $	Can. $	U.K. £
Girl with hat	325.00	500.00	200.00

Shape 364   Girl with beret, wall mask

Designer: Unknown
Issued: c.1935 - by 1940
Size: Unknown
Colour: Unknown - gloss

Description	U.S. $	Can. $	U.K. £
Girl with beret	325.00	500.00	200.00

Shape 365   Girl with beret, wall mask

Designer: Unknown
Issued: c.1935 - by 1940
Size: Unknown
Colour: Unknown - gloss

Description	U.S. $	Can. $	U.K. £
Girl with beret	325.00	500.00	200.00

Photograph not
available
at press time

Shape 366   Girl with hat, wall mask

Designer: Unknown
Issued: c.1935 - by 1940
Size: Unknown
Colour: Unknown - gloss

Description	U.S. $	Can. $	U.K. £
Girl with hat	325.00	500.00	200.00

Shape 367   **Girl with hat (facing left), wall mask**

Designer: Unknown
Issued: c.1935 - by 1940
Size: Unknown
Colour: Unknown - gloss

Description	U.S. $	Can. $	U.K. £
Girl with hat	325.00	500.00	200.00

Shape 380   **Young girl with bonnet, wall mask**

Designer: Mr. Owen in 1936
Issued: 1936 - by 1940
Height: 9", 22.9 cm
Colour: Blonde hair, pink bonnet with green bow - gloss

Description	U.S. $	Can. $	U.K. £
Young girl with bonnet	325.00	500.00	200.00

Shape 393   **Girl with plaits, wall mask**

Designer: Miss Greaves in 1936
Issued: 1936 - by 1940
Size: 8 ½", 21.6 cm
Colour: Unknown - gloss

Description	U.S. $	Can. $	U.K. £
Girl with plaits	325.00	500.00	200.00

Shape 433   **Wall vase**

Designer: Mr. Symcox in 1936
Issued: 1936 - by 1940
Size: 8 ½", 21.6 cm
Colour: 1. Assorted decorations - satin matt
         2. White - matt

Market	Range
U.S.A.	$75.00 - 100.00
Canada	$125.00 - 150.00
U.K.	£45.00 - 60.00

Shape 436 **Hyacinth lady, wall mask**

Designer:	Miss Greaves in 1936
Issued:	1936 - by 1954
Height:	12″, 30.5 cm
Colour:	1. Fair or dark hair, blue flowers, red beads - satin matt
	2. Stone - satin matt 3. White - matt

Description	U.S. $	Can. $	U.K. £
1. Colour	325.00	500.00	200.00
2. Stone	300.00	450.00	175.00
3. White	175.00	250.00	100.00

Shape 449 **Lady with hat and scarf, wall mask**

Designer:	Mr. Owen in 1936
Issued:	1936 - by 1940
Height:	12 ½″, 31.7 cm
Colour:	Unknown - gloss

Description	U.S. $	Can. $	U.K. £
Lady with hat and scarf	500.00	750.00	300.00

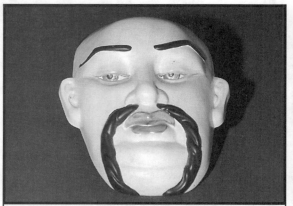

Shape 457 **Genie, wall mask**

Designer:	Miss Greaves in 1936
Issued:	1936 - by 1940
Size:	9 ¼″, 23.5 cm
Colour:	Black hat and moustache - gloss

Description	U.S. $	Can. $	U.K. £
Genie	300.00	450.00	175.00

Shape 467 **Wall vase**

Designer:	Mr. Symcox in 1937
Issued:	1937 - by 1959
Size:	9″, 22.9 cm
Colour:	1. Assorted decorations - satin matt
	2. White - matt

Market	Range
U.S.A.	$75.00 - 100.00
Canada	$125.00 - 150.00
U.K.	£45.00 - 60.00

Shape 470   George VI, coronation plaque

Designer: Mr. Weiss in 1937
Issued: 1937 - 1937
Size: Unknown
Colour: Ivory - satin matt

Colour	U.S. $	Can. $	U.K. £
Coronation plaque		Rare	

Shape 483   Girl with headdress, wall mask

Designer: Miss Greaves in 1937
Issued: 1937 - by 1940
Length: 9", 22.9 cm
Colour: Light brown hair, light grey-blue headdress; beige with yellow flowers

Description	U.S. $	Can. $	U.K. £
Girl with headdress	425.00	650.00	250.00

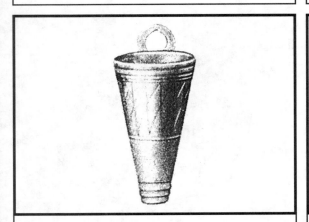

Shape 490   Wall vase, in two sizes

Designer: Mr. Owen in 1937
Issued: 1937 - by 1940
Sizes: 1. 8 ½", 21.6 cm
             2. 10", 25.4 cm
Colour: 1. Assorted decorations - satin matt
             2. White - matt

Market	Range 490/1	Range 490/2
U.S.A	$75.00 - 100.00	$75.00 - 125.00
Canada	$125.00 - 150.00	$125.00 - 175.00
U.K.	£45.00 - 60.00	£45.00 - 75.00

Shape 492   Wall vase

Designer: Mr. Owen in 1937
Issued: 1937 - by 1940
Height: 7 ½", 19.1 cm
Colour: 1. Assorted decorations - satin matt
             2. White - matt

Market	Range
U.S.A.	$75.00 - 100.00
Canada	$125.00 - 150.00
U.K.	£45.00 - 60.00

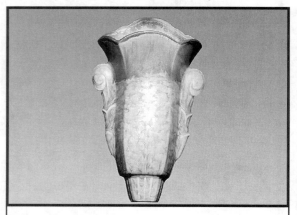

Shape 498   **Wall vase**

Designer:	Mr. Owen in 1937
Issued:	1937 - by 1940
Height:	11 ½", 29.2 cm
Colour:	1. Assorted decorations - satin matt
	2. White - matt

Market	Range
U.S.A.	$75.00 - 125.00
Canada	$125.00 - 175.00
U.K.	£45.00 - 75.00

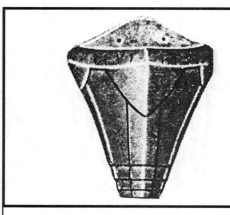

Shape 503   **Wall vase**

Designer:	Mr. Owen in 1937
Issued:	1937 - by 1940
Height:	9", 22.9 cm
Colour:	1. Assorted decorations - satin matt
	2. White - matt

Market	Range
U.S.A.	$75.00 - 100.00
Canada	$125.00 - 150.00
U.K.	£45.00 - 60.00

Shape 506   **Wall vase**

Designer:	Mr. Owen in 1937
Issued:	1937 - by 1940
Size:	Unknown
Colour:	1. Assorted decorations - satin matt
	2. White - matt

Market	Range
U.S.A.	$75.00 - 100.00
Canada	$125.00 - 150.00
U.K.	£45.00 - 60.00

Shape 507   **The Gleaners**

Designer:	Mr. Watkin in 1937
Issued:	1937 - 1940
Size:	11", 27.9 cm
Colour:	Green rim with scene in various shades of brown - satin matt

Description	U.S. $	Can. $	U.K. £
The Gleaners	250.00	375.00	150.00

Note: This plaque is a pair with shape 508.

Shape 508   The Angelus

Designer:	Mr. Watkin in 1937
Issued:	1937 - 1940
Size:	11", 27.9 cm
Colour:	Green rim with scene in various shades of brown - satin matt

Description	U.S. $	Can. $	U.K. £
The Angelus	250.00	375.00	150.00

Note: This plaque is a pair with shape 507.

Shape 551   Flowers in basket, plaque

Designer:	Mr. Hayward in 1937
Issued:	1938 - by 1954
Height:	10", 25.4 cm
Colour:	Flowers in various colours, basket in beige and light brown - satin matt

Description	U.S. $	Can. $	U.K. £
Flowers in basket	125.00	175.00	65.00

Shape 556   Flowers in basket plaque

Designer:	Mr. Watkin in 1937
Issued:	1938 - by 1954
Height:	10 ½", 26.7 cm
Colour:	Flowers in various colours, basket in beige and light brown - satin matt

Description	U.S. $	Can. $	U.K. £
Flowers in basket	125.00	175.00	65.00

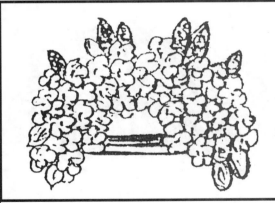

Shape 557   Spray of flowers, plaque

Designer:	Miss Greaves in 1937
Issued:	1938 - by 1954
Size:	6 ½", 16.5 cm
Colour:	Flowers in various colours, yellow bowl - satin matt

Description	U.S. $	Can. $	U.K. £
Spray of flowers	135.00	200.00	75.00

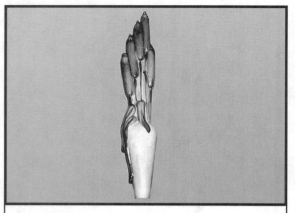

Shape 564   **Bulrushes, plaque**

Designer: Miss Greaves in 1937
Issued: 1938 - by 1954
Height: 14", 35.5 cm
Colour: Brown bulrushes in blue or white holder - satin matt

Description	U.S. $	Can. $	U.K. £
Bulrushes	85.00	125.00	50.00

Shape 565   **Anemones, plaque**

Designer: Unknown
Issued: 1938 - by 1954
Size: 5 ½", 14.0 cm
Colour: Flowers in various colours, holder in yellow - satin matt

Description	U.S. $	Can. $	U.K. £
Anemones	135.00	200.00	75.00

Shape 571   **Bowl of roses, plaque**

Designer: Miss Greaves in 1938
Issued: 1938 - by 1954
Height: 4 ½", 11.9 cm
Colour: Pink and yellow flowers with green leaves - satin matt

Description	U.S. $	Can. $	U.K. £
Bowl of roses	135.00	200.00	75.00

Shape 572   **Robin on bough, plaque**

Designer: Miss Greaves in 1938
Issued: 1938 - by 1954
Size: Unknown
Colour: Bird natural colour, brown bough, foliage green - satin matt

Description	U.S. $	Can. $	U.K. £
Bird on bough	135.00	200.00	85.00

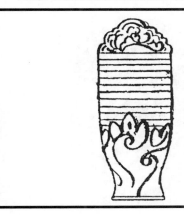

Shape 574 **Three blue tits, plaque**

Designer: Miss Greaves in 1938
Issued: 1938 - by 1954
Size: 10" x 5 ", 25.4 x 12.7 cm
Colour: Yellow, blue, green and brown - satin matt

Description	U.S. $	Can. $	U.K. £
Three blue tits	135.00	200.00	85.00

Shape 583 **Wall vase**

Designer: Mr. Symcox in 1938
Issued: 1938 - by 1940
Size: Unknown
Colour: 1. Assorted decorations - satin matt
2. White - matt

Market	Range
U.S.A.	$75.00 - 125.00
Canada	$125.00 - 175.00
U.K.	£45.00 - 75.00

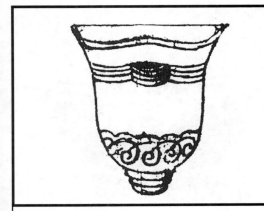

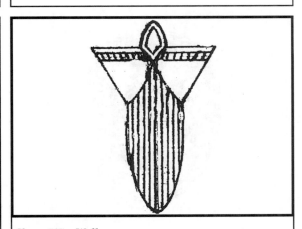

Shape 584 **Wall vase**

Designer: Mr. Symcox in 1938
Issued: 1938 - by 1940
Size: Unknown
Colour: 1. Assorted decorations - satin matt
2. White - matt

Market	Range
U.S.A.	$75.00 - 125.00
Canada	$125.00 - 175.00
U.K.	£45.00 - 75.00

Shape 585 **Wall vase**

Designer: Mr. Symcox in 1938
Issued: 1938 - by 1940
Size: 9", 22.9 cm
Colour: 1. Assorted decorations - satin matt
2. White - matt

Market	Range
U.S.A.	$75.00 - 125.00
Canada	$125.00 - 175.00
U.K.	£45.00 - 75.00

Shape 612   Young boy's head, wall mask

Designer:	Mr. Owen in 1938
Issued:	1938 - by 1954
Size:	7 ¼", 18.4 cm
Colour:	Brown hair, face in natural colour - satin matt

Descripton	U.S. $	Can. $	U.K. £
Young boy's head	400.00	650.00	250.00

Shape 614   Butterfly, wall vase

Designer:	Mr. Watkin in 1938
Issued:	1938 - by 1954
Size:	Unknown
Colour:	Blue, green, yellow, brown and cream - satin matt

Description	U.S. $	Can. $	U.K. £
Butterfly	135.00	200.00	85.00

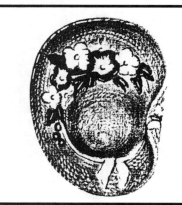

Shape 651   Hat with flowers, wall vase

Designer:	Mr. Watkin in 1938
Issued:	1938 - by 1965
Size:	9 ¼", 23.5 cm
Colour:	Stone or straw coloured hat with flowers in various colours - gloss or matt

Description	U.S. $	Can. $	U.K. £
Hat with flowers	135.00	200.00	85.00

Shape 693   Modelle, wall vase

Designer:	Unknown
Issued:	1939 - by 1963
Length:	13", 33 cm
Colour:	1. Assorted decorations - satin matt
	2. White - matt

Market	Range
U.S.A.	$75.00 - 125.00
Canada	$125.00 - 175.00
U.K.	£45.00 - 75.00

Shape 708   Cupid, wall vase

Designer:	Arthur Gredington in 1939
Issued:	1939 - by 1954
Size:	6 ¾, 17.2 cm
Colour:	Natural coloured body with pale green wings and blonde hair - satin matt

Description	U.S. $	Can. $	U.K. £
Cupid, wall vase		Rare	

Shape 710   Courting couple, plaque

Designer:	Arthur Gredington in 1939
Issued:	1939 - by 1954
Size:	8", 20.3 cm
Colour:	Green background, white dress with pink and yellow flowers, man in red jacket, yellow, waistcoat, green breeches and white hose - gloss

Description	U.S. $	Can. $	U.K. £
Courting couple	200.00	300.00	125.00

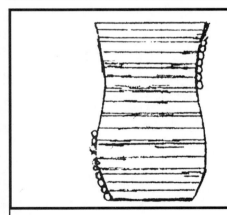

Shape 713   Wall vase

Designer:	Albert Hallam in 1939
Issued:	1939 - by 1954
Size:	Unknown
Colour:	1. Assorted decorations - satin matt 2. White - matt

Market	Range
U.S.A.	$75.00 - 100.00
Canada	$125.00 - 150.00
U.K.	£45.00 - 60.00

Shape 714   "Hear no evil, say no evil, see no evil," motto plaque or letter rack

Designer:	Arthur Gredington in 1939
Issued:	1939 - by 1954
Size:	6 x 4 ½, 15 cm x 11.9 cm
Colour:	Grey/blue, green and brown on light background - gloss

Description	U.S. $	Can. $	U.K. £
"Hear no evil....."	200.00	300.00	125.00

Shape 715 "A world without friends would be like a garden without flowers," motto plaque

Designer: Mr. Owen in 1939
Issued: 1939 - by 1954
Size: 9 ½" x 7 ½", 24.0 x 19.1 cm
Colour: 1. Multi-coloured border - satin matt
2. White - matt

Colour	U.S. $	Can. $	U.K. £
1. Multi-coloured border	100.00	175.00	65.00
2. White	65.00	100.00	40.00

Photograph not
available
at press time

Shape 719 "One of the best things to have up your sleeve is a funny bone," motto plaque

Designer: Mr. Owen in 1939
Issued: 1939 - by 1954
Size: 9 ½" x 7 ½", 24.0 x 19.1 cm
Colour: 1. Multi-coloured border - satin matt
2. White - matt

Colour	U.S. $	Can. $	U.K. £
1. Multi-coloured border	100.00	175.00	65.00
2. White	65.00	100.00	40.00

Shape 723 "Those who bring sunshine to the lives of others cannot keep it from themselves," motto plaque

Designer: Mr. Owen in 1939
Issued: 1939 - by 1954
Size: 9 ¼" x 7 ¼", 23.5 x 18.4 cm
Colour: 1. Multi-coloured border - satin matt
2. White - matt

Colour	U.S. $	Can. $	U.K. £
1. Multi-coloured border	100.00	175.00	65.00
2. White	65.00	100.00	40.00

Photograph not
available
at press time

Shape 724 "Don't worry it may never happen," motto plaque

Designer: Mr. Owen in 1939
Issued: 1939 - by 1954
Size: 8" x 8 ¾", 20.3 x 22.0 cm
Colour: 1. Multi-coloured border - satin matt
2. White - matt

Colour	U.S. $	Can. $	U.K. £
1. Multi-coloured border	100.00	175.00	65.00
2. White	65.00	100.00	40.00

Photograph not
available
at press time

Shape 733   **Cupid, wall vase**

Designer: Arthur Gredington in 1939
Issued: 1939 - by 1954
Size: 6 ¾", 17.2 cm
Colour: Natural coloured body with pale green wings
and blonde hair - satin matt

Description	U.S. $	Can. $	U.K. £
Cupid		Rare	

Shape 739   **"Lifes a melody if youll only hum the tune,"
motto plaque**

Designer: Mr. Owen in 1939
Issued: 1939 - by 1954
Size: 8" x 8 ¾", 20.3 x 22.0 cm
Colour: 1. Multi-coloured border - satin matt
           2. White - matt

Colour	U.S. $	Can. $	U.K. £
1. Multi-coloured border	100.00	175.00	65.00
2. White	65.00	100.00	40.00

Shape 740   **"When you are up to your neck in hot water,
think of the kettle and sing," motto plaque**

Designer: Mr. Owen in 1939
Issued: 1939 - by 1954
Size: 8" x 8 ¾", 20.3 x 22.0 cm
Colour: 1. Multi-coloured border - satin matt
           2. White - matt

Colour	U.S. $	Can. $	U.K. £
1. Multi-coloured border	100.00	175.00	65.00
2. White	65.00	100.00	40.00

Shape 741   **Courting couple, plaque**

Designer: Arthur Gredington in 1939
Issued: 1939 - by 1954
Size: 8", 20.3 cm
Colour: Unknown

Description	U.S. $	Can. $	U.K. £
Courting couple	200.00	325.00	125.00

Shape 806   **Horse head, tie rack, wall ornament**

Designer:	Mr. Owen in 1938
Issued:	1939 - 1968
Size:	7 ¼", 18.4 cm
Height:	6", 15 cm
Colour:	Brown - gloss

Description	U.S. $	Can. $	U.K. £
Horse head, tie rack	125.00	175.00	75.00

Note: Modelled from no. 686 (flat back) but with raised back.

Shape 807   **Horse head, tie rack, wall ornament**

Designer:	Mr. Owen in 1938
Issued:	1939 - 1968
Size:	7 ¼," 18.4 cm
Height:	6", 15 cm
Colour:	Brown - gloss

Description	U.S. $	Can. $	U.K. £
Horse head, tie rack	125.00	175.00	75.00

Note: Modelled from no. 687 (flat back) but with raised back.

Photograph not
available
at press time

Shape 837   **Plain plaque**

Designer:	Albert Hallam in 1940
Issued:	1940 - by 1954
Diameter:	16", 40.5 cm
Colour:	Unknown

Description	U.S. $	Can. $	U.K. £
Plain plaque	Possibly not put into production		

Shape 842   **Gargoyle/cat, plaque**

Designer:	Miss Joachim in 1940
Issued:	1940 - by 1954
Size:	4 ½" x 4 ½", 11.5 x 11.5 cm
Colour:	Dark grey/black - gloss

Description	U.S. $	Can. $	U.K. £
Gargoyle/cat		Rare	

Shape 1209 "As You Like It," Shakespeare plaque

Designer:	Arthur Gredington in 1950
Issued:	1951 - 1968
Diameter:	12", 30.5 cm
Colour:	Multi-coloured scene - gloss

Description	U.S. $	Can. $	U.K. £
"As You Like It", plaque	175.00	250.00	100.00

Note: This plaque is a pair with shape 1210.

Shape 1210 "Romeo and Juliet," Shakespeare plaque

Designer:	Arthur Gredington in 1950
Issued:	1951 - 1968
Diameter:	12", 30.5 cm
Colour:	Multi-coloured scene - gloss

Description	U.S. $	Can. $	U.K. £
'Romeo and Juliet", plaque	175.00	250.00	100.00

Note: This plaque is a pair with shape 1209.

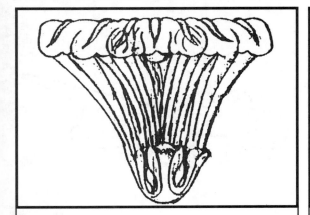

Shape 1322 Corner wall vase

Designer:	Albert Hallam and Mr. Hayward in 1953
Issued:	1954 - by 1956
Size:	Unknown
Colour:	Unknown

Description	U.S. $	Can. $	U.K. £
Corner wall vase	85.00	125.00	50.00

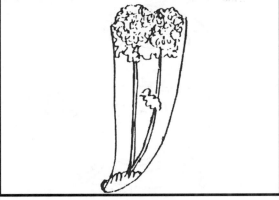

Shape 1609 Chrysanthemum, wall vase

Designer:	Albert Hallam in 1959
Issued:	1959 - by 1963
Size:	Unknown
Colour:	Coloured flowers on a white background - satin matt

Description	U.S. $	Can. $	U.K. £
Chrysanthemum, wall vase	85.00	125.00	50.00

Note: Set of nine with vases nos. 1602, 1604,1605, 1606, 1607, 1608, bowl 1603 and basket 1668

Shape 1632 Yacht GP14, plaque

Designer: Albert Hallam in 1959
Issued: 1960 - by 1963
Height: 7 ¾", 19.7 cm
Colour: White sails, blue boat on shaded
            blue-green sea - satin matt

Description	U.S. $	Can. $	U.K. £
Yacht GP14	150.00	200.00	85.00

Note: Set of four with ornaments 1610, 1633 and 1634.

Shape 1679 Double Diamond pub, plaque

Designer: Albert Hallam in 1960
Issued: Unknown
Size: Unknown
Colour: Pub - brown roof, stone coloured walls and
            blue sills; green leaves on tree - gloss

Description	U.S. $	Can. $	U.K. £
Double Diamond pub	400.00	625.00	250.00

Note: Special Commission.

Shape 1680 Double Diamond man, plaque

Designer: Albert Hallam in 1960
Issued: Unknown
Height: 7", 17.8 cm
Colour: Black hat and jacket, black and white striped
            trousers with white shirt - gloss

Description	U.S. $	Can. $	U.K. £
Double Diamond man	250.00	375.00	150.00

Note: Special Commission.

Shape 1681 Double Diamond dog, plaque

Designer: Albert Hallam in 1960
Issued: Unknown
Size: Unknown
Colour: Unknown - gloss

Description	U.S. $	Can. $	U.K. £
Double Diamond dog	250.00	375.00	150.00

Note: Special Commission.

Shape 2060 Hunts plaque

Designer:	Albert Hallam in 1966
Issued:	Unknown
Height:	7 ½", 19.1 cm
Colour:	Grey horse, green tree and grass with brown fence - gloss

Description	U.S. $	Can. $	U.K. £
Hunts plaque	300.00	450.00	175.00

Note: Special Commission.

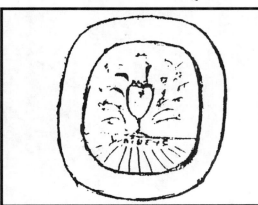

Shape 2079 Watneys plaque

Designer:	Graham Tongue in 1966
Issued:	Unknown
Size:	6 ¼", 15.9 cm
Colour:	Unknown - gloss

Description	U.S. $	Can. $	U.K. £
Watneys plaque	100.00	165.00	65.00

Note: Special Commission.

Shape 2233 Cat and dog plaque

Designer:	Graham Tongue in 1968
Issued:	1968 - unknown
Size:	9" x 6 ¼", 22.9 x 15.9 cm
Colour:	Unknown - gloss

Description	U.S. $	Can. $	U.K. £
Cat and dog plaque	100.00	150.00	65.00

Shape 2235 Basset dog plaque, concave

Designer:	Graham Tongue in 1968
Issued:	1968 - unknown
Size:	4 ½" x 6 ¼", 11.9 x 15.9 cm
Colour:	Tan and white dog with black background - gloss

Description	U.S. $	Can. $	U.K. £
Basset dog plaque	125.00	175.00	75.00

Shape 2236 Cat plaque

Designer:	Graham Tongue in 1968
Issued:	1968 - unknown
Size:	6 ¼" x 9", 15.9 x 22.9 cm
Colour:	Ginger cat, with yellow eyes, on a dark pewter background - gloss

Description	U.S. $	Can. $	U.K. £
Cat plaque	100.00	150.00	65.00

Shape 2237 Babycham plaque

Designer:	Graham Tongue in 1968
Issued:	c.1970 - c.1975
Size:	3" x 6 ¼", 7.6 x 15.9 cm
Colour:	Unknown - gloss

Description	U.S. $	Can. $	U.K. £
Babycham plaque	175.00	225.00	100.00

Note: Special Commission.

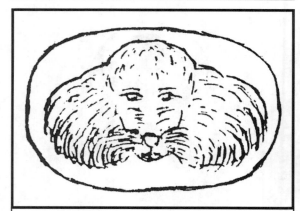

Shape 2268 Poodle plaque

Designer:	Graham Tongue in 1969
Issued:	1969 - unknown
Size:	6" x 4 ½", 15 x 11.9 cm
Colour:	Unknown - gloss

Description	U.S. $	Can. $	U.K. £
Poodle plaque	175.00	250.00	95.00

Shape 2376 Christmas 1972, Latama plaque

Designer:	Albert Hallam in 1971
Issued:	1972 only
Size:	11 ¼" x 5 ½", 28.5 x 14 cm
Colour:	Multi-coloured scene - gloss

Description	U.S. $	Can. $	U.K. £
Christmas 1972	250.00	375.00	150.00

Note: Developed from shape 2375 Christmas 1972 Tankard "The Carol Singers."

Shape 2393 Christmas Plaque, England 1972

Designer:	Albert Hallam in 1971
Issued:	1972 - 1972
Size:	8" x 8", 20.3 x 20.3 cm
Colour:	Multi-coloured scene

Description	U.S. $	Can. $	U.K. £
England 1972	60.00	90.00	35.00

Shape 2419 Christmas Plaque, Mexico 1973

Designer:	Albert Hallam in 1972
Issued:	1973 - 1973
Size:	8" x 8", 20.3 x 20.3 cm
Colour:	Multi-coloured scene

Description	U.S. $	Can. $	U.K. £
Mexico 1973	60.00	90.00	35.00

Shape 2430 Christmas 1973, Latama plaque

Designer:	Albert Hallam in 1972
Issued:	1973 only
Size:	11 ¼" x 5 ½", 28.5 x 14 cm
Colour:	Multi-coloured scene - gloss

Description	U.S. $	Can. $	U.K. £
Christmas 1973	175.00	250.00	100.00

Note: Developed from Shape 2423 Christmas
1973 Tankard "A Christmas Carol."

Shape 2443 Regent Street, Latama plaque

Designer:	Albert Hallam in 1972
Issued:	1973 - unknown
Length:	11 x 7", 27.9" x 17.8 cm
Colour:	Multi-coloured scene - gloss

Description	U.S. $	Can. $	U.K. £
Regent Street	175.00	250.00	100.00

Shape 2462 Christmas Plaque, Bulgaria 1974

Designer:	Albert Hallam in 1973
Issued:	1974 - 1974
Size:	8" x 8", 20.3 x 20.3 cm
Colour:	Multi-coloured scene

Description	U.S. $	Can. $	U.K. £
Bulgaria 1974	60.00	90.00	35.00

Shape 2522 Christmas Plaque, Norway 1974

Designer:	Graham Tongue in 1974
Issued:	1975 - 1975
Size:	8" x 8", 20.3 x 20.3 cm
Colour:	Multi-coloured scene

Description	U.S. $	Can. $	U.K. £
Norway 1974	60.00	90.00	35.00

Shape 2538 Christmas Plaque, Holland 1976

Designer:	Mr. Lyttleton, Graham Tongue in 1976
Issued:	1976 - 1976
Size:	8" x 8", 20.3 x 20.3 cm
Colour:	Multi-coloured scene

Description	U.S. $	Can. $	U.K. £
Holland 1976	60.00	90.00	35.00

Shape 2567 Christmas Plaque, Poland 1977

Designer:	Mr. Plant, Graham Tongue in 1977
Issued:	1977 - 1977
Size:	8" x 8", 20.3 x 20.3 cm
Colour:	Multi-coloured scene

Description	U.S. $	Can. $	U.K. £
Poland 1977	60.00	90.00	35.00

Shape 2594 Jemima Puddleduck and Foxy Whiskered Gentleman Plaque, Beatrix Potter plaque

Designer: David Lyttleton, Harry Sales in 1977
Issued: 1978 - 1982
Size: 7 ½" x 7 ½", 19.1 x 19.1 cm
Colour: White duck, brown fox in woodland scene of greens and browns - gloss

Description	U.S. $	Can. $	U.K. £
Jemima/Foxy	200.00	300.00	125.00

Note: Set of three with shape nos. 2650 and 2685.

Shape 2598 Christmas Plaque, America 1978

Designer: Albert Hallam in 1978
Issued: 1978 - 1978
Size: 8" x 8", 20.3 x 20.3 cm
Colour: Multi-coloured scene

Description	U.S. $	Can. $	U.K. £
America 1978	60.00	90.00	35.00

Shape 2650 Peter Rabbit in Vegetable Patch, Beatrix Potter plaque

Designer: David Lyttleton, Harry Sales in 1979
Issued: 1980 - 1982
Size: 7 ½" x 7 ½", 19.1 x 19.1 cm
Colour: Blue jacket; orange carrots; background greens and browns - gloss

Description	U.S. $	Can. $	U.K. £
Peter Rabbit	200.00	300.00	125.00

Note: Set of three with shape nos. 2594 and 2685.

Shape 2685 Mrs. Tittlemouse at the Door, Beatrix Potter plaque

Designer: Harry Sales in 1981
Issued: 1982 - 1982
Size: 7 ½" x 7 ½", 19.1 x 19.1 cm
Colour: White and pink striped dress with white apron; background greens and browns - gloss

Description	U.S. $	Can. $	U.K. £
Mrs. Tittlemouse	250.00	375.00	150.00

Note: Set of three with shape nos. 2594 and 2650.

Shape 2393 Christmas Plaque England 1972

SECTION THREE

NOVELTIES

Bookends, serviette holders, cruet sets, teapots, toothbrush holders, lemon squeezers, money boxes and hen baskets are some of the items to be found in this "fun" section. Here we find animals featuring in the majority of the shapes and some pieces actually modelled in the shapes of animals, eg. teapots.

It is hardly surprising that animals feature so prominently, as the House of Beswick was internationally known for its realistic and true to life modelling of a wide variety of animals (see *The Charlton Standard Catalogue of Beswick Animals*).

As with the Miscellaneous Section most of the items listed here are individuals, there is a good variety and some are very imaginative, such as the mirror featuring a polar bear (shape 287) a delightful piece, which is also very rare.

Although numbers were allocated to the shapes listed below, there is no indication that these items were ever put into commercial production: No 2346 Cat sellotape holder, 2354 and 2355 Mushroom salt and pepper, 2812 and 2813 Cat's Fun cups and 2818 Cat's Fun teapot.

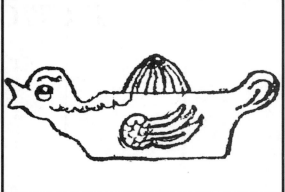

Shape 87   **Dog bookends**

Designer: Unknown c.1933
Issued: 1934 - by 1963
Height: 6 ¼", 15.9 cm
Colour: 1. Assorted decorations - satin matt
     2. White - matt

Description	U.S. $	Can. $	U.K. £
1. Various	150.00	225.00	85.00
2. Blue	200.00	300.00	125.00
3. White	150.00	225.00	85.00

Shape 283   **Duck lemon squeezer**

Designer: Mr. Symcox c.1934
Issued: 1935 - by 1954
Height :   Unknown
Colour: 1. Assorted decorations - satin matt
     2. White - matt

Description	U.S. $	Can. $	U.K. £
Duck lemon squeezer		Rare	

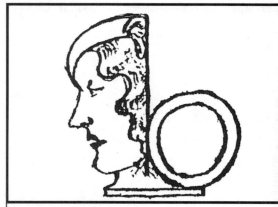

Shape 284   **Lady with beret, serviette holder**

Designer: Mr. Watkin c.1934
Issued: 1935 - by 1940
Height: Unknown
Colour: Blonde hair with either a black or blue
     beret - gloss

Description	U.S. $	Can. $	U.K. £
Serviette holder	125.00	175.00	75.00

Shape 287   **Stand with mirror and polar bear**

Designer: Mr. Watkin in 1934
Issued: 1935 - by 1954
Height: 6 ¾", 17.2 cm
Colour: White bear on blue ice - gloss

Description	U.S. $	Can. $	U.K. £
Stand with mirror and polar bear	175.00	250.00	100.00

Shape 311 **Duck serviette holder**

Designer:	Miss Greaves in 1934
Issued:	1935 - by 1940
Height:	2 ½", 6.4 cm
Colour:	1. Assorted decorations - satin matt
	2. White - matt

Market	Range
U.S.A.	$75.00 - 125.00
Canada	$125.00 - 175.00
U.K.	£45.00 - 75.00

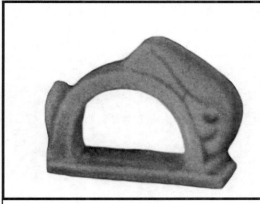

Shape 312 **Rabbit serviette holder**

Designer:	Miss Greaves in 1934
Issued:	1935 - by 1940
Height:	2 ½", 6.4 cm
Colour:	1. Assorted decorations - satin matt
	2. White - matt

Market	Range
U.S.A.	$75.00 - 125.00
Canada	$125.00 - 175.00
U.K.	£45.00 - 75.00

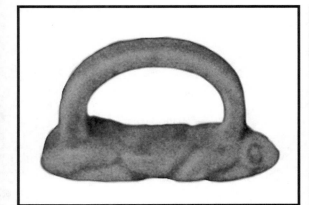

Shape 313 **Rabbit serviette holder**

Designer:	Miss Greaves in 1934
Issued:	1935 - by 1940
Size:	2 ½", 6.4 cm
Colour:	1. Assorted decorations - satin matt
	2. White - matt

Market	Range
U.S.A.	$75.00 - 125.00
Canada	$125.00 - 175.00
U.K.	£45.00 - 75.00

Shape 376 **Rabbit place card holder**

Designer:	Unknown
Issued:	1936 - by 1954
Height:	2 ¼", 5.7 cm
Colour:	1. Assorted decorations - satin matt
	2. White - matt

Description	U.S. $	Can. $	U.K. £
Rabbit place card holder	85.00	125.00	50.00

Shape 401   Lemon squeezer, two pieces

Designer:	Unknown
Issued:	1936 - 1970
Height:	3 ½", 8.9 cm
Colour:	Lemon, red or orange base, white top - gloss

Description	U.S. $	Can. $	U.K. £
Lemon squeezer	40.00	60.00	25.00

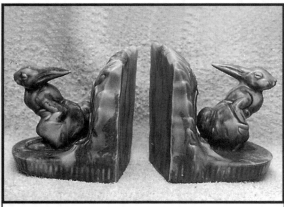

Shape 455   Rabbit bookends

Designer:	James Hayward in 1936
Issued:	1937 - by 1954
Size:	6 3/4", 17.2 cm
Colour:	1. Assorted decorations - satin matt
	2. Blue - gloss 3. White - matt

Colourways	U.S. $	Can. $	U.K. £
1. Assorted decorations	100.00	150.00	65.00
2. Blue	135.00	200.00	85.00
3. White	100.00	150.00	65.00

Shape 460   Cruet, Dutch boy and girl (salt and pepper) in boat with capstan (mustard)

Designer:	Mr. Symcox in 1936
Issued:	1937 - by 1940
Size:	Unknown
Colour:	1. Assorted decorations - satin matt
	2. White - matt

Description	U.S. $	Can. $	U.K. £
Cruet		Rare	

Photograph not
available
at press time

Shape 472   George VI bookends

Designer:	Mr. Weiss in 1937
Issued:	1937 - 1937
Size:	Unknown
Colour:	1. Assorted decorations - satin matt
	2. White - matt

Market	Range
U.S.A.	$75.00 - 125.00
Canada	$125.00 - 175.00
U.K.	£45.00 - 75.00

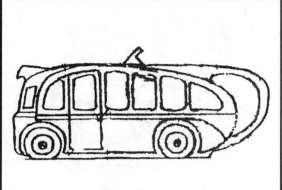

Shape 575 Laurel and Hardy cruet

Designer: Mr. Watkin in 1938
Issued: 1938 - 1968
Height: 4 ¼", 10.8 cm
Colour: Black, white, brown, with flesh coloured
           faces - gloss

Description	U.S. $	Can. $	U.K. £
Laurel and Hardy cruet	150.00	200.00	75.00

Shape 576 Bus teapot

Designer: Mr. Watkin in 1938
Issued: 1938 - by 1954
Size: Unknown
Colour: Unknown - gloss

Description	U.S. $	Can. $	U.K. £
Bus teapot		Rare	

Shape 577 Caravan preserve

Designer: Mr. Watkin in 1938
Issued: 1938 - by 1954
Size: 4 ½" x 3 ¾, 11.9 x 9.5 cm incl. knob
Colour: Green, black and silver - gloss

Description	U.S. $	Can. $	U.K. £
Caravan preserve		Rare	

Photograph not
available
at press time

Shape 590/610 Speedboat preserve

Designer: Mr. Watkin in 1938
Issued: 1938 - by 1954
Size: Unknown
Colour: Unknown

Description	U.S. $	Can. $	U.K. £
Speedboat preserve		Rare	

Shape 609 **Chess cruet — salt, pepper, mustard, base**

Designer:	Mr. White in 1938		
Issued:	1938 - by 1954		
Size:	Unknown		
Colour:	1. Assorted decorations		
	2. White - matt		

Description	U.S. $	Can. $	U.K. £
Chess cruet		Rare	

Shape 613 **Soldier cruet**

Photograph not available at press time

Designer:	Mr. White in 1938
Issued:	1938 - by 1954
Size:	Unknown
Colour:	Unknown

Description	U.S. $	Can. $	U.K. £
Soldier cruet		Rare	

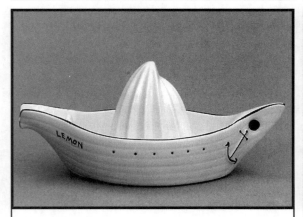

Shape 619 **Yacht lemon squeezer**

Designer:	Mr. Hayward in 1938
Issued:	1938 - 1970
Height:	2 ¼", 5.7 cm
Colour:	Orange, red, yellow or white - gloss

Colour	U.S. $	Can. $	U.K. £
Lemon squeezer	40.00	60.00	25.00

Shape 624 **Dog toothbrush holder**

Designer:	Miss Catford in 1938
Issued:	1938 - by 1954
Size:	4", 10.1 cm
Colour:	1. Blue - gloss
	2. Various - satin matt
	3. White - matt

Colour	U.S. $	Can. $	U.K. £
1. Blue	175.00	250.00	100.00
2. Various	250.00	375.00	150.00
3. White	175.00	250.00	100.00

Shape 625   Rabbit cruet

Designer:	Miss Catford in 1938
Issued:	1938 - by 1954
Size:	Unknown
Colour:	1. Assorted decorations - satin matt
	2. White - matt

Description	U.S. $	Can. $	U.K. £
Rabbit cruet		Rare	

Shape 663   Elephant toothbrush holder

Designer:	Miss Catford in 1938
Issued:	1938 - by 1954
Size:	4 ½", 11.9 cm
Colour:	1. Assorted decorations - satin matt
	2. Blue - gloss
	3. White - matt

Description	U.S. $	Can. $	U.K. £
1. Assorted decorations	265.00	400.00	165.00
2. Blue	250.00	350.00	150.00
3. White	250.00	350.00	150.00

Shape 664   Fox toothbrush holder

Designer:	Miss Catford in 1938
Issued:	1938 - by 1954
Size:	4 ¾", 12.1 cm
Colour:	1. Assorted decorations - satin matt
	2. Blue - gloss
	3. White - matt

Description	U.S. $	Can. $	U.K. £
1. Assorted decorations	250.00	350.00	150.00
2. Blue	225.00	325.00	135.00
3. White	225.00	325.00	135.00

Shape 665   Rabbit toothbrush holder

Designer:	Miss Catford in 1938
Issued:	1938 - by 1954
Size:	4 ¾", 12.1 cm
Colour:	1. Assorted decorations - satin matt
	2. Blue - gloss
	3. White - matt

Description	U.S. $	Can. $	U.K. £
1. Assorted decorations	250.00	350.00	150.00
2. Blue	225.00	325.00	135.00
3. White	225.00	325.00	135.00

Shape 742   **Panda teapot (First version)**

Designer:	Mr. Watkin in 1939
Issued:	1939 - by 1954
Size:	6", 12.7 cm
Colour:	Black and white panda with beige/yellow bamboo shoot - gloss

Description	U.S. $	Can. $	U.K. £
Panda teapot	275.00	400.00	165.00

Shape 751   **Guard in sentry box bookend**

Designer:	Mr. Watkin in 1939
Issued:	1939 - by 1954
Size:	6", 15.0 cm
Colour:	Black busby, red jacket and black trousers - gloss

Description	U.S. $	Can. $	U.K. £
Guard in sentry box	175.00	275.00	100.00

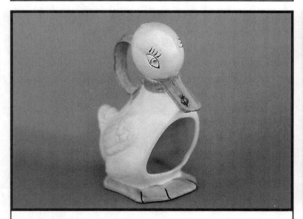

Shape 769   **Duck night light holder**

Designer:	Mr. Watkin in 1939
Issued:	1939 - by 1954
Size:	6", 15 cm
Colour:	White and yellow duck, orange beak - gloss

Description	U.S. $	Can. $	U.K. £
Duck night light holder		Rare	

Shape 940   **Anderson Shelter bookends (pair)**
                          Family (left), Warden (right)

Designer:	Unknown
Issued:	1941 - by 1954
Size:	Unknown
Colour:	Ivory - gloss

Description	U.S. $	Can. $	U.K. £
Bookends	350.00	500.00	200.00

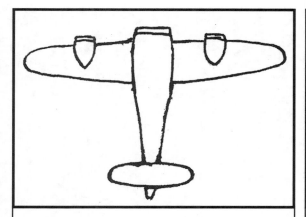

Shape 945   Aeroplane

Designer: Mr. White in 1941
Issued: 1941 - by 1954
Size: Unknown
Colour: Unknown

Description	U.S. $	Can. $	U.K. £
Aeroplane		Rare	

Shape 952   Army co-operation bookends (pair)

Designer: Unknown
Issued: 1941 - by 1954
Size: Unknown
Colour: Unknown

Description	U.S. $	Can. $	U.K. £
Bookends	450.00	600.00	275.00

Shape 1099   Cock and hen, salt and pepper

Designer: Unknown
Issued: 1947 - 1959
Height: 2", 5.0 cm
Colour: Teal green, brown, yellow and red - gloss

Description	U.S. $	Can. $	U.K. £
Salt and pepper	60.00	90.00	35.00

**Shape 1201   Friar liqueur set
                Monk, tray and six measures**

Designer: Arthur Gredington, Albert Hallam in 1950
Issued: 1950 - 1950
Size: 8 ¼", 21.0 cm
Colour: Brown with cream inners to measures - gloss

Description	U.S. $	Can. $	U.K. £
Friar liqueur set	100.00	150.00	65.00

Note: Special Commission for Heatmaster.

Shape 1760 Piggy bank

Designer:	Albert Hallam in 1961
Issued:	1961 - 1967
Height:	8 ½", 21.6 cm
Colour:	White, grey and pink - gloss

Description	U.S. $	Can. $	U.K. £
Piggy bank	125.00	175.00	75.00

Shape 1761 Foxy bank

Designer:	Albert Hallam in 1961
Issued:	1961 - 1967
Height:	8 ½", 21.6 cm
Colour:	Tan, brown and black on white - gloss

Description	U.S. $	Can. $	U.K. £
Foxy bank	125.00	175.00	75.00

Shape 1869 Dubonnet stand

Designer:	Albert Hallam in 1963
Issued:	Unknown
Size:	Unknown
Colour:	Blue with red lettering - gloss

Description	U.S. $	Can. $	U.K. £
Dubonnet stand	175.00	250.00	100.00

Shape 1870 Dubonnet bottle

Designer:	Albert Hallam in 1963
Issued:	Unknown
Height:	5 ½", 14.0 cm
Colour:	Unknown

Description	U.S. $	Can. $	U.K. £
Dubonnet bottle	40.00	60.00	25.00

Shape 1871 Dubonnet poodle

Designer: Albert Hallam in 1963
Issued: Unknown
Height: 4", 10.1 cm
Colour: White - gloss

Description	U.S. $	Can. $	U.K. £
Dubonnet poodle	125.00	185.00	75.00

Shape 1872 Dubonnet bulldog

Designer: Albert Hallam in 1963
Issued: Unknown
Height: 3 ¾", 9.5 cm
Colour: White - gloss

Description	U.S. $	Can. $	U.K. £
Dubonnet bulldog	125.00	185.00	75.00

Note: The four items (1869 to 1872) create one display. Special Commission. The dogs were available separately until 1967.

Shape 2135 Loaf, butter dish

Designer: Albert Hallam in 1967
Issued: 1968 - 1970
Size: 5 ½" x 3 ¾", 14 x 9.5 cm
Colour: Brown with dark brown top - gloss

Description	U.S. $	Can. $	U.K. £
Loaf, butter dish	40.00	60.00	25.00

Shape 2156-2157 Cat pepper and salt

Designer: Harry Sales, Graham Tongue in 1967
Issued: 1968 - 1969
Height: 5 ½", 14 cm
Colour: 1. Shape — 2156 black - gloss
             2. Shape — 2157 white - gloss

Description	U.S. $	Can. $	U.K. £
1. Shape 2156 — black cat	60.00	90.00	35.00
2. Shape 2157 — white cat	60.00	90.00	35.00

Shape 2298 Hen basket

Designer:	Graham Tongue in 1969
Issued:	1970 - 1974
Height:	4 ½", 11.9 cm
Colour:	Brown with light brown basket - gloss

Description	U.S. $	Can. $	U.K. £
Hen basket	40.00	60.00	25.00

Shape 2306 Hen basket

Designer:	Graham Tongue in 1970
Issued:	1970 - 1980
Height:	8", 20.3 cm
Colour:	Brown with light brown basket - gloss

Description	U.S. $	Can. $	U.K. £
Hen basket	125.00	175.00	75.00

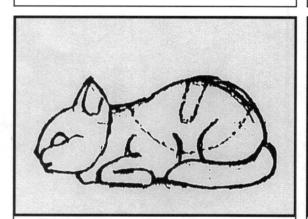

Shape 2346 Cat sellotape holder

Designer:	Unknown
Issued:	Unknown
Size:	Unknown
Colour:	Unknown - gloss

Description	U.S. $	Can. $	U.K. £
Cat sellotape holder		Possibly not issued	

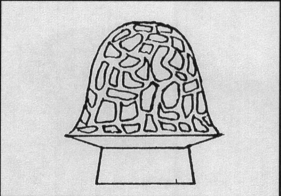

Shape 2354-2355 Mushroom pepper and salt (pair)

Designer:	Graham Tongue in 1971
Issued:	Unknown
Height:	3 ½", 8.9 cm
Colour:	Unknown - gloss

Colour	U.S. $	Can. $	U.K. £
1. Shape 2354 — Pepper		Possibly not issued	
2. Shape 2355 — Salt			

Shape 2397   Hen basket

Designer:	Albert Hallam, Graham Tongue in 1972
Issued:	1972 - 1972
Size:	8" x 8 ½", 20.3 x 21.6 cm
Colour:	Brown, light brown basket - gloss

Description	U.S. $	Can. $	U.K. £
Hen basket	125.00	175.00	75.00

Shape 2761   Cat on chimney pot, salt and pepper

Designer:	Unknown
Issued:	1982 - 1985
Size:	4", 10.1 cm
Colour:	White and gold - gloss
Series:	Fun ceramics

Description	U.S. $	Can. $	U.K. £
Salt and pepper	135.00	175.00	85.00

Shape 2792   Daisy the cow creamer

Designer:	Graham Tongue in 1982
Issued:	1982 - 1989
Height:	5 ¾", 14.6 cm
Colour:	Floral decorations, blue or yellow being the most common, on a white background - gloss
Series:	Fun ceramics

Description	U.S. $	Can. $	U.K. £
1. Blue	125.00	150.00	75.00
2. Yellow	125.00	150.00	75.00

Shape 2805   Cat on post box, money box

Designer:	Unknown
Issued:	1983 - 1986
Height:	6 ¼", 15.9 cm
Colour:	White cat on red post box
Series:	Fun ceramics

Description	U.S. $	Can. $	U.K. £
Money box	125.00	150.00	75.00

Shape 2808 Money box — Saving for a rainy day

Designer:	Unknown
Issued:	1983 - 1986
Height:	5 ¼", 13.3 cm
Colour:	Shaded browns with red umbrella - gloss
Series:	Fun ceramics

Description	U.S. $	Can. $	U.K. £
Money box	125.00	175.00	75.00

Shape 2810 Cat egg cup

Designer:	Unknown
Issued:	1983 - 1986
Height:	2 ½", 6.4 cm
Colour:	Ginger kitten with white egg cup - gloss
Series:	Fun ceramics

Description	U.S. $	Can. $	U.K. £
Cat egg cup	65.00	100.00	40.00

Shape 3015-3105 Panda teapot

Designer:	Mr. Platt and Mr. Alcock in 1987
Issued:	1989 - 1990
Height:	6", 15 cm
Colour:	Black and white panda - gloss

Description	U.S. $	Can. $	U.K. £
Panda teapot	125.00	175.00	65.00

Note: Set of four with nos. 3138, 3139 and 3142.

Shape 3138 Cat teapot

Designer:	Mr. Alcock in 1988
Issued:	1989 - 1990
Size:	7 ¼", 18.4 cm
Colour:	1. Black and white - gloss
	2. White - gloss

Desription	U.S. $	Can. $	U.K. £
1. Black/white	200.00	225.00	75.00
2. White	125.00	175.00	65.00

Note: Set of four with nos. 3105, 3139 and 3142.

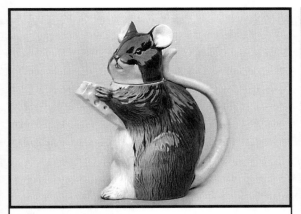

Shape 3139 Mouse teapot

Designer:	Warren Platt in 1988
Issued:	1989 - 1990
Height:	7", 17.8 cm
Colour:	White and brown mouse - gloss

Description	U.S. $	Can. $	U.K. £
Mouse teapot	150.00	225.00	65.00

Note: Set of four with nos. 3105, 3138 and 3142.

Shape 3142 Squirrel teapot

Designer:	Amanda Hughes in 1988
Issued:	1989 - 1990
Height:	7 ¼", 18.4 cm
Colour:	Red squirrel, with white - gloss

Description	U.S. $	Can. $	U.K. £
Squirrel teapot	150.00	200.00	65.00

Note: Set of four with nos. 3105, 3138 and 3139.

Note: Price ranges are retail market indicators of prices for models under the following conditions:
- Lower end of range = price of monochrome models
- Higher end of range = price of multicoloured models

MISCELLANEOUS

The shapes listed here do not fit into any of the other chapters in this book. Included are some items of tableware, preserve pots, honey pots, biscuit containers, cruets and ornaments. Most of these shapes are individual pieces and are not members of larger groups and sets.

For ornamental figures please see *The Charlton Standard Catalogue of Royal Doulton Beswick Figurines.*

Shape 377, an Edward VIII motif for use on other items, Shape 451 a Bust of Edward VIII and Shape 458 an Edward VIII jar were designed in anticipation of his coronation, and although a few were made, they were not put into full commercial production.

Shape 53   **Rome preserve**

Designer: Unknown
Issued: 1931 - by 1940
Height: 3 ½", 8.9 cm
Colour: 1. Assorted decorations - gloss
        2. White

Market	Range
U.S.A.	$45.00 - 65.00
Canada	$65.00 - 100.00
U.K.	£25.00 - 45.00

Shape 89   **Cigarette box**

Designer: Unknown
Issued: 1933 - by 1940
Size: 12", 30.5 cm
Colour: 1. Assorted decorations - satin matt
        2. White

Market	Range
U.S.A.	$45.00 - 65.00
Canada	$65.00 - 100.00
U.K.	£25.00 - 45.00

Note: Illustration is missing cover of cigarette box.

Shape 170   **Biscuit container**

Designer: Mr. Owen in 1933
Issued: 1933 - by 1954
Size: 4 ¾" x 5", 12.0 x 12.7 cm
Colour: 1. Assorted decorations - satin matt
        2. White

Market	Range
U.S.A.	$45.00 - 65.00
Canada	$65.00 - 100.00
U.K.	£25.00 - 45.00

Shape 202/2 Globe teapot

Designer: Unknown
Issued: 1933 - by 1940
Size: Unknown
Colour: 1. Assorted decorations - satin matt
        2. White

Market	Range
U.S.A.	$75.00 - 125.00
Canada	$125.00 - 175.00
U.K.	£45.00 - 75.00

Shape 206 **Apple shaped preserve with stand, (stalk used as a knob)**

Designer:	Mr. Symcox 1933
Issued:	1933 - 1940
Height:	5", 12.7 cm incl. stand
Colour:	1. Assorted decorations - gloss
	2. White

Market	Range
U.S.A.	$35.00 - 70.00
Canada	$50.00 - 100.00
U.K.	£20.00 - 40.00

Shape 207/1/2 **Preserve (available with or without stand)**

Designer:	1. Shape 207/1 — Mr. Symcox in 1933
	2. Shape 207/2 — Albert Hallam in 1950
Issued:	1. Shape 207/1 — 1933 - 1950
	2. Shape 207/2 — 1950 - 1970
Diameter:	3 ¾", 9.5 cm
Colour:	Lime green, orange, red or yellow - gloss

Market	Range 207/1	Range 207/2
U.S.A.	$35.00 - 70.00	$35.00 - 70.00
Canada	$50.00 - 100.00	$50.00 - 100.00
U.K.	£20.00 - 40.00	£20.00 - 40.00

Photograph not available at press time

Photograph not available at press time

Shape 209 **Baby plate**

Designer:	Albert Hallam in 1933
Issued:	1933 - by 1954
Size:	Unknown
Colour:	Unknown - gloss

Description	U.S. $	Can. $	U.K. £
Baby plate		Rare	

Shape 264 **Baby plate**

Designer:	Albert Hallam in 1933
Issued:	1933 - by 1954
Size:	Unknown
Colour:	Unknown - gloss

Description	U.S. $	Can. $	U.K. £
Baby plate		Rare	

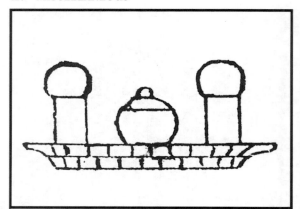

Shape 278   **Cruet, three pieces on a stand**

Designer: Mr. Symcox in 1933
Issued: 1934 - by 1940
Size: Unknown
Colour: 1. Assorted decorations - gloss
             2. White

Description	U.S. $	Can. $	U.K. £
Cruet		Rare	

Shape 318   **Preserve with lid**

Designer: Mr. Symcox in 1933
Issued: 1934 - by 1940
Size: Unknown
Colour: 1. Assorted decorations - gloss
             2. White

Market	Range
U.S.A.	$35.00 - 70.00
Canada	$50.00 - 100.00
U.K.	£20.00 - 40.00

Shape 319   **Cruet**

Designer: Mr. Symcox in 1933
Issued: 1934 - by 1954
Size: Unknown
Colour: Green, blue, yellow, pink on cream
             background - gloss

Description	U.S. $	Can. $	U.K. £
Cruet	65.00	100.00	40.00

Photograph not
available
at press time

Shape 400   **Teapot**

Designer: Mr. White in 1936
Issued: 1936 - by 1954
Size: Unknown
Colour: 1. Assorted decorations - gloss
             2. White

Market	Range
U.S.A.	$75.00 - 125.00
Canada	$125.00 - 175.00
U.K.	£45.00 - 75.00

Shape 402   **Beehive honey pot with base**

Designer:	Unknown
Issued:	1936 - by 1962
Height:	4 ¾", 12.1 cm
Colour:	1. Brown or white - gloss
	2. White with coloured bees - gloss

Market	Range
U.S.A.	$45.00 - 65.00
Canada	$65.00 - 100.00
U.K.	£25.00 - 45.00

Photograph not
available
at press time

Shape 403   **Rectangular honey container**

Designer:	Unknown
Issued:	1936 - by 1954
Height:	4 ½", 11.9 cm
Colour:	Brown, white or white and gold - gloss

Description	U.S. $	Can. $	U.K. £
Honey container		Rare	

Shape 456   **Biscuit container**

Designer:	Mr. Symcox in 1936
Issued:	1936 - by 1954
Length:	7 ½", 19.1 cm
Colour:	1. Assorted decorations - satin matt
	2. White - matt

Market	Range
U.S.A.	$45.00 - 65.00
Canada	$65.00 - 100.00
U.K.	£25.00 - 45.00

Shape 468   **Bust of George VI**

Designer:	Mr. Weiss in 1937
Issued:	1937 - 1937
Size:	Unknown
Colour:	Ivory - satin matt

Description	U.S. $	Can. $	U.K. £
Bust of George VI	200.00	300.00	125.00

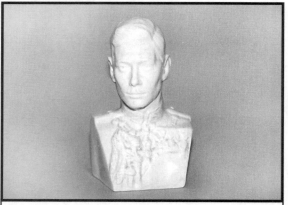

Shape 469   **Bust of George VI**

Designer: Mr. Weiss in 1937
Issued: 1937 - 1937
Size: Unknown
Colour: Ivory - satin matt

Colour	U.S. $	Can. $	U.K. £
Ivory	175.00	250.00	100.00

Photograph not
available
at press time

Shape 471   **Head of George VI**

Designer: Mr. Weiss in 1937
Issued: 1937 - 1937
Size: Unknown
Colour: Ivory - satin matt

Colour	U.S. $	Can. $	U.K. £
Ivory	125.00	175.00	75.00

Shape 474   **Clock case**

Designer: Mr. Symcox in 1937
Issued: 1937 - by 1954
Size: Unknown
Colour: 1. Assorted decorations - satin matt
            2. White - matt

Market	Range
U.S.A.	$85.00 - 125.00
Canada	$125.00 - 175.00
U.K.	£50.00 - 75.00

Shape 559   **Biscuit container**

Designer: Mr. Owen in 1937
Issued: 1937 - by 1954
Height: 5 ¼", 13.3 cm
Colour: 1. Assorted decorations - satin matt
            2. White - matt

Market	Range
U.S.A.	$45.00 - 65.00
Canada	$65.00 - 100.00
U.K.	£25.00 - 45.00

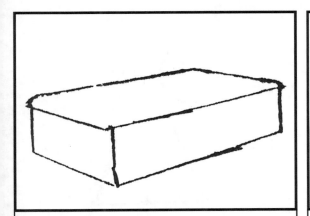

Shape 587   Cigarette box

Designer:	Mr. Symcox in 1938
Issued:	1938 - by 1954
Size:	Unknown
Colour:	1. Assorted decorations - satin matt
	2. White - matt

Market	Range
U.S.A.	$30.00 - 75.00
Canada	$45.00 - 100.00
U.K.	£10.00 - 25.00

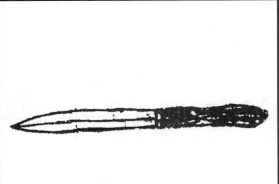

Shape 598   Butter knife

Designer:	Mr. White in 1938
Issued:	1938 - by 1954
Size:	Unknown
Colour:	1. Assorted decorations - satin matt
	2. White - matt

Market	Range
U.S.A.	$40.00 - 60.00
Canada	$25.00 - 40.00
U.K.	£15.00 - 25.00

Shape 599   Spoon

Designer:	Mr. White in 1938
Issued:	1938 - by 1954
Size:	Unknown
Colour:	Assorted decorations - satin matt

Market	Range
U.S.A.	$40.00 - 60.00
Canada	$25.00 - 40.00
U.K.	£15.00 - 25.00

Photograph not
available
at press time

Shape 622   Bust of Mr. Chamberlain

Designer:	Mr. Owen in 1938
Issued:	1938 - 1938
Size:	Unknown
Colour:	Ivory - satin matt

Description	U.S. $	Can. $	U.K. £
Bust of Chamberlain	85.00	125.00	50.00

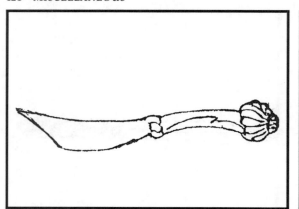

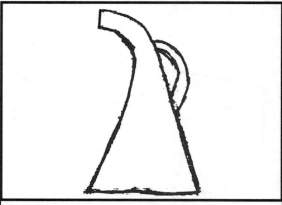

Shape 650   Butter knife

Designer:	Mr. Watkin in 1938
Issued:	1938 - by 1954
Size:	Unknown
Colour:	Assorted decorations - satin matt

Market	Range
U.S.A.	$40.00 - 60.00
Canada	$25.00 - 40.00
U.K.	£15.00 - 25.00

Shape 684   Bath salts container

Designer:	Mr. Owen in 1939
Issued:	1939 - by 1954
Size:	Unknown
Colour:	1. Assorted decorations - satin matt
	2. White - matt

Market	Range
U.S.A.	$45.00 - 65.00
Canada	$65.00 - 100.00
U.K.	£25.00 - 45.00

Photograph not
available
at press time

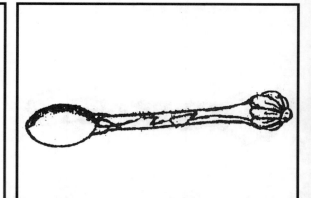

Shape 695/1/2 Butter dish

Designer:	Unknown
Issued:	1939 - by 1954
Size:	Unknown
Colour:	1. Assorted decorations - satin matt
	2. White - matt

Market	Range
U.S.A.	
Canada	Rare
U.K.	

Shape 730   Spoon

Designer:	Mr. Watkin in 1939
Issued:	1939 - by 1954
Size:	Unknown
Colour:	Assorted decorations - gloss

Market	Range
U.S.A.	$40.00 - 60.00
Canada	$25.00 - 40.00
U.K.	£15.00 - 25.00

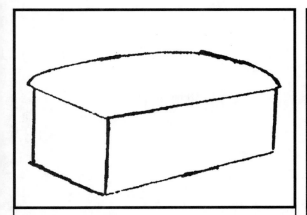

Shape 744   Cigarette box

Designer: Mr. Owen in 1939
Issued: 1939 - by 1954
Size: Unknown
Colour: 1. Assorted decorations - satin matt
             2. White - matt

Market	Range
U.S.A.	$35.00 - 60.00
Canada	$50.00 - 90.00
U.K.	£20.00 - 35.00

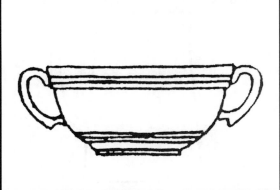

Shape 958/959 Soup bowl and soup saucer

Designer: Albert Hallam in 1941
Issued: 1941 - by 1954
Size: Unknown
Colour: White

Description	U.S. $	Can. $	U.K. £
Soup bowl and soup saucer	20.00	30.00	10.00

Shape 960   Tea caddy

Designer: Albert Hallam in 1941
Issued: 1941 - 1954
Size: Unknown
Colour: White

Description	U.S. $	Can. $	U.K. £
Tea caddy	40.00	60.00	25.00

Shape 983   R.A.F. Teapot

Designer: Unknown
Issued: 1942
Size: Unknown
Colour: Unknown

Description	U.S. $	Can. $	U.K. £
R.A.F. Teapot	50.00	75.00	30.00

Note: Special Commission in 1942.
          Set of four with shapes 984, 985 and 986.

Photograph not
available
at press time

Shape 984   R.A.F. Jug

Designer:	Unknown
Issued:	1942
Size:	Unknown
Colour:	Unknown - gloss

Description	U.S. $	Can. $	U.K. £
R.A.F. Jug	40.00	60.00	25.00

Note: Special commission in 1942.
Set of four with shapes 983, 985 and 986.

Shape 985   R.A.F. Cup and saucer

Designer:	Unknown
Issued:	1942
Size:	Unknown
Colour:	Unknown - gloss

Description	U.S. $	Can. $	U.K. £
R.A.F. Cup and saucer	25.00	40.00	15.00

Note: Special commission in 1942.
Set of four with shapes 983, 984 and 986.

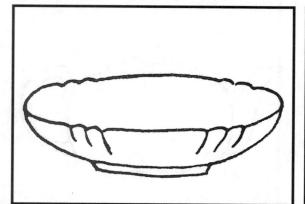

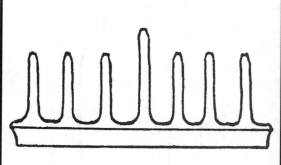

Shape 986   R.A.F. Jam dish

Designer:	Unknown
Issued:	1942
Size:	Unknown
Colour:	Unknown - gloss

Description	U.S. $	Can. $	U.K. £
R.A.F. Jam dish	30.00	45.00	15.00

Note: Special commission in 1942.
Set of four with shapes 983, 984 and 985.

Shape 989   Toast rack, six slices

Designer:	Mr. Watkin in 1942
Issued:	1942 - by 1954
Size:	Unknown
Colour:	Unknown - gloss

Colour	U.S. $	Can. $	U.K. £
Unknown	25.00	40.00	15.00

Shape 1339 Goblet

Designer:	Albert Hallam in 1954
Issued:	1954 - by 1963
Size:	Unknown
Colour:	1. Assorted decorations - satin matt
	2. White - matt

Market	Range
U.S.A.	$35.00 - 60.00
Canada	$50.00 - 90.00
U.K.	£20.00 - 35.00

Shape 1341 Minton tea cup

Designer:	Albert Hallam in 1954
Issued:	1954 - by 1965
Size:	Unknown
Colour:	Assorted decorations - gloss

Market	Range
U.S.A.	$7.00 - 12.00
Canada	$10.00 - 20.00
U.K.	£5.00 - 8.00

Photograph not
available
at press time

Photograph not
available
at press time

Shape 1376 Muffin

Designer:	Albert Hallam in 1955
Issued:	1955 - by 1959
Size:	8", 20.3 cm
Colour:	1. Assorted decorations - gloss
	2. White

Description	U.S. $	Can. $	U.K. £
Muffin	Possibly not put into production		

Shape 1600/1601 Minton breakfast cup and saucer

Designer:	Albert Hallam in 1959
Issued:	1959 - by 1962
Size:	Unknown
Colour:	Assorted decorations - gloss

Market	Range
U.S.A.	$20.00 - 35.00
Canada	$30.00 - 50.00
U.K.	£10.00 - 20.00

Shape 1610 Firefly dinghy

Designer:	Albert Hallam in 1959
Issued:	1959 - by 1963
Size:	5 ½", 14 cm
Colour:	1. Blue boat with F261 on the sail - gloss
	2. Red boat with F126 on the sail - gloss

Description	U.S. $	Can. $	U.K. £
1. Blue boat	160.00	235.00	95.00
2. Red boat	160.00	235.00	95.00

Note: Set of four with no. 1633, 1634 and
1632 (wall plaque).

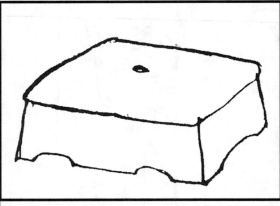

Shape 1619 Covered square butter

Designer:	Mr. Garbet in 1959
Issued:	Unknown
Size:	Unknown
Colour:	Unknown - gloss

Colour	U.S. $	Can. $	U.K. £
Unknown	25.00	40.00	15.00

Photograph not
available
at press time

Shape 1621 Covered scallop

Designer:	Albert Hallam in 1959
Issued:	Unknown
Size:	Unknown
Colour:	Unknown - gloss

Colour	U.S. $	Can. $	U.K. £
Unknown		Rare	

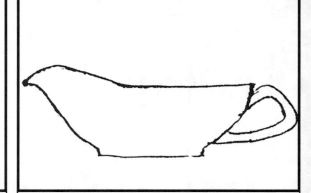

Shape 1622 Gravy boat

Designer:	Albert Hallam in 1959
Issued:	Unknown
Size:	Unknown
Colour:	Unknown - gloss

Colour	U.S. $	Can. $	U.K. £
Unknown	20.00	30.00	10.00

Shape 1630/1/2/3 Urn, three sizes

Designer:	Albert Hallam in 1959
Issued:	1959 - 1971
Sizes:	1. Shape 1630/1 — 10", 25.4 cm
	2. Shape 1630/2 — 8", 20.3 cm
	3. Shape 1630/3 — 6", 12.7 cm
Colour:	1. Various decorations - satin matt
	2. White or black - matt
	3. Copper - lustre

Market	Range
Shape 1630/1	
U.S.A.	$75.00 - 125.00
Canada	$125.00 - 175.00
U.K.	£45.00 - 75.00
Shape 1630/2	
U.S.A.	$75.00 - 100.00
Canada	$125.00 - 150.00
U.K.	£45.00 - 60.00
Shape 1630/3	
U.S.A.	$65.00 - 100.00
Canada	$100.00 - 150.00
U.K.	£40.00 - 60.00

Shape 1633 Yacht GP 14

Designer:	Albert Hallam in 1959
Issued:	1959 - by 1963
Height:	11 ¾", 29.8 cm
Colour:	Red boat with 2242 on the sail - satin matt

Colour	U.S. $	Can. $	U.K. £
Red	225.00	350.00	135.00

Note: Set of four with nos. 1610, 1634 and 1632 (wall plaque)

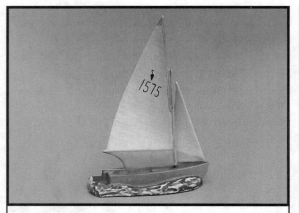

Shape 1634 Yacht Heron

Designer: Albert Hallam in 1959
Issued: 1959 - by 1963
Height: 9", 22.9 cm
Colour: Red or blue boat with 1575 on the sail -
              satin matt

Colour	U.S. $	Can. $	U.K. £
1. Red	175.00	250.00	100.00
2. Blue	175.00	250.00	100.00

Note: Set of four with nos. 1610, 1633 and
1632 (wall plaque).

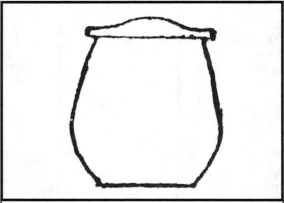

Shape 1697 Mustard

Designer: Albert Hallam in 1960
Issued: Unknown
Size: Unknown
Colour: Unknown - gloss

Description	U.S. $	Can. $	U.K. £
Mustard	Possibly not put into production		

Note: Replaced by shape 1719 in 1960.

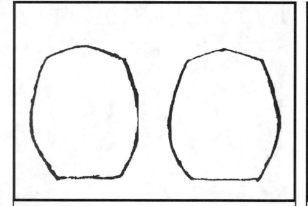

Shape 1698/1699 Salt and pepper

Designer: Albert Hallam in 1960
Issued: Unknown
Size: Unknown
Colour: Unknown - gloss

Description	U.S. $	Can. $	U.K. £
Salt and pepper	Possibly not put into production		

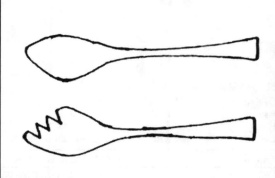

Shape 1700 Servers

Designer: Albert Hallam in 1960
Issued: Unknown
Size: Unknown
Colour: Various decorations - gloss

Description	U.S. $	Can. $	U.K. £
Servers	Possibly not put into production		

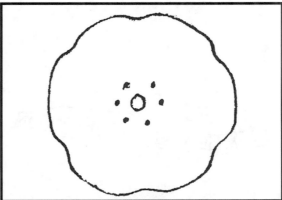

Shape 1739 Shave lotion container, replica of an 18th century gunpowder flask

Designer:	Albert Hallam in 1961
Issued:	Unknown
Size:	Unknown
Colour:	Ivory background with decoration in blues and greys - gloss

Description	U.S. $	Can. $	U.K. £
Shave lotion container	60.00	90.00	35.00

Note: Special commission for Royal Stag by Kosler.

Shape 1764 Cress drainer for fruit bowl

Designer:	Albert Hallam in 1961
Issued:	1961 - Unknown
Size:	Unknown
Colour:	Assorted decorations - gloss

Description	U.S. $	Can. $	U.K. £
Cress drainer	20.00	30.00	10.00

Shape 1797 Urn on pedestal with or without cover

Designer:	Albert Hallam in 1962
Issued:	1962 - 1968
Height:	1. 9 ½", 22.9 with cover
	2. 7 ½", 19.1 cm without cover
Colour:	1. Various decorations - satin matt
	2. White or black - matt
	3. Copper - lustre

Market	Range With Cover
U.S.A.	$75.00 - 125.00
Canada	$125.00 - 175.00
U.K.	£45.00 - 75.00

Market	Range Without Cover
U.S.A.	$65.00 - 100.00
Canada	$100.00 - 150.00
U.K.	£40.00 - 60.00

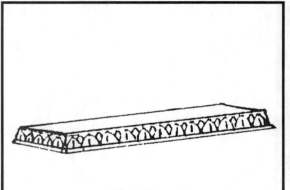

Shape 1809 Stand for horse

Designer: Albert Hallam in 1962
Issued: 1962 - Unknown
Size: Unknown
Colour: 1. Brown - gloss
             2. Copper - lustre

Colour	U.S. $	Can. $	U.K. £
1. Brown	20.00	30.00	10.00
2. Copper	20.00	30.00	10.00

Shape 1810 Urn with cover

Designer: Albert Hallam in 1962
Issued: 1962 - 1969
Height: 1. 6 ½", 16.5 cm with cover
             2. 4 ½", 11.9 cm without cover
Colour: 1. Various decorations - satin matt
             2. White or black - matt
             3. Copper - lustre

Market	Range 1810/1	Range 1810/2
U.S.A.	$65.00 - 100.00	$45.00 - 65.00
Canada	$100.00 - 150.00	$65.00 - 100.00
U.K.	£40.00 - 60.00	£25.00 - 45.00

Shape 1819 Beehive honey pot

Designer: Albert Hallam in 1962
Issued: 1962 - 1972
Height: 3 ¾", 9.5 cm
Colour: 1. Brown or white - gloss
             2. White with coloured bees and flowers - gloss

Colour	U.S. $	Can. $	U.K. £
1. Brown or white	50.00	75.00	30.00
2. White with coloured bees	50.00	75.00	30.00

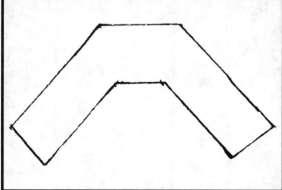

Shape 1863 Stand for bull and cow or pigs

Designer: Albert Hallam in 1963
Issued: c.1963
Height: 1", 2.54 cm
Colour: Unknown - gloss

Colour	U.S. $	Can. $	U.K. £
Unknown	18.00	25.00	10.00

Shape 1893/1894 Sugar and creamer

Designer:	Albert Hallam in 1963
Issued:	1964 - 1971
Size:	Sugar — 6" x 3", 15 x 7.6 cm
	Creamer - 4 ½", 11.9 cm
Colour:	1. Various decorations - satin matt
	2. White or black - matt
	3. Copper - lustre

Market	Range
Shape1893 — Sugar	
U.S.A.	$10.00 - 20.00
Canada	$15.00 - 30.00
U.K.	£5.00 - 10.00
Shape 1894 — Creamer	
U.S.A.	$10.00 - 20.00
Canada	$15.00 - 30.00
U.K.	£5.00 - 10.00

Shape 1893 — Sugar bowl

Shape 1894 — Creamer

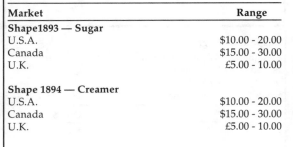

Shape 1895 Grapefruit bowl

Designer:	Albert Hallam in 1963
Issued:	1964 - 1972
Height:	3 ¼", 8.3 cm
Colour:	Blue, mauve, maroon, green, pink
	or yellow - lustre or satin matt

Description	U.S. $	Can. $	U.K. £
Grapefruit bowl	15.00	25.00	10.00

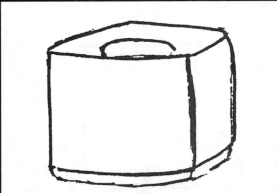

Shape 1914 Table lighter

Designer:	Albert Hallam in 1963
Issued:	1963 - unknown
Height:	8 ½", 21.6 cm
Colour:	Unknown - gloss

Description	U.S. $	Can. $	U.K. £
Table lighter	25.00	40.00	15.00

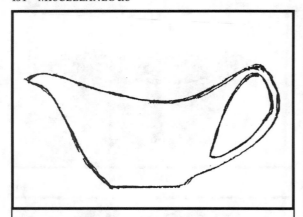

Shape 1920 Gravy boat and stand

Designer:	Albert Hallam in 1963
Issued:	1963 - unknown
Size:	Unknown
Colour:	Unknown - gloss

Description	U.S. $	Can. $	U.K. £
Gravy boat and stand		Rare	

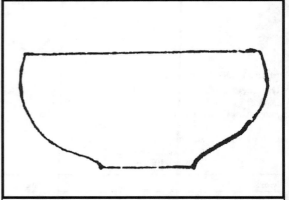

Shape 1921 Sugar

Designer:	Albert Hallam in 1964
Issued:	Unknown
Size:	Unknown
Colour:	Unknown - gloss

Description	U.S. $	Can. $	U.K. £
Sugar		Rare	

Shape 1931 Apothecary jar

Designer:	Albert Hallam in 1964
Issued:	1964 - unknown
Height:	6 ½", 16.5 cm
Colour:	Unknown - gloss

Description	U.S. $	Can. $	U.K. £
Apothecary jar	60.00	90.00	35.00

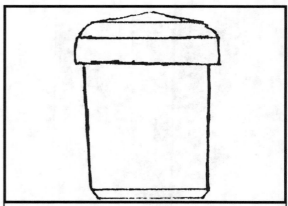

Shape 1945 Jar with lid

Designer:	Albert Hallam in 1964
Issued:	1964 - unknown
Size:	Unknown
Colour:	Unknown - gloss

Description	U.S. $	Can. $	U.K. £
Jar with lid		Rare	

Shape 1999 Bath oil bottle (pair with shape 2000)

Designer:	Albert Hallam in 1965
Issued:	c.1965
Size:	Unknown
Colour:	Very light lime green, light yellow or pink pearl - satin matt

Market	Range
U.S.A.	$20.00 - 25.00
Canada	$30.00 - 40.00
U.K.	£10.00 - 15.00

Note: Special commission for Cussons.

Shape 2000 Bath salts container (pair with shape 1999)

Designer:	Albert Hallam in 1965
Issued:	c.1965
Height:	6 ¼", 15.9 cm incl. lid
Colour:	Very light lime green, light yellow or pink pearl - satin matt

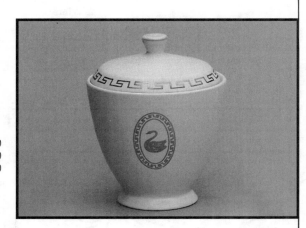

Market	Range
U.S.A.	$20.00 - 25.00
Canada	$30.00 - 40.00
U.K.	£10.00 - 15.00

Note: Special commission for Cussons.

Note: Price ranges are retail market indicators of prices for models under the following conditions:
- Lower end of range = price of monochrome models
- Higher end of range = price of multicoloured models

Shape 2040

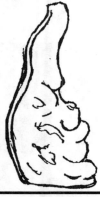
Shape 2041

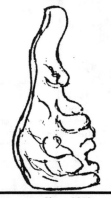
Shape 2042

Shape 2040-2041-2042 Vinegar, Salt and Pepper

Designer:	Albert Hallam in 1965
Issued:	c.1965
Size:	1. Shape 2040 — 5 ¼″, 13.3 cm
	2. Shape 2041 — 5 ½″, 14.0 cm
	3. Shape 2042 — 5 ½″, 14.0 cm
Colour:	1. Various decorations - satin matt
	2. White or black - matt

Market	Range
U.S.A.	$10.00 - 20.00
Canada	$15.00 - 30.00
U.K.	£5.00 - 10.00

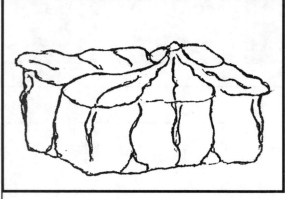

Shape 2043 Butter dish

Designer:	Albert Hallam in 1965
Issued:	c.1965
Size:	5 ¾″ x 3 ½″, 14.6 x 8.9 cm
Colour:	1. Various decorations - satin matt
	2. White or black - matt

Market	Range
U.S.A.	$20.00 - 40.00
Canada	$30.00 - 60.00
U.K.	£10.00 - 25.00

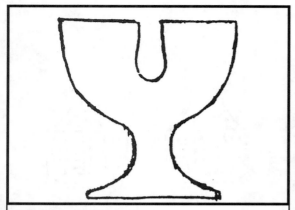

Shape 2054 Double egg cup

Designer:	Albert Hallam in 1966
Issued:	1966 - 1969
Height:	4", 10.1 cm
Colour:	1. Various decorations - satin matt
	2. White or black - matt
	3. Copper - lustre

Market	Range
U.S.A.	$10.00 - 25.00
Canada	$15.00 - 40.00
U.K.	£5.00 - 15.00

Shape 2074 Porringer

Designer:	Graham Tongue in 1966
Issued:	1967 - 1971
Diameter:	5 ½", 14 cm
Colour:	1. Various decorations - satin matt
	2. White or black - matt
	3. Copper - lustre

Market	Range
U.S.A.	$20.00 - 30.00
Canada	$30.00 - 50.00
U.K.	£10.00 - 20.00

Shape 2091 Double egg cup

Designer:	Graham Tongue in 1967
Issued:	1967 - 1969
Height:	3 ¾", 9.5 cm
Colour:	Blue or yellow - gloss

Description	U.S. $	Can. $	U.K. £
Double egg cup	20.00	30.00	10.00

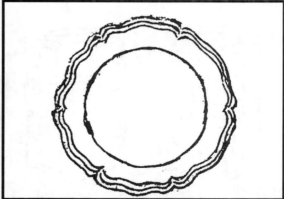

Shape 2136/1/2/3 Chippendale plates

Designer:	Albert Hallam, 1967 (1) and 1968 (2 and 3)
Issued:	Shape 2136/1/2 — c.1968
	Shape 2136/3 — 1968 - 1971
Size:	Shape 2136/1 — 5", 12.7 cm
	Shape 2136/2 — 7", 17.8 cm
	Shape 2136/3 — 10", 25.4 cm

Market	Range
U.S.A.	$20.00 - 60.00
Canada	$30.00 - 90.00
U.K.	£10.00 - 35.00

Shape 2138 Wine taster

Designer:	Albert Hallam in 1967
Issued:	1968 - 1970
Height:	5 ½", 14.0 cm
Colour:	1. Black - matt
	2. Copper lustre with black gloss inner
	3. Pewter - satin matt

Market	Range
U.S.A.	$20.00 - 30.00
Canada	$30.00 - 50.00
U.K.	£10.00 - 20.00

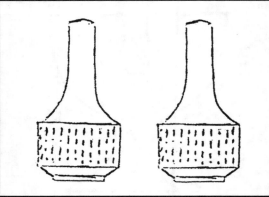

Shape 2151-2152 Salt and pepper

Designer:	Shape 2151 — G. Tongue, H. Sales in 1967
	Shape 2152 — G. Tongue
Issued:	1967 - unknown
Height:	5", 12.7 cm
Colour:	Unknown - gloss

Market	Range
U.S.A.	$20.00 - 25.00
Canada	$30.00 - 40.00
U.K.	£10.00 - 15.00

Shape 2154 -2155 Chimney - Pepper and salt

Designer:	Graham Tongue in 1967
Issued:	1967 - unknown
Height:	4", 10.1 cm
Colour:	Unknown - gloss

Market	Range
U.S.A.	$20.00 - 25.00
Canada	$30.00 - 40.00
U.K.	£10.00 - 15.00

Shape No 2179 - Honey pot

Designer:	Albert Hallam in 1968
Issued:	1968 - unknown
Height:	3 ¼", 8.3 cm
Colour:	Brown - gloss

Description	U.S. $	Can. $	U.K. £
Honey pot	40.00	60.00	25.00

Shape 2213 Bust of Shakespeare

Designer:	Graham Tongue in 1968
Issued:	1968 - unknown
Height:	3", 7.6 cm
Colour:	Unknown - satin matt

Description	U.S. $	Can. $	U.K. £
Bust of Shakespeare	60.00	90.00	35.00

Shape 2220/1/2/3 Measures

Designer:	Shape 2220/1 — Albert Hallam in 1968
	Shape 2220/2/3/ — Graham Tongue in 1968
Issued:	1969 - 1972
Height:	Shape 2220/1 — 5", 12.7 cm
	Shape 2220/2 — 4", 10.1 cm
	Shape 2220/3 — 3", 7.6 cm
Colour:	1. Pewteramic - satin matt
	2. White or black - matt
	3. Copper - lustre

Market	Range
Shape 2220/1	
U.S.A.	$10.00 - 30.00
Canada	$15.00 - 50.00
U.K.	£5.00 - 20.00
Shape 2220/2	
U.S.A.	$10.00 - 25.00
Canada	$15.00 - 40.00
U.K.	£5.00 - 15.00
Shape 2220/3	
U.S.A.	$10.00 - 15.00
Canada	$15.00 - 25.00
U.K.	£5.00 - 10.00

Shape 2227 Shakespeare book

Designer:	Graham Tongue in 1968
Issued:	1968 - unknown
Length:	6", 15.0 cm
Colour:	Unknown - satin matt

Description	U.S. $	Can. $	U.K. £
Shakespeare book	60.00	90.00	30.00

Shape 2243 Shakespeare bust on pedestal

Designer:	Graham Tongue in 1968
Issued:	1968 - unknown
Height:	5", 12.7 cm
Colour:	Ivory - satin matt

Description	U.S. $	Can. $	U.K. £
Bust on pedestal	85.00	125.00	50.00

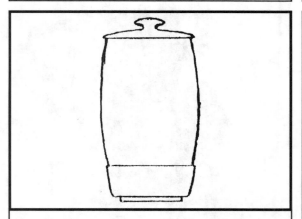

Shape 2260 Bemax jar

Designer:	Albert Hallam in 1969
Issued:	c.1969
Size:	Unknown
Colour:	Unknown - gloss

Description	U.S. $	Can. $	U.K. £
Bemax jar	20.00	30.00	10.00

Note: Special Commission.

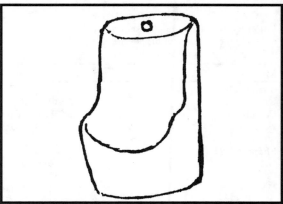

Shape 2270 Shaving brush stand

Designer:	Graham Tongue in 1969
Issued:	c.1969
Height:	4 ½", 11.9 cm
Colour:	Unknown - gloss

Description	U.S. $	Can. $	U.K. £
Shaving brush stand	20.00	30.00	10.00

Note: Special Commission. Pair with shape 2313.

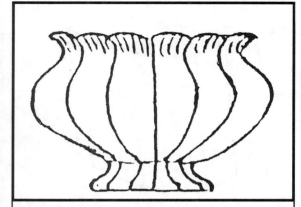

Shape 2289 Sugar (pair with shape 2290)

Designer:	Graham Tongue in 1969
Issued:	1969 - 1970
Height:	2 ¼", 5.7 cm
Colour:	1. Various decorations - satin matt
	2. White or black - matt
	3. Copper - lustre

Market	Range
U.S.A.	$10.00 - 25.00
Canada	$15.00 - 40.00
U.K.	£5.00 - 15.00

Shape 2290 Cream Jug (pair with shape 2289)

Designer:	Graham Tongue in 1969
Issued:	1969 - 1970
Height:	3 ½", 8.9 cm
Colour:	1. Various decorations - satin matt
	2. White or black - matt
	3. Copper - lustre

Market	Range
U.S.A.	$10.00 - 25.00
Canada	$15.00 - 40.00
U.K.	£5.00 - 15.00

Shape 2295 Display Stand for Beatrix Potter Figures

Designer:	A. Brindley in 1969
Issued:	1969 - 1989
Size:	12 ½" X 2 ½", 31.7 x 6.4 cm
Colour:	Shaded browns and greens - gloss

Description	U.S. $	Can. $	U.K. £
Display stand	150.00	125.00	75.00

Note: Transferred to Royal Albert backstamp.

Shape 2304 Honey Jar Container

Designer:	Albert Hallam in 1970
Issued:	1970 - 1972
Size:	Unknown
Colour:	Brown - gloss

Description	U.S. $	Can. $	U.K. £
Honey jar container	50.00	75.00	30.00

Shape 2313 Shaving brush handle (pair with 2270)

Designer:	Graham Tongue in 1969
Issued:	c.1969
Size:	Unknown
Colour:	Unknown - gloss

Description	U.S. $	Can. $	U.K. £
Shaving brush handle	15.00	25.00	10.00

Note: Special Commission

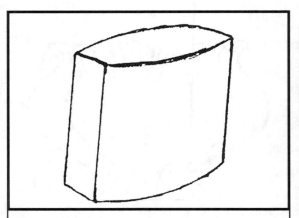

Shape 2347 Napkin holder

Designer:	Unknown
Issued:	Unknown
Size:	4", 10.1 cm
Colour:	Unknown - gloss

Description	U.S. $	Can. $	U.K. £
Napkin holder	15.00	25.00	10.00

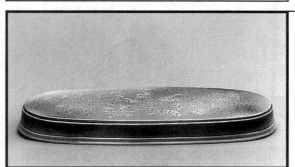

Shape 3017

Shape 3044

Shape 3017-3028-3029-3044-3068 Ceramic plinths

Designer:	Graham Tongue 1986-1987
Issued:	c.1987
Length:	Shape 3017 — 11"
	Shape 3028 — 5 ½"
	Shape 3029 — 13"
	Shape 3044 — 9 ½"
	Shape 3068 — unknown (circular)
Colour:	Green top, brown sides - gloss

Market	Range
U.S.A.	$10.00 - 25.00
Canada	$15.00 - 40.00
U.K.	£5.00 - 15.00

Note: These ceramic plinths were used for mounting animal models for Special Commissions (see *The Charlton Standard Catalogue of Beswick Animals*.)

Warning: Surplus plinths were made available to the public and have since been found mounted with other makes of animals not produced by Beswick.

INDEX